BIOHAZARD

BIOHAZARD

THE HOT ZONE AND BEYOND

Mankind's Battle Against Deadly Disease

Peter Brookesmith

Consultant Editor: Professor Roy Porter

BARNES
&NOBLE
BOOKS
NEW YORK

This book is dedicated to my mother, Marjory Beale Brookesmith, who survived diphtheria by having very tough skin on her teeth and saved my sisters' lives and mine more than once. We should live so long!

This edition published by Barnes & Noble, Inc
by arrangement with Brown Packaging Books Ltd
1997 Barnes & Noble Books

ISBN: 0 7607 0512 7

Printed in Italy by Vincenzo Bona Turin

M 10 9 8 7 6 5 4 3 2 1

Conceived and produced by
Brown Packaging Books Ltd
255-257 Liverpool Road
London N1 1LX

Medical consultant: Dr Fiona Payne
Editor: Lesley Riley
Design: wda
Picture research: Adrian Bentley
Additional research: Maury M. Breecher

CONTENTS

MICROBES VERSUS MANKIND

NEW BATTLES LOOM AGAINST OUR OLDEST ENEMY

Vaccines, antibiotics and extraordinary advances in medical technology in recent decades have created an impression that we are all but impervious to disease. Then came the realization that AIDS could infect anybody, and there was no cure for it, and little hope of creating an effective vaccine. Almost at the same time, other new and horrifically destructive diseases emerged from distant corners of the earth. Hospitals were revealed as breeding grounds for frightening new superbugs. These are the 'biohazards' we now face. What went wrong?

On one thing, at least, the Bible and the followers of Charles Darwin would agree: humanity is the crown of creation. We may believe God created Adam from clay, or that humanity evolved over millions of years to emerge as *Homo sapiens* in southern Africa some 100,000 years ago. But we tend to take it for granted that, of all the creatures of the earth, we are supreme. No other animal can match our powers of calculation, communication or creativity. While

The Four Horsemen of the Apocalypse, who herald the end of the world, as depicted by Albrecht Dürer in 1498. On the heels of the first three – war, famine and death – rides the most feared: plague.

world religions have always taught that this apparent supremacy brings with it deep obligations and special responsibilities, in practice humanity has treated the world and its riches as its own, to order as it pleases.

This has been especially so in the past two centuries, and particularly in Europe and the Americas, where a continuing industrial revolution has given people unprecedented abilities to manipulate and control the conditions of life. The last 60 or 70 years have seen an amazing victory over nature – the control and even eradication of some of the most lethal diseases in history. In this book, we look at the shattering effects on human societies and the horrific symptoms that have afflicted millions, and at the sometimes

heroic work of medical scientists who led the way in defeating some of these scourges. Even as the battle against infection seemed to be won, however, nature was preparing to take revenge. Many of the drugs that revolutionized medicine after World War II are less effective than they were, and some have even encouraged the rise of apparently insuperable 'superbugs'. Since the 1970s the world has seen a phenomenal growth in terrorism and the rise of a dangerous minority of national leaders with large ambitions and few scruples. Biological weaponry has become disturbingly attractive to both.

Further, we now face a fresh array of devastating, incurable diseases. Thanks to the speed and pervasiveness of modern transport, any one of them may burgeon from a local sickness and transform itself into a full-blown plague. Such a plague would not be limited to a single continent: it could wing its way around the world in hours. We know, because it has already happened. Without highways, trucks and jet planes, AIDS would still be hidden in a few remote villages in Central Africa. And, against all the evidence, AIDS is still seen as a minor threat in the West, partly because it takes years to develop. In contrast, the most virulent of the new diseases, against which modern science is defenseless, can spread and kill in days.

As a little-regarded background to these grim prospects we have to face the possibility that we are all more susceptible to disease than we were half a century ago. Environmentalists say that a mounting reservoir of pollution from the very industry that has provided the wealth to improve hygiene, nutrition and medical care in many parts of the world threatens us through holes in the ozone layer, the prospect of global warming, and radical but hardly visible effects on the human immune system. As a result of global warming, diseases that are now limited to a few specific areas could flourish across vast new tracts of the globe.

How did things turn out this way?

Winning the first round

By the beginning of the 20th century industrialization, science and technology created unprecedented affluence in the nations where they developed, and these rich societies were able to afford equally exceptional efforts to prevent and control disease. This century has seen an astonishingly effective onslaught on diseases that were once deemed a grim and inevitable part of the human condition. Smallpox, first challenged by inoculation in Western countries in 1720, was still killing over two million people a year, and disfiguring millions more survivors in 1967, when the World Health Organization (WHO) began its global assault on the disease. Over 250 million vaccine doses were dispensed over the next decade, and by 1977 smallpox existed only as carefully guarded samples in secure laboratories. Other scourges already banished or reduced to negligible levels in the world's wealthier nations included diphtheria, polio, tuberculosis and tertiary syphilis. The last killed 13,000 people in the USA in 1940; by 1949, after the introduction of antibiotic treatment, the number was down to 6000, and by 1970 only some 400 Americans succumbed to the disease. As a result, over the next decade, many medical schools in the USA closed departments dedicated to the study of sexually transmitted disease.

At the time it seemed that diseases could be defeated, worldwide, given the will, the money and the know-how, just as people had conquered other scientific and technical problems. It was a mistake. The flaw in the thinking sprang from a misconception of the place of humanity in the scheme of things, and from an ignorance of the way many diseases – or the agents that caused them – reacted to such radical treatment as that afforded by 'miracle cures' like antibiotics.

Humanity appears to have no natural predators, apart from other people. That doesn't mean a hungry bear or an angry lion won't attack a human being. But superior intelligence, skill with weapons, foresight and cunning have allowed people to outwit and defeat larger or more fearsome creatures, or taught us to avoid them or, in a few cases, to domesticate them. The crown of creation walked on two legs but still lorded it over the earth.

But there were always the microbes. And no sooner had we learned about them, and how to defeat them, than we forgot them. Especially overlooked until recently were the viruses which, unlike bacteria, cannot be combated once they have invaded the body.

The greatest single discovery

For most of our history, of course, we have been unaware of microbes. Plagues and diseases were thought to be the work of capricious and unpredictable gods, or were punishment for sins committed sometimes by individuals, sometimes by whole societies. It was not until the 1860s that the great breakthrough in understanding came. The French chemist Louis Pasteur was asked to suggest a cure for a disease that was afflicting silkworms, threatening to ruin France's silk industry. Using his microscope, Pasteur found that both the ailing silkworms and the mulberry leaves on which they fed were infested with tiny organisms. He suggested that affected worms and bushes both be destroyed, and the remainder used to give the industry a fresh start. The drastic solution worked, but Pasteur did not stop thinking about his discovery. He reasoned that *all* infectious diseases were caused by what he called 'germs' – tiny creatures, invisible to the naked eye, that traveled through the air, in water, or by direct contact to attack a healthy organism. Pasteur's insight has justly been called the greatest single discovery ever made in medicine. One of his immediate proposals was that medical instruments and bandages should be boiled to kill the would-be invaders before they could cause any damage.

Pasteur's 'germs' were identified more and more precisely over the next 80 years. In the 1930s chemists developed sulfa drugs (synthetic compounds containing sulfur), which had spectacular curative effects on bacterial infections. Then came the antibiotics, first reported in the late 1920s and devel-

Children being vaccinated at a clinic in Nigeria. Such programs have largely failed to defeat most endemic diseases in the Third World: lack of funds has stopped them reaching enough people to be fully effective.

oped as a medical treatment during World War II. Far more potent than sulfa drugs against harmful bacteria, antibiotics decimated diseases that had afflicted mankind for eons.

A profound consequence of these extraordinary victories was a misplaced optimism about our capacity to deal with disease. Although strains of bacteria soon appeared that resisted the power of antibiotics, medical science developed new treatments to counter them. And because the war against 'germs' was won in principle, by human ingenuity and understanding, it seemed that it should be only a matter of time before all diseases could be analyzed, attacked and wiped out. In its own eyes, at least, humanity had

retained the right to its crown in the scheme of things.

Only after it became possible to analyze the very building blocks of life – contained in deoxyribonucleic acid (DNA) in the cells of all living things – did it become apparent to scientists that, far from being set above all other living creatures, humanity has been preyed upon and changed by microbes, especially viruses, over millions of years. As Nobel prizewinner Joshua Lederberg has noted:

it is a pyrrhic victory for a virus to eradicate its host!... From the virus's perspective, its ideal would be a virtually symptomless infection, in which the host is quite oblivious of providing shelter and

nourishment for the indefinite propagation of the virus's genes. Our own genome probably carries hundreds of thousands of such stowaways. The boundary between them and the 'normal genome' is quite blurred; intrinsic to our own ancestry and nature are not only Adam and Eve, but any number of invisible germs that have crept into our chromosomes.... As much as 95 per cent of our DNA may be 'selfish', parasitic in origin.

In the light of that history – and the schoolbook history we all know about the Black Death in medieval times and, much more recently, the devastations of cholera, yellow fever and malaria in the Americas – Lederberg reminds us:

> We have no guarantee that the natural evolutionary competition of viruses and the human species will always find ourselves the winner.... The countercultural protest against technology posits a benign nature, whose balance we now disturb with diabolical modernities. But man himself is a fairly recent emergent on the planet; the sheer growth of our species since the paleolithic [age] is the major source of disturbances to that hypothetical balance.... We are complacent to trust that nature is benign; we are arrogant to assert that we have the means to except ourselves from the competition [that occurs among all living things].... Our principal competitors for dominion, outside our own species, are the microbes: the viruses, bacteria, and parasites. *They remain an interminable threat to our survival.*

Nothing reminded humanity of its complacency and arrogance so harshly or so uncompromisingly as the emergence of AIDS as a global threat in the 1980s. In the USA, the recognition of the scope and seriousness of that peril was – it now seems amazing – delayed first by political obstacles and then by a refusal to admit that the disease raging among men and women in Africa was the same one that was devastating gay men in America. For years, research proposals were disregarded, and budgets were non-existent. In Africa, political leaders long denied the very existence of AIDS in their countries. Even when those obstacles were overcome, and the AIDS virus identified, the intractable problem remained: how to kill or neutralize the virus – any virus – without also killing its human host.

The power of plagues

AIDS can fairly be called a plague, and since it emerged other potentially devastating diseases against which we have no known defense have flourished unexpectedly and, sometimes mysteriously, faded back into obscurity. We have been starkly reminded of our vulnerability and our mortality. A number of writers have been inspired to look again at plagues of the past to see these new threats in the context and perspective of history – and perhaps to prepare us, to help us imagine the unimaginable that now flickers uneasily around the edges of our consciousness.

One lesson of the past is inescapable: diseases, especially in lethal epidemics, have altered the course of history time and again. To illustrate the point here, we can take a single yet profoundly potent example from the Roman empire. In 542 CE, the emperor Justinian was engaged in an enormously ambitious plan to conquer all the territories of the old Roman empire, including its rump around Rome itself. He had already taken much of North Africa, Sicily, and parts of Spain. Then bubonic plague struck. It came out of Egypt, hit the Byzantine capital Constantinople (today Istanbul), and spread west across Europe. The people of Constantinople suffered for three months, into the winter, when the plague changed to its even more virulent and contagious pneumonic form. At its height, 10,000 people a day were dying; when the crisis subsided, 40 per cent of the city's population were dead. Other cities suffered as badly as the disease raged across Europe over the next six years, eventually reaching Ireland and Denmark. It returned at intervals (sometimes within three or four years) until about 590; by 600 CE, according to one estimate, it had killed half of Europe's people. By 610 it had reached China.

Apart from the famine and civil disorder that came in its wake, the plague shattered Justinian's so nearly realized ambitions, and the remnant of the old Roman empire; the loss of Rome's last civilizing influences in Europe ushered in the period of political confusion and cultural decline known as the Dark Ages. Britain's destiny was altered, as the Celtic population was unable to resist invading Saxons from Germany. In North Africa in the following century, it is certainly possible that 'Islam marched so swiftly through so many lands because the plague had battered them physically, psychologically and culturally' – with consequences for future ages that we are still witnessing today.

A quarantine in force in the USA in 1916, during a polio epidemic. The quarantine was designed to stop people from leaving the area of infection, as well as to keep the healthy away from the sick.

In China, the plague contributed dramatically to a loss of faith in the old religions and the rise of Buddhism. The disease decided the future of millions of people from one end of the vast Eurasian landmass to the other.

The deadly city

More subtle, perhaps, than the way disease affects history is the way human activity can release epidemics on a huge scale, or lay the foundations for the spread of so-called 'slow' diseases, like the AIDS virus, which can take years to produce symptoms. One of the least obvious of these contributors to plagues – because we take it for granted in the modern world

– is the city itself. Throughout history great urban centers have served as a magnet for humanity's finest talents, and as a gathering place for its oldest enemies, the microbes. Until the last hundred years or so the mass of people lived without running water, effective sewage disposal or a decent diet; germs were in paradise. The urban poor, packed into substandard housing, were particularly vulnerable to infection. Statistics for ancient Rome show that only 30 per cent of Romans lived beyond the age of 30, whereas 70 per cent of those living in the countryside did. It was worse for the urban poor. 'If the Roman patricians occasionally suffered dysentery because of bacteria in the aqueducts,' writes medical journalist Laurie Garrett, 'the plebeians downstream were guaranteed a double exposure due to the additional bacterial burden of the patricians' contaminated waste.'

Once an epidemic got under way in

such conditions, it could pass from person to person with incredible speed and lethality. Especially when the population had no natural defense against the microscopic invader.

In 1519, when Spanish conquistadores sailed to Mexico to join their leader Hernando Cortés in the Aztecs' great capital of Tenochtitlán (now Mexico City), among the company was an African slave suffering from a mild case of smallpox. The Spanish seem to have had enough antibodies in their systems to resist the infection. But the Aztecs in their splendid capital died in droves. Cortés and his band were driven out of the city, but they stormed in again, after a three-month siege. In that time, half the 300,000 inhabitants had died: 'A man could not set his foot down unless on the corpse of an Indian,' Cortés recounted. As survivors fled, they carried the smallpox with them across Mexico. In less than 50 years the population of the region had

This shanty town, known as Manila Smokey Mountain, is built on a huge rubbish dump in the Philippines. Disease thrives in the squalid and overcrowded conditions in which the poor are forced to live.

shriveled from 25 million to three million; within a century it was almost half that. Here, a disease changed history, but human action had ushered in and then amplified the affliction.

Western cities may on the whole be far more sanitary today, but cities anywhere are still happy hunting grounds for deadly microbes, and are likely to become more so. Historian Arno Karlen points out:

Two centuries ago, 98 per cent of the world's people were farmers

and villagers. Soon half will be urbanites, many living in megacities of 10 million or more. Such cities put huge strains on water and waste systems, infrastructure, social order, and public health programs. At the same time, demographic profiles will shift. Developed nations, their growth slowed or stopped, will have more older citizens.... In developing countries, populations will be skewed strongly toward youth and early adulthood. Those most at risk from new infections will be 'the immunosuppressed and subpopulations of the young, old and poor' of the megacities. Karlen warns: 'if the young lack food, jobs and hope, they become social and medical time bombs and disseminators of disease.'

Still more tragic are epidemics that spring from the best of intentions. The road that runs east from Pointe-Noire on the Congo's Atlantic coast, through Zaire and Uganda and on to the Indian Ocean at Mombasa in Kenya, is no smooth-metaled interstate highway. 'The road was once a dirt track that wandered through the heart of Africa,' writes Richard Preston, 'almost impossible to traverse along its complete length. Long sections of it were paved in the 1970s, and the trucks began rolling through....' The track was turned into a modern commercial artery thanks to foreign aid. As the truck traffic grew, so did the number of *femmes libres* along the way, the 'free women' who charged cash to serve the basic instincts of the truck drivers.

Somewhere on that highway, after a brief stop not far from Lake Victoria, someone climbed into his cab with the AIDS virus as a stowaway in his body. Or perhaps he left it behind him for his temporary consort to pass unwittingly to the next (and the next, and the next) client. No one knows. No one is entirely sure how, precisely, the AIDS virus arose among the people of Central Africa, either. But a key route for its spread from coast to coast across the waist of Africa was a road built in the belief that it would improve the lot of all within reach of it. Today it is called the 'AIDS Highway'. It was, quite literally, a road to hell that had been paved with good intentions.

We shall come upon other examples of routes to real or potential disaster. They may not be actual paths across a solid landscape, but the good intentions have been authentic enough, and so have the awful consequences. The apparently incurable human tendency to meddle with the natural world – usually in the hope of improving it – has rarely been indulged without creating worse problems in the process.

The fourth horseman

Today we face a series of threats to human health that seem to be without parallel. In fact they are nothing of the kind. So many historical instances have been quoted here just to underline that point. But they appear to us, in the Western world in the last years of the 20th century, to be uniquely threatening, because for generations we have known nothing as cataclysmic as the fate that befell Constantinople nearly 1500 years ago. The most widespread and virulent plague to have attacked humanity this century occurred in 1918–19, and killed 20 million

people. This event is just within individual living memory, yet it is all but forgotten by society at large. Perhaps this is because, unlike the victims of the Black Death, the dead were not piled in the streets, and nor were whole towns and villages emptied by its scourge. Perhaps too it has been overshadowed by the memory of World War I, with its far more potent images of destruction and death. And the killer was a common, and usually harmless ailment: influenza.

For some of the same reasons we do not see AIDS. The infection can be invisible in individuals for years and, in the West, the dying fade from sight into homes and hospices. While there are few of us who have not personally known a victim, we do not see the mass of the dead. Still less do we see those dying today of the same disease in Africa. Yet by the end of the century the AIDS virus is likely to have infected between 40 and 100 million people worldwide and may have killed 20 million adults and one million children. We in the West may begin to take notice sometime before 2010, when it is likely that the disease will cause one in two deaths in Africa south of the Sahara. By then, the images of medieval plagues will have come to life again on our television screens, and in our dreams nightly.

We tend to think of a plague as sudden, lethal, and devastating in its effects – like the Ten Plagues that were visited on Egypt, as told in the book of Exodus in the Bible. The word 'plague' has also been used for all kinds of widespread diseases, such as cancer. But whether descending like a whirlwind or slow and insidious, plagues are usually highly lethal, spreading fast and far enough to disrupt an entire society.

In that sense, AIDS is a plague, especially in Central Africa.

The words we use for outbreaks of disease are often rather vaguely defined and used rather loosely. Medical anthropologists tend to use the word *illness* to describe one's personal experience of a disorder, and the word *disease* to describe the objective reality. Longstanding and widespread diseases are called *endemic*: a non-lethal example would be the common cold, and a deadlier one the presence of malaria throughout much of the 'undeveloped' world. Epidemiologists use *epidemic* to describe an unusual instance of an ailment. Strictly speaking, an epidemic of a disease can consist of just one sick person, but the word is normally used when a disease becomes prevalent at a particular time and place. But if a disease rampages across a country or a continent, we would face a *pandemic* – an epidemic of enormous proportions, like the Black Death that wiped out up to a third of Europe's population in the 14th century. We shall try, at least, to use these terms consistently in these senses in this book.

In it, we will meet all these variations in the way our well-being can be deranged. We will see how plagues and pandemics have afflicted humanity throughout history and how, in a brief bright window of time, they seemed to have been banished or controlled. And then we will look at the emerging threats to that cozy view of the world, and assess the chances that Pestilence, the dread fourth horseman of the Apocalypse, may yet come thundering down upon humanity again – and soon. It is possible that we are about to witness a new and more savage phase of the endless struggle between mankind and its oldest enemy.

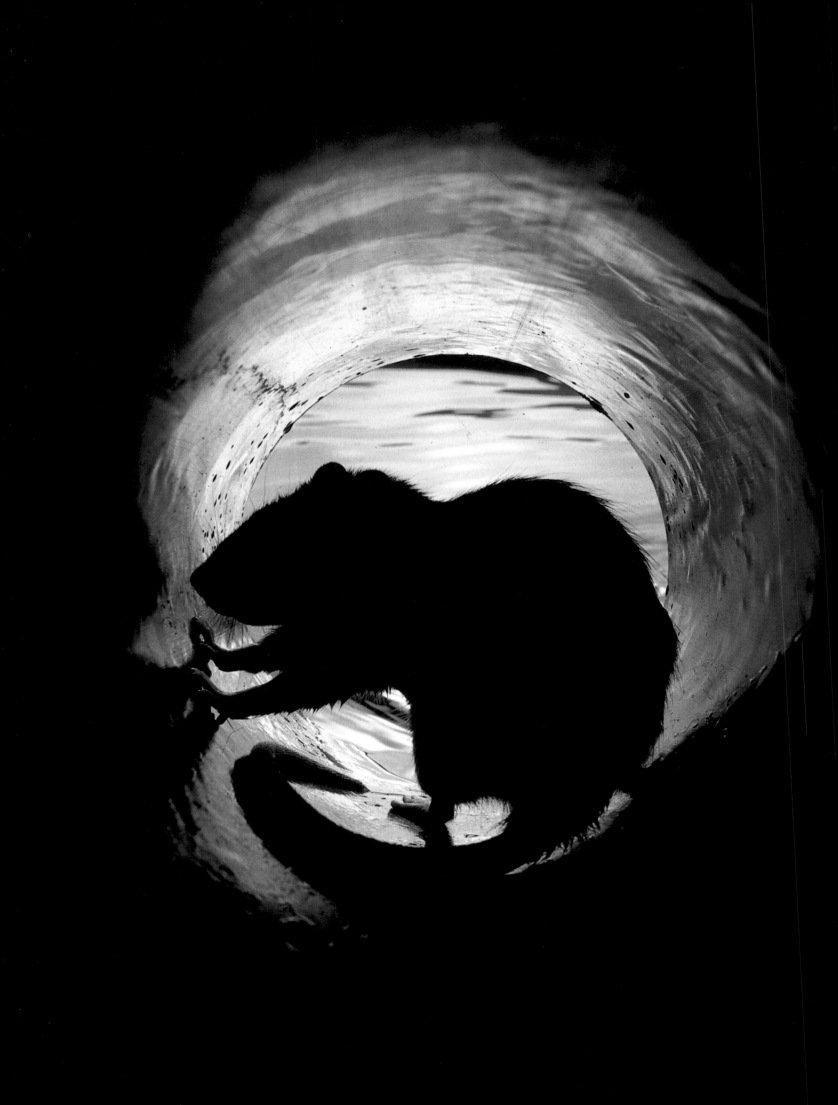

CHAPTER ONE

SCOURGES OF THE GODS

PLAGUES THAT HAUNT HUMANITY

To most of us the word 'plague' conjures up the bubonic plague.
It is six centuries since the disease slaughtered tens of millions in
Europe, and yet its name still sends shudders down the spine.
But it was far from the only plague to ravage whole nations.
How did those afflicted deal with their terrible experiences?

No scourge so destructive of human life is anywhere on record, wrote the Greek historian Thucydides of the plague that devastated Athens in 430 BCE. 'As for the gods,' he remarked, 'it seemed to be the same thing whether one worshiped them or not, when one saw the good and the bad dying indiscriminately.'

Athens, then at the height of its glory, never really recovered from that visitation of death. The year before, the city had found itself at war with its rival Sparta, whose invading forces had driven villagers off the land and into Athens for refuge. Some 200,000 people were crammed behind the walls

Bubonic plague travels on the backs of rats – the disease is caused by Yersinia pestis *bacteria, which breed in the gut of the fleas that infest the rodents. The plague is the most feared of more than 30 infections that rats can share with mankind.*

and in Piraeus, the nearby port. It was here the sickness began, rapidly spreading into Athens. Thucydides recorded the symptoms for posterity:

People in good health were all of a sudden attacked by violent heats in the head, and redness and inflammation in the eyes, the inward parts, such as the throat or tongue, becoming bloody and emitting an unnatural and fetid breath. These symptoms were followed by sneezing and hoarseness, after which the pain soon reached the chest and produced a hard cough. When it fixed in the stomach, it upset it; and discharges of bile of every kind named by physicians ensued, accompanied by very great distress.

With the vomiting and diarrhea came a terrible thirst, while the victim's body broke out in sores that turned ulcerous. Unable to sleep or to bear the touch of bedding, some sufferers wandered naked in the streets in search of

water, until they died. Even dogs died of the disease, as did crows and buzzards that ate the corpses that lay everywhere. People who survived might have lost their fingers or toes, eyes, or memory.

As up to half the population and a quarter of the city-state's army perished, the social fabric of Athens collapsed. No malefactor expected to live long enough to be punished, and there was a parallel epidemic of theft, murder and rape. Athenians were demoralized, in all senses of the word. Pericles, king of the city in all but name, died at sea in the second great wave of the disease in 429 BCE, along with 4000 soldiers of the Athenian fleet. In the years that followed, the Athenian empire unraveled. What should have been a short decisive war with Sparta stretched on for 30 years, sapping resources and ending in defeat. Athens' political power shrank, and its Golden Age became a memory.

entirely within five years. Historian Arno Karlen speculates: 'It may have been the violent European debut of measles, scarlet fever, smallpox, typhoid, or some disease that no longer exists. Another guess is that an epidemic of influenza or something like it was complicated by staphylococcus infections, producing a toxic shock syndrome. We will never be sure.'

Ancient and modern

In 1996, Dr Patrick Olson of the San Diego Medical Center suggested in the journal *Emerging Infectious Diseases* that the Ebola virus lay behind the Athens plague. He had noticed similarities between Thucydides' account and reports of an outbreak of Ebola fever in Zaire in 1995. The journal *New Scientist* suggested another connection: it noted that ancient frescoes on islands near Athens depicted green monkeys which, scientists suspected, had passed the Ebola virus to humans in Kikwit, Zaire, in 1995. Kevin DeCock, of the London School of Hygiene and Tropical Medicine, was not impressed by Dr Olson's suggestion: he remarked that one of the main symptoms of Ebola is copious bleeding (from hemorrhages), which does not feature in Thucydides' account.

Here in microcosm is the stark difference between the ancient and the modern approaches to a terrible epidemic. In the 5th century BCE, Thucydides, for all his dispassionate, careful and deliberate recording of symptoms – specifically so that later ages might recognize the mystery disease – despairs of the gods. Today, scientists argue courteously over a diagnosis against a background of medical knowledge that reaches down to the fundamental stuff of life. At the

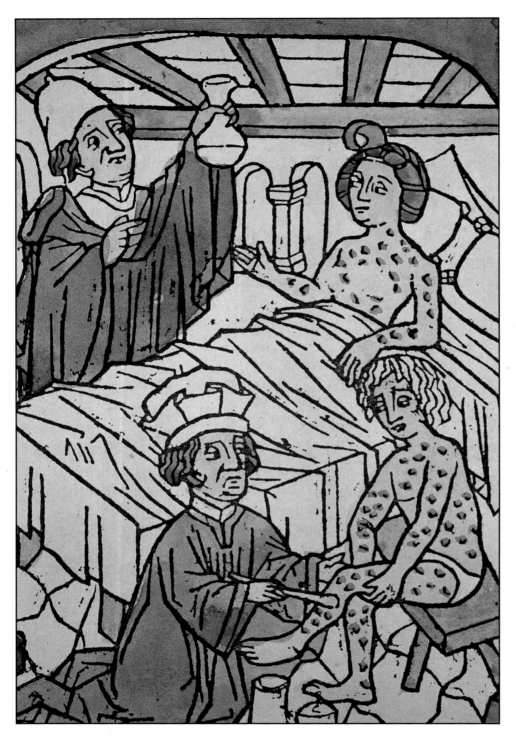

When syphilis first appeared in the 15th century, its 'great pocks' were hideously disfiguring – and were seen as a mark of divine wrath. As late as 1826 Pope Leo XII banned the use of condoms because they prevented the immoral evildoers from suffering diseases that were believed to be the just punishment for their sin.

Still no one is certain what caused the plague of Athens. Thucydides said that it had first begun 'in the ports of Ethiopia…and thence descended into Egypt and Libya and into most of [Persia].' In Greece it afflicted only Athens and 'the most populous of other towns', and it had vanished

same time, both the doctors of the 1990s could be wrong. We may never know what ravaged Athens in 430 BCE, because science has shown us that microbes can adapt, evolve and mutate extraordinarily quickly. The Ebola virus that we know today is unlikely to be the same as it was 24 centuries ago, and may not produce exactly the same symptoms. When syphilis first burst upon Europe at the end of the 15th century, the symptoms began with genital sores, progressed to a general rash, and then to revolting abscesses and scabs all over the body. The sores became ulcers that could eat into bones and destroy the nose, lips, eyes, throat, and genitals. There were agonizing pains in the muscles and bones.... The disease could be fatal in years or even months.

By the time antibiotics were first used to attack syphilis, at the end of World War II, the visible symptoms had receded to the genital area and victims might live into old age – albeit mad, in the tertiary stage of the disease, it is true. The more virulent (or 'fulminant') forms of the bacterium that causes syphilis had largely died out as early as the end of the 16th century, simply by killing their hosts and dying with them; while surviving Europeans were more resistant to the disease. The first outbreak of a previously unknown pestilence, like the plague of Athens, is almost always more horrific than its later, more settled forms – and it is this that makes ancient infections, after such a span of years, so difficult to identify.

Nevertheless it is possible to identify how such diseases were transmitted, turning epidemics into pandemics through the relatively scattered populations of the ancient, medieval and

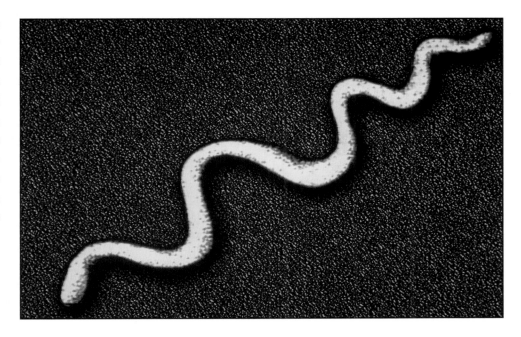

early modern world. As might be guessed from several examples already given, one of the major channels along which infections spread was warfare. Then as now, armies traveled vast distances in the interests of expanding empires. The centers of those empires were inevitably cities, whose cramped inhabitants were fed and clothed using the resources of the surrounding countryside. As the cities grew, they demanded both more resources to maintain themselves and more room for their burgeoning populations.

The urban menace

The size of some cities rivaled those of today, certainly as a proportion of the area and total population they governed. At the time Jesus of Nazareth was born, Rome boasted a population of one million – a figure not surpassed by a city in the West until the growth of London in the 19th century – and was consuming 6000 tonnes of grain a week. Its empire of 50 million people stretched from Britain and Spain in the west to the Red Sea in the east, encircled the Mediter-

The Treponema pallidum *spirochete bacterium that causes syphilis. The first stage of syphilis creates short-lived skin lesions. But the bacteria continue to attack, sometimes for years, and then tumor-like masses appear all over the body. Blindness, heart damage or madness may result.*

ranean Sea and reached beyond the Alps into Germany.

Microbes thrive in the dense crowds of cities, where people are in constant physical contact, breathe in what others breathe, cough or sneeze out, have a potentially huge range of sexual partners, take drinking water from the same river that they use as a sewer, and generate massive quantities of garbage. In such an intimate throng a single person has contact with so many others, directly and indirectly, that microbes – already thriving in water, waste, houses, furniture and food – can spread like fire on a parched prairie. Over time – usually a century or two – the people and the microbes will generally come to an accommodation: ravaging diseases will, for instance, be reduced to brief childhood sicknesses, not eradicated but not lethal or disruptive either. In 16th-century Spain, for example, smallpox had largely been reduced to a nuisance no worse than modern measles, but it killed nine out of 10 of the vulnerable Mexican population.

Warfare and pestilence

Throughout history, armed and aggressive emissaries of expanding empires have taken their diseases with them. In the 14th century BCE, for instance, an Egyptian army brought a plague to the Hittites that lasted for three generations. Sometimes armies met their match in the shape of diseases that were tolerable among those they wished to conquer but fatal to the invaders. The results of one such instance can still be seen today in modern India. From about 800 BCE, the urbanized Hindu civilization of the arid plains of northwestern India began to expand from the Indus valley south and east through the forests of the subcontinent. In the ensuing encounters, the invaders and the forest tribes each carried microbes that were lethal to the other, although not sufficiently to halt the tide of invasion. The forest people were not assimilated by their new masters, but were kept apart from them as subject castes. Physical contact of any kind, no matter how casual, between the castes was forbidden, and there were elaborate rituals of purification for those chance occasions when the taboo was broken. Although officially the caste system has been abolished in India, it remains a part of everyday life. While it offended Western egalitarians, it had the effect of preserving the religious, cultural and social traditions of the conquered peoples – which explains how Hinduism has accumulated such a vast panoply of gods, and why India is a nation still of over 1600 distinct languages and dialects.

Armies that extended imperial bounds or enforced imperial rule ran the risk of carrying highly contagious, unknown diseases back to the hub of the empire – should they survive them in the first place. The beginning of the fall of the Roman empire can be dated from the great plague that struck the city – by then housing some two million people – in 165 CE, brought there by troops returning from quelling a rebellion in Syria. The accounts of survivors are not detailed enough to identify the disease precisely, although smallpox is reckoned the most likely

A woman of the 'untouchable' caste sweeps a street in New Delhi. Hindus cannot escape the caste into which they are born; this rigid class system may be the relic of an ancient form of quarantine against disease.

The Triumph of Death *by Pieter Brueghel the Elder, painted around 1560. Medieval and early modern Europe was a killing field for rival princes, and plagues and epidemics followed close in the footsteps of war.*

culprit. At the plague's height, 2000 people a day died in Rome, and over the next 14 years it raged across the empire. In Europe, somewhere between four and seven million people died.

In turn, the disease may have been a kind of microbial bow-wave of the Huns, ferocious horsemen who were then migrating west across the Asian steppes. Those displaced by their depre-

dations brought chaos and disease to the borders of the Roman empire. Still worse was the plague that killed as many as 5000 people a day in Rome in 251 CE and continued to ravage the city and its provinces until 266. This seems to have come out of Ethiopia, and may have been another strain of smallpox, or possibly measles. Over the next two centuries a combination of encroaching Huns, epidemics and uprisings sapped the strength of Rome and ate away at its empire. Taxes raised in the depopulated Mediterranean cities were no longer enough to pay the garrisons in the barbaric hinterland; with the collapse of military order, the empire became

unprotected and unprotectable, and fell in upon itself. Ironically, when the Huns eventually reached the gates of Rome in 452, an epidemic was once again doing its dreadful work within the city walls, and it attacked the invaders too. It may have been this, as much as the gold donated by Pope Leo I, that persuaded the Huns to retreat from Rome, by now a spent and broken power.

Warfare remains a trailblazer and amplifier for potent epidemics. In 1994 an outbreak of cholera in refugee camps in Tanzania and Zaire directly followed an orgy of indiscriminate bloodletting between the Hutu and Tutsi peoples in neighboring Rwanda,

and was contained only by prompt medical action – which included ridding rivers of the corpses that clogged them, purifying water, and providing rehydration therapy and antibiotics for those stricken. The half-century of continuous warfare in Southeast Asia has contributed directly to the growth of resistance in malarial microbes to virtually every drug that has been thrown at them – as we shall discuss in a later chapter.

Trading in disease

While plagues of disease follow the plague of war, microbes have been no less keen to follow in the tracks of peaceful traders. Intercontinental trade between North Africa and Europe was thriving at least 4000 years ago, while the entrepreneurial, seagoing Phoen-

icians from the Levantine coast established their colony at Carthage, in modern Tunisia, in 814 BCE. The Romans had trading ships of 1000 tonnes plying the Mediterranean. From the coastal settlements Arab slave traders penetrated the interior of Africa, while the Nile served as a huge artery for trade. The Mediterranean thus formed a pool of disease that also included many African infections: the area was malarial, for example, until the end of World War II. Desert, sea and mountains long formed natural barriers between the region and the other two great pools of disease in the ancient world, China and India.

China harbored malaria and schistosomiasis in its southern Yangtze flood plain; the north was prey to smallpox, measles and possibly bubonic plague,

Dead and dying soldiers in Goma, eastern Zaire, in the mid-1990s. While warfare may disturb hidden microbes in the rain forest, the unburied fallen create new opportunities for diseases to burst out and become epidemics.

which arrived from vast underground colonies of rodents on the Asian steppes. Smallpox seems to have broken out early in the 2nd century BCE, and a series of epidemics over the next 700 years or so reduced the population of some southern regions by as much as 80 per cent. Southern India too had malaria, dengue (or breakbone) fever, perhaps cholera, and smallpox – which may have originated there as a disease of cattle.

While occasional traders reached

the Mediterranean from China and India, communications were so sporadic and populations so sparse where traders did meet that any infection they may have carried had no chance to take hold to any significant degree. During the 1st century CE, however, trade both by ship and by overland caravan became well established between large centers of population. A caravan was a prodigious undertaking, demanding the transport of sufficient goods to pay for food, fodder, and garrisons dotted along the route to make the venture safe – indeed possible at all – with enough left over for a profit. The growth of the caravan trade thus meant a movement of thousands of people and animals through communities that themselves soon grew large enough to sustain an epidemic caused by disease-bearing microbes, should they appear. And should a new microbe emerge, to which the population had never been

exposed, such an epidemic was bound to be carried down the caravan route and create a pandemic.

The major trade between China and the Mediterranean was in silk; and the caravan route between northwestern China and Roman Syria, known to the Romans as the Silk Road, stretched across the Asian steppes, home to bubonic plague. Down this channel, in all likelihood, came the plague that infected Roman soldiers in Syria and struck Rome in 165 CE. The series of pandemics that followed left a European population too weak to resist the bubonic plague that raced out from Constantinople in 542 (described in the Introduction). Europe took four centuries to recover from this microbial battering. While bubonic plague died out, smallpox and measles were reduced in the remaining, resistant humans to childhood illnesses. The population of Europe slowly returned to its previous level, and between about 1000 and

1300 CE actually doubled. Neither warfare nor venturesome traders brought horrific epidemics in their wake. Leprosy, tuberculosis and a now extinct disease known as 'the sweats' enjoyed epidemics, but none had the destructive power of early outbreaks of smallpox, measles or the pneumonic plague. But then came famine, and the Great Dying.

An unnatural presence

Justinian's plague, as it has become known, may have come down the Silk Road to Egypt and thence to the Byzantine capital in 542 CE. It may, just as likely, have come by sea from India to Ethiopia and gone from there to Egypt. In either case it most probably originated among wild rodents – rats, field mice, marmots and burrowing squirrels – in Asia. But how did it break into the human population?

Bubonic plague is not 'natural' to human beings, which is one reason why it wreaks such terrible havoc when it takes hold among them. Its direct cause is a bacillus, a rod-shaped bacterium called *Yersinia pestis*, which breeds in the gut of the fleas that live on the blood of the rodents. Eventually the flea's gut becomes blocked with a massive plug of teeming bacteria, so that when it feeds it injects some of the bacteria into its host. The rodent is then infected with the plague, and its fleas will carry the bacteria to other animals in the same colony.

Once in an animal (or a human), the bacteria attack the lymphatic

Camels bring goods from Asia to Europe in the 16th century. Trade brought new contact between peoples – and with the exotic silks and spices came exotic new diseases.

The rat flea Xenopsylla cheopis, *harbor of the bacteria that cause bubonic plague. Pockets of the disease still linger in the USA.*

Long before it reached Europe tales were told of the horrors that had already been visited on India and China: only one in 10 people survived an early outbreak in the province of Hopei in 1331. Across Asia the scourge came down trade routes to reach the Crimea, on the Black Sea, in 1346, where for three years the port of Kaffa (now Feodosiya) had been besieged by a Tartar army. When the plague struck, the Tartars called off the siege but not, according to legend, before first hurling diseased corpses over the walls of Kaffa with their catapults. Whether because of this grisly demonstration or simply by way of the parallel army of rats that inevitably scurried between the Tartars and the city, the people who emerged from Kaffa brought the plague out with them. A group of Genoese merchants who had been trapped within the walls reached Messina, Sicily, in the late fall of 1347; from there the plague raced around the Mediterranean by ship and along the main rivers of Europe. As winter came, the pneumonic form emerged, and the pace of infection accelerated. By 1348 plague had reached Britain, and was on its way to Moscow and into North Africa.

In Europe there were possibly 30 million dead by the time the pestilence ebbed in 1351. Between a quarter and a third of the population perished, and in places the proportion was far higher. London lost an estimated 35,000 people out of an original 60,000. The city of Smolensk, south of Moscow, boasted a mere five survivors. What

system, killing cells at a phenomenal rate and creating grotesque buboes, the size of small apples; these are swollen lymph nodes in the groin and armpits. From here bacteria can migrate to the liver, spleen and brain, making them hemorrhage and bringing on dementia. Black and purple spots appear on the skin; they are the sign of certain death, which comes within two or three days, unless the buboes burst – in which case survival is possible. In cold weather the bacillus changes its target and attacks the lungs – creating pneumonic plague, which can now spread directly from person to person as the deadly bacteria are coughed or breathed out – and breathed in by the next victim. The death rate from pneumonic plague was close to 100 per cent, and victims might die within 24 hours of infection.

In the wild, bubonic plague seems to become epidemic in rodent colonies in response to sudden, critical increases in the size of the colony – which themselves occur as good weather produces an increase in the food supply. This is what appears to have happened sometime around the 1st century CE. At that time, wild rodents were in contact with the black rats that scavenge on human communities. As the black rats died from the plague, their infected fleas sought food from people. The black rat, besides being a scavenger, is also a nimble climber: mooring ropes and gangplanks made it easy for the creature to board ships to raid cargo holds and galleys in search of food. Thus, Justinian's plague, festering in black rats, could well have come to Asia Minor overland from the steppes. Or it may have come by sea from India, where a pool of the disease seems to have existed at the conjunction of India, Burma and China.

A worldwide horror

Plague came again to Europe in the late 1340s. Sometime in the previous decade the wild Asian rodents experienced another population explosion, plague broke out among them, and was soon on the rampage in all directions.

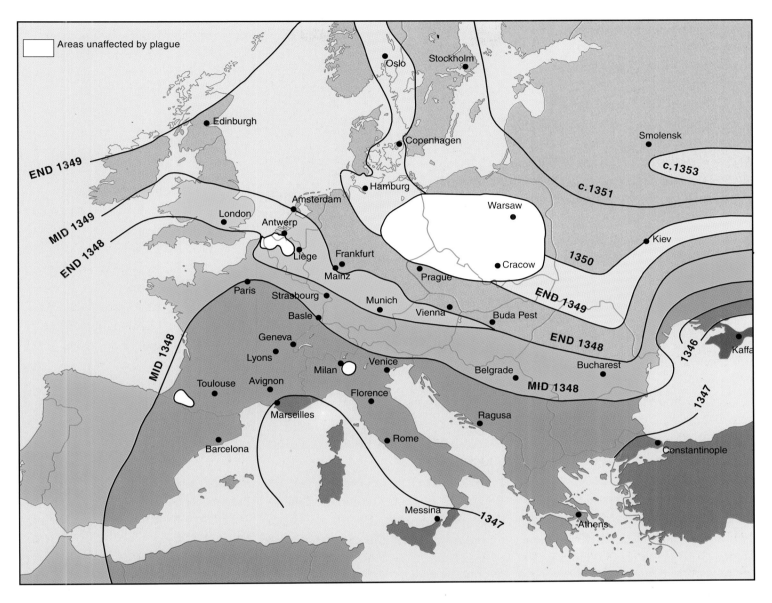

Areas unaffected by plague

How the bubonic plague spread across Europe in the middle of the 14th century, gripping all but a few isolated spots. How much faster might it travel if it broke out today?

was most terrifying was the rate at which people succumbed. In Paris, 800 a day died, in Vienna 600, and Givry, France, lost 1500 a day. Of major European cities, only Milan was unscathed. In the southern Mediterranean and the Levant, similar numbers perished: chroniclers reported that Egypt and Syria lost about a third of their populations between 1347 and 1349, and Egypt saw recurrences of the plague until the middle of the 20th century. Eastward, it ravaged China again, killing up to two thirds of the population in 1353 and 1354.

The Black Death, or Great Dying, as it was then known, might have killed fewer people in Europe and Asia had the conditions of life been less precarious. For half a century the weather had gradually been growing colder and stormier; harvests failed disastrously. In 1309 the worst famine in Europe's history began, and it lasted for 10 years. By 1325 more than one person in 10 had starved to death, and sickness was rife among the remainder. Famine recurred for another 20 years, and in the midst of it the Hundred Years' War between England and France erupted, soon to degenerate into a series of disruptive guerrilla

struggles. The Great Dying began among a weakened, ailing people. In China, in 1333, drought and famine followed the first onset of plague, and then a series of natural disasters from floods to earthquakes combined with a general insurrection against the Mongol empire to bring incessant turbulence to daily life. Epidemics were an inevitable consequence, leaving the

23

people even more than usually vulnerable to the bubonic plague when it struck China again in 1353. And no matter where it struck, workforces were disrupted or destroyed, communications broken, crops left unsown or unharvested; and famine and further sickness followed among the depleted and demoralized population.

Desperate measures

Reactions to the Great Dying varied, as might be expected, according to the culture on which it descended. There were endless desperate attempts to cure or palliate the appalling symptoms: laxatives and emetics, bleeding, fumigating houses, cauterizing the buboes or placing dried toads on them, and even bathing in urine were tried to no effect. Some efforts at controlling the spread of the plague had a basis in common sense. In 1349, King Edward

III instructed the Lord Mayor of London that 'all the human excrement and other filth lying in the streets is to be removed. You are to cause the city to be cleared from all bad smells so that no more people will die from such smells.' The Italian poet Boccaccio lamented that the plague raced through Florence in 1348 'in spite of all that human forethought could think of to avoid it, such as the cleaning of the city from many impurities, the refusal of entrance to all sick folk and humble prayers to God. Any that touched the cloaks of the sick seemed to catch the disease.'

Since the plague could not be treated, the next best thing was to try to keep it out, as Florence had tried to do, or at a distance, should it appear again. In Christian countries, quarantine was applied where it could be, following biblical injunctions for

Flagellants in the Netherlands in the 14th century. These bands of self-proclaimed martyrs hoped to take upon themselves the burden of sin which, they believed, had brought the plague upon humanity.

dealing with lepers. The first port to apply a quarantine to visiting ships was Ragusa, Italy, in 1465, followed by Venice in 1485; over the following century quarantine slowly became common throughout the Mediterranean at least. Ships were required to anchor in an isolated spot and remain there for 40 days, with no one aboard permitted to come ashore. Unfortunately the isolated anchorage was not always available, the rule was not always enforced – and the rats, together with their fleas, were perfectly capable of swimming ashore. During the Great Dying itself, a cruder form of quarantine was occasionally administered by terrified citizens: they simply nailed up the houses of victims, leaving them to starve within.

Speculation as to the cause of the plague was hardly less various than the efforts to cure it. The universally revered French surgeon Guy de Chauliac suggested that it was possible to catch the disease simply by looking at a victim. The medical doctors at the University of Paris pronounced that the astrological conjunction of Saturn, Mars and Jupiter in Aquarius that occurred on 20 March 1345 was responsible, which says as much about the value of astrology in any age as it does about the effectiveness of medicine at the time. Other candidates included earthquakes, comets, cats and dogs (whose intestinal worms were thought to carry the dread disease), lepers, gypsies, and sin. Christian zealots in Germany and neighboring countries, who were convinced that the weight of individual and collective wickedness had brought the plague as punishment from an angry deity, took the wrath of God upon themselves. They marched in procession through the cities and towns of Europe, flogging one another with whips embedded with small iron spikes and chanting 'Mea maxima culpa' ['I am most guilty']. The ritual often proved as lethal to the participants as the plague. Many of these Flagellant bands evolved from being holy beggars, modeled on the orders of friars, into bandits and muggers. Pope Clement VI at first had blessed them for their altruism; then, as they made their rejection of both church and law increasingly blatant, he had them put to the sword.

Besides blaming the sins of the world for the plague, the Flagellants encouraged their Christian brethren to seek more visible culprits: the Jews, whom they accused of poisoning wells, and physically attacked at every opportunity. Pogroms broke out everywhere, whipped up by demented priests and usually carried out by small tradesmen and artisans. They began in what is now Switzerland, where the burghers of Basel voted to kill all Jews, demolish their homes, and ban Jews from the city for 200 years. In Mainz, Germany, 12,000 Jews were burned alive. In Strasbourg, 16,000 were murdered. Such organized killings were not seen again until the Nazis conquered Europe in the 1940s.

While some European aristocrats stood aside from the slaughter – many openly hoped to be rid of their Jewish creditors – others reacted more nobly. King Casimir of Poland managed to prevent any pogroms in his country, and Duke Albert of Austria gave hundreds of Jewish families sanctuary in his castle. Pope Clementine sheltered Jews in his palace in Avignon and pronounced the Jews innocent of all crime, as did Emperor Charles VI of France and the great schools of medicine at Paris and Montpellier, but to little effect.

Reign of chaos

The orgy of misplaced vengeance upon European Jewry was part of a general collapse of rationality and social order in the face of inconceivable horror. Historian Arno Karlen writes:

Chronicles and diaries of the plague years still challenge the imagination. There are stories of infants sucking at the breasts of their dead mothers, lone survivors of entire towns walking through empty manors in robes and jewels, naked orgies in the streets, ghost ships manned only by corpses adrift at sea.

In the Islamic world, in North Africa and the Balkans, the response to the Great Dying was different. The prophet Mohamed reportedly remarked that anyone who died in an epidemic was a martyr (and therefore the recipient of divine favor), while the plague was 'a punishment that God inflicts on whom he wills, but he has granted a modicum of clemency with respect to believers'. The sayings of Mohamed are a powerful part of Moslem tradition which, together with the unspoken theme of predestination in the Koran, clearly implied that nothing could, or indeed should, stand in the way of the

An electron micrograph of Yersinia pestis *bacteria, cause of bubonic plague. The microbes enter the human bloodstream from infected fleas that feed on human blood.*

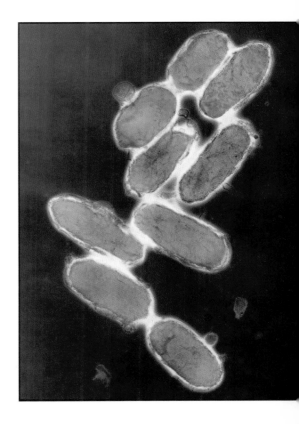

plague. Historian William McNeill comments that by the 16th century Moslem views had

> hardened against efforts to escape the will of Allah. This is well illustrated by the Ottoman [Turkish] Sultan's response to a request from [a Christian] ambassador…for permission to change his residence because plague had broken out in the house assigned to him: 'Is not the plague in my own palace, yet I do not think of moving?' Moslems regarded Christian health measures with amused disdain, and thereby exposed themselves to heavier losses from plague than prevailed among their Christian neighbors.

As McNeill points out, this fatalism turned out to be a handicap in countries that had a Moslem ruling class or imperial élite. That class tended to live in towns, which were magnets for plagues and epidemics of all kinds, and the Moslems suffered disproportionate losses as a result. In the Balkans, McNeill notes, 'the human basis for Moslem dominion speedily began to wear thin' and the Christian population's nationalist aspirations began to have some rational hope of success. The first to throw the Moslems out was Greece, in 1821, but Balkan history before and after is a confusion of attempts to break free of Islamic rule.

The persistent ravages of pandemic diseases in China probably contributed to the spread of the fatalistic Buddhist religion there and perhaps in Japan – ironically, for Buddhist missionaries from Korea brought a major epidemic disease, possibly smallpox, with them to Japan in 552 CE. Buddhism, like Christianity, taught that death was a release from the miseries of earthly existence: it put the random, unjust and inexplicable visita-

tion of uncontrollably lethal epidemics into a comprehensible scheme of things.

Christians might not welcome the immediate pain and suffering of a dreadful epidemic; God notoriously moved in mysterious ways that were incomprehensible to mere mortals, but they could at least make sense of the torment. On the one hand it was a just punishment for sin; on the other, a blessed release. Cyprian, bishop of Carthage, wrote while a plague devastated his city in 251 CE:

> This mortality is a bane to the Jews and pagans and enemies of Christ; to the servants of God it is a salutary departure…The just are called to refreshment, the unjust are carried off to torture; protection is more quickly given to the faithful; punishment to the faithless.

Such simple and sustaining faith probably explains why, when the Great Dying of the 14th century was at last over, European societies had not collapsed into anarchy. True, questions were asked more frequently than before about the worldliness, élitism and venality of the church, and poets such as Boccaccio and Chaucer mercilessly satirized the hypocrisy of monks, friars and others. This skeptical movement found final expression in the Reformation, a century and a half later. But Christianity's fundamental hold on the religious imagination of Europe remained essentially unchallenged.

Medicine without science

The church itself was ambivalent about medicine. While many religious orders were pioneers in founding hospitals all over Europe, some churchmen resisted the idea of intervening in the course of an infection. In the 12th century St Bernard, founder of the Cistercian

order of monks, held that 'to buy drugs, to consult physicians, befits not religion'. For centuries the church forbade dissection, hindering any advance in anatomical knowledge. Surgery was effective enough for relatively minor problems, within the limits of medical knowledge, lack of anesthetics, and ignorance of the virtues of antiseptics. That is, it worked if the patient could stand the pain, and if no infection set in from the operation itself. Herbal treatments and folk remedies, dispensed by 'wise women' or simply part of the common stock of knowledge, worked for some ailments: stopping the bleeding of a minor wound with a spider's web, or giving henbane to dull pain, for example. (The association of folk remedies with ancient paganism and witchcraft may have lain behind St Bernard's sour comment on using drugs.) Some treatments were prescribed according to a system of sympathetic magic: a heart-shaped leaf for an illness ascribed to the heart, for example, while the soothing effect of putting honey on a bee-sting could be taken as a sign of God's benevolence – and the sting as a signal that one had sinned.

Physicians diagnosed illness in line with the theory that four key fluids, blood, phlegm, yellow bile and black bile – called 'humors' – in the body had slipped out of balance. Too much blood (which could arise from overindulging in red meat, for instance), or hot blood, would cause fever; too much phlegm would make the body too cold, or too moist. These conditions in turn could as easily be 'caused' by astrological circumstances. A doctor faced with a foot ailment might well consider the state of the planets in Pisces (associated with the feet) before deciding on a suitable treatment.

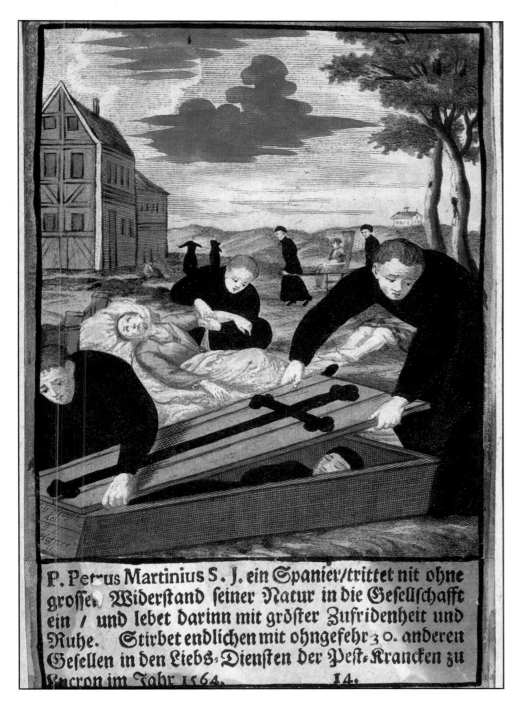

P. Petrus Martinius S. J. ein Spanier/trittet nit ohne
grosser Widerstand seiner Natur in die Gesellschafft
ein / und lebet darinn mit gröster Zufridenheit und
Ruhe. Stirbet endlichen mit ohngefehr 30. anderen
Gesellen in den Liebs-Diensten der Pest-Krancken zu
Ancron im Jahr 1564. 14.

Jesuit Father Petrus Martinius nurses and buries bubonic plague victims in Spain in 1564. The disease continued to strike in Europe for over 300 years after its initial devastating outbreak in 1347.

stomach of a Persian goat. By noon the king was dead. He was 53 years old.

Such 'treatments' were characteristic of an age that believed that lettuce was an anti-aphrodisiac, whereas eating figs could 'stere a man to veneryous actes'. There was, however, a kind of logic behind the relentless application of purges, emetics and bleeding. The idea was to cleanse the body of superfluous or tainted 'humors' and allow it to regain its natural balance. But even when pre-scientific medicine worked, it was powerless in the face of an epidemic, pandemic or plague. No one knew what caused a disease, be it smallpox, cholera or bubonic plague, and no one knew how to contain or cure it. As cancer specialist Lewis Thomas has commented, 'One reason why medical history is not much taught in medical schools is that so much of it is an embarrassment.' And even though the mechanisms of disease and the human body were gradually uncovered from the 18th century onward, it was not until the 1930s, and the discovery of sulfa drugs, that afflictions could be cured with any certainty.

So curious efforts to cure the incurable continued, and blame was apportioned with as much certainty. Syphilis, which was one of the first diseases to succumb to 20th-century science, first broke out in 1494, in Barcelona, where Nicolas Squillacio described its symptoms in a letter to a friend. In February 1495 it appeared in Italy among the army of the French king Charles VIII,

The medications themselves could border on the surreal, and no doubt often hastened death. On 2 February 1685, King Charles II of England 'felt some unusual disturbance in his brain, soon followed by loss of speech and convulsions'. His doctors responded by drawing off 16 ounces of blood and then immediately giving the king an emetic, followed by pills 'to drain away the humours', which they 'supplemented' with an enema. His head was then shaved and blistering agents applied. Next day, 10 ounces of blood were drawn off. On 4 February, the king was given 40 drops of spirit of human skull mixed in an ounce an a half of julep. Two days later, once an hour, he was taking 2 scruples of bezoar stone, which was a stone from the

who had just successfully completed a siege of Naples. When the king discharged his 50,000 mercenary soldiers, they spread the disease across Europe as they returned to their homes in Switzerland, Flanders, Spain, France and Italy. In 1498 syphilis reached India, with the sailors aboard Vasco da Gama's expedition from Lisbon to Calcutta, and from there had made its way to China by 1505 and Japan by 1512. If not precisely a plague, syphilis certainly had a profound effect on European, and perhaps more farflung, attitudes to sex. Being a sexual disease, it was easily linked with the Original Sin of Adam

and Eve: churchmen have always preferred to smudge the distinction between sexual and intellectual knowledge that was gained in Eden. As biologist Christopher Wills puts it, syphilis 'injected a new element of terror and guilt into one of our most basic drives'.

In 1495 the emperor Maximilian I declared that the affliction was a punishment for blasphemy. Such an 'explanation' presupposed the spontaneous appearance of disease through the omnipotence of God, but more materialistic notions about the new affliction were sometimes hardly rational. At the trial for treason of Cardinal

Christopher Columbus makes landfall in the Americas in 1492. The belief that Columbus's sailors caught syphilis there and brought it home with them is not entirely borne out by the available evidence.

Wolsey, Lord Chancellor of England, in 1529, it was alleged that he had given King Henry VIII syphilis by whispering in his ear. Generally, there was a rapid recognition that the disease was associated with sex, and within a decade a prosaic account of its origins was being offered. This remained the conventional wisdom among medical historians until very recently: the so-called Great Pox had been brought back from the New World by Christopher Columbus's sailors.

It is true that by 1498 syphilis was rampant in Columbus's tiny colony on Hispaniola in the West Indies, but whether it was taken there by its founders in 1494 or contracted from the natives is open to question, especially as the natives were by no means welcoming or hospitable. Claims by Amerindians that disease was a thing unknown in the Americas until the white men arrived need to be treated with caution. Almost any conditions before the advent of Europeans must very soon have seemed like a golden age and, besides, the archeological record shows that endemic maladies in the Americas included scurvy, arthritis, anemia, and other ailments associated with malnutrition, hookworms and tapeworms, mastoid infections, dysentery, tuberculosis and bartonellosis. To Europeans, Amerindians seemed young, hale and strong, and they were: they were the survivors of a deadly obstacle course of disease that killed 40 per cent of the population before it reached the age of 20, while the life expectancy of most Amerindians was not much above 30, with tribal élites living perhaps 10 years longer on average.

Direct evidence of syphilis among native Americans amounts to a single skeleton of a child showing the characteristic deformed teeth of one born with the disease. The picture is enormously complicated by the centuries-old existence of two diseases, yaws and bejel, in Africa and the Middle East as well as in pre-Columbian America. Both are caused by spirochetes that appear to be absolutely identical to the syphilis spirochete bacteria, even under electron microscopes and in the details of their DNA, yet are transmitted by ordinary contact with broken skin, not specifically sexually. Yaws produces different, far milder symptoms; in extreme cases bejel can produce the bone deformations, tissue collapse and skin lesions seen in the final stages of syphilis. Given the highly complex web of trade links between Europe, Arabia and Africa, the ability of bacteria to mutate spontaneously into different forms and the extraordinary similarity between the three bacteria involved, it is at present anyone's guess as to whether syphilis arose in the New World or the Old, and how or why.

While moralists pronounced syphilis a divine punishment for humanity's wanton behavior, physicians came up with a cure – of sorts. Arab doctors had found that breathing the fumes of heated cinnabar created enormous quantities of saliva and could make the lesions of bejel disappear, especially those around the mouth. European doctors borrowed the treatment for syphilis. Cinnabar is essentially mercuric sulfide, and mercury, we know today, is a poison that causes horrific brain damage.

Carnage in the New World

Even if syphilis was brought to Europe from the Americas, it was hardly a fair exchange for the diabolical host of diseases that Europeans unleashed among the native peoples they encountered. Historian William McNeill was inspired to begin *Plagues and Peoples*, his classic study of the influence of disease on human affairs, by the realization that the Spanish conquest of Aztec Mexico must have been boosted immeasurably by the conquistadores' unwitting but implacable ally, smallpox.

The plagues that almost erased the native Mexicans within 50 years (from an estimated 25 million people in 1518 to around three million in 1568) started with smallpox, which raced south to shatter both the Maya and Inca civilizations in Central America and Peru by the late 1520s; then came measles in 1530 and 1531, followed in 1546 by another European disease, possibly typhus. Influenza ravaged the continent, and most of the rest of the world, in 1558 and 1559; Amerindians, with no resistance at all to these Old World endemics, suffered worst. In 1589 a still-unidentified horror launched itself upon Peru. Beginning with kidney pains and headaches, it soon brought on delirium, while lesions went so deep that flesh could fall from the body. Facial skin, noses and lips could be stripped away, exposing the bones. The gruesome affliction spread into Chile, killing three in four of the population.

Over the next century mumps, scarlet fever and diphtheria arrived and took their toll, along with further sporadic outbreaks of smallpox and measles. While the Aztec, Maya and Inca civilizations were agricultural and heavily urbanized, even the relatively scattered populations of hunter, forest and pueblo tribes across the continent collapsed under the onslaught of infections. 'The Indians die so easily,' wrote a German missionary as late as 1699, 'that the bare look and smell of a Spaniard causes them to give up the ghost.' The story was repeated in the north. Arno Karlen provides a chilling sketch of how smallpox and measles felled the native peoples in North America:

Bubonic plague breaks out in Manchuria in 1911. The disease was carried by marmots, which newly arrived Chinese immigrants had begun trapping for their fur. Local tradition held that the animals should only be shot, and that sick ones were untouchable. But the newcomers caught sick and healthy marmots alike – and were at once struck down by the plague.

Le Petit Journal

ADMINISTRATION
61, RUE LAFAYETTE, 61
Les manuscrits ne sont pas rendus
On s'abonne sans frais
dans tous les bureaux de poste

5 CENT. SUPPLÉMENT ILLUSTRÉ 5 CENT.
22 me Année — Numéro 1.057
DIMANCHE 19 FÉVRIER 1911

ABONNEMENTS
SEINE et SEINE-ET-OISE... 2 fr. 3 fr. 50
DÉPARTEMENTS............ 2 fr. 4 fr. »
ÉTRANGER .... 2 50 5 fr. »

LA PESTE EN MANDCHOURIE

As in Latin America, smallpox and measles returned again and again into the nineteenth century, never absent for more than two or three decades. Amerindians perished by the village, town, and tribe. Epidemics reduced the number of Indian towns in the lower Mississippi valley by 80 per cent from 1550 to 1600; thus ended the Mound Builders' civilization. In 1645, smallpox killed half the Hurons and sent the survivors in flight from the warring Iroquois, who in turn were halved by the disease in 1684. In 1738, smallpox killed half of the Cherokees in the Charleston area; in the early nineteenth century, it destroyed two thirds of the Omahas, and in 1837–1838 almost all of the Mandans. As in Latin America, it often preceded white explorers; when George Vancouver entered Puget Sound in 1792, he was met by Indians with pockmarked faces, and found a beach strewn with human bones and skulls.

Close behind the Spanish, and later the French and English, came the first African slaves, and around the mid-17th century they brought malaria and yellow fever to the Americas. Europeans were as susceptible to malaria and yellow fever as Amerindians. Puritan preacher Cotton Mather described a 1693 outbreak of yellow fever in Boston, Massachusetts, as 'a most pestilential fever…which in less than a week's time carried off my neighbors, with very direful symptoms, of turning yellow, vomiting and bleeding in every way and so dying.' (Mather, incidentally, was one of the first to promote the new system of inoculation against smallpox in 1721.) Both yellow fever and malaria remained scourges in the New World from the tropics as far north as Canada until the 20th century; as late as the 19th century malaria was believed to be caused, if not by God, by 'miasmata' – poisonous gases emanating from the ground or stagnant water.

The Americas supported some 100 million people when the Europeans arrived and let their microbes loose on the inhabitants. By the early 19th century, the native population had been reduced to perhaps 10 million. This accidental conspiracy between man – or some men – and microbe explains how, regardless of their cavalry and firearms, so few Europeans could conquer so many Amerindians so quickly. So devastating were the white men's diseases, especially in South America, that traditional structures of authority fell apart. But this only partly explains the ease with which the Spaniards dominated the natives.

A shared belief

By a curious coincidence, both sides in the unequal battle agreed that divine providence had intervened on behalf of the invaders. Both shared a belief that plagues were a sign of divine displeasure, and it was all too plain that the Spanish were virtually immune to the scourge that fell upon the Amerindians. 'The old gods seemed to have abdicated,' as William McNeill puts it, and the natives converted to Christianity in droves. Spanish belief in the righteousness of their cause was inevitably reinforced.

In 1548 San Domingo's Spanish governor deduced from the destruction of the island's indigenous population, from an original one million to a mere 500, that 'God repented having made such ugly, vile and sinful people'.

In North America, a similar attitude prevailed. In 1630, incipient hostilities between the 10-year-old English colony in Massachusetts and the Saugast Indians ceased, according to Increase Mather (father of Cotton) because 'God ended the controversy by sending the smallpox among the Indians.... Whole towns of them were swept away,' he noted, although not one of the 300 colonists succumbed; proof enough of which people the deity favored. Four years later, William Bradford, governor of the colony, described Indians dying of smallpox 'like rotten sheep', while 'by the marvelous goodness and providence of God not one of the English was...in the least measure tainted with this disease.' This perspective was part of the long tradition of seeing higher meanings in sickness, and sickness as a species of communication from God. As historian Professor Roy Porter says, in pre-industrial societies

illness was standardly seen not as a random assault from outside, but as a deeply significant life-event, integral to the sufferer's whole being, spiritual, moral, physical, and life-course, past, present and future.... In earlier centuries life was precarious, death commonly struck in the very prime of life, and the salvation of the immortal soul was paramount: in such circumstances, each illness...had to be scrutinized for its deeper portents and meanings. And...sickness was interpreted as packed with moral, spiritual and religious messages... [and] as one of the many ways through which God revealed his will to man.

So, following the conquest of the New World, as native populations in Siberia, Polynesia, New Zealand and Australia collapsed under the weight of European microbes in the 17th and 18th centuries, the colonists could be sure that they were executing the will of God. But from the 18th century on, as well, human curiosity about the way God's creation worked led to an exponential increase in knowledge of the natural world. Disease would slowly begin to be seen not as a matter for fear, awe and desperate measures, but as a challenge to reason and science. The great breakthrough came in the middle of the 20th century, with the discovery of antibiotics.

And then came the backlash – the rise of the superbug.

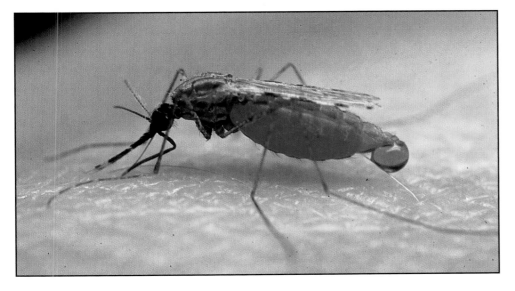

A mosquito feeding on human blood – and so gorged that it is excreting excess fluid. Yellow fever, malaria and dengue came to the Americas in mosquitoes that accompanied slaves shipped from Africa.

CHAPTER TWO

THE MIRACLE THAT FAILED

HOW WONDER DRUGS CREATED SUPERBUGS

In the late 1940s, some of the world's most formidable diseases suddenly lost their menace. Diphtheria, scarlet fever, 'strep throat', syphilis, pneumonia and other common and incurable killers were being stopped in their tracks with antibiotics. The new drugs seemed to bring the total defeat of disease within reach of humanity. Fifty years later, it had become evident that antibiotics were not only losing their power – they were actually encouraging the emergence of yet more deadly infections.

Staphylococcus aureus is one of the deadliest bacteria on earth, and one of the most common. It lurks in the human body, in pet animals, and even in the soil in fields and gardens. Usually kept at bay by the body's innate immune system, it can, given the opportunity, cause blood poisoning (septicemia), septic arthritis, infections within the bone (osteomyelitis) and, in its most virulent form, toxic shock syndrome – all of which can kill.

It was 'staph' bacteria that, in the 1920s, the Scottish bacteriologist

Testing a new antibiotic. Bacteria are placed on a neutral medium on the dishes, and pellets of the drug added. If the antibiotic works, a clear area, free of bacteria, will appear around the pellets.

Alexander Fleming saw being destroyed by a mold on one of his petri dishes – a chance event that led 20 years later to the development of wonder-working antibiotic drugs and a revolution in medicine.

At the beginning of the 1950s, when that revolution was well under way, penicillin – the original antibiotic drug – was able to stop a staph infection in its tracks in virtually 100 per cent of cases. Just 30 years later, penicillin was effective in fewer than one in 10 critical cases. The bacterium had mutated into a 'superbug', resisting all but a few new and expensive antibiotics. Nor was it alone in turning from an apparently feeble organism that the original antibiotics destroyed at a stroke into a tough, resilient, all-too-efficient killer. Penicillin was also used

to deal with another common bacterium, *Streptococcus*, which caused scarlet fever, impetigo, rheumatic fever and a host of other diseases. Some, like scarlet fever, were both common and frequently lethal. In the 1940s a four-day course of 10,000 units of penicillin a day would deal with most strep-related infections, and by the early 1950s scarlet fever had become virtually unheard-of in Europe and the USA. But in 1992, it took a daily dose of 24 million units of penicillin to combat a strep infection, and there was still no guarantee that it might not kill.

Dozens of antibiotics that had once cured an extraordinary range of infections were failing to work after only a few decades. The so-called 'Age of Antibiotics' was beginning to look like no more than a brief breathing space in the war between man and microbe. Experts warned that a new age of incurable and untreatable diseases might be dawning. Only one or two human generations would have had the benefits of antibiotic drugs. Worse, many of the deadly superbugs that were treating life-saving antibiotics as if they did not exist were thriving in uncounted billions in the very places people went to be cured. Superbugs especially flourish in hospitals.

What went wrong? Where did the superbugs come from? Have we any defense against them?

To answer those questions, we need to see how antibiotics work, and how bacteria react to them. And we also need to see how people have used antibiotics. It was not only doctors who were both over-enthusiastic and insufficiently cautious about employing these 'miracle' drugs.

Bacteria are minuscule creatures that consist of a single biological cell. They are named for their shapes: 'cocci' are round, 'bacilli' are rod-shaped, 'vibrios' look like commas, and those that resemble coils or spirals are called 'spirochetes'. The larger bacilli reach 10 microns (a hundredth of a millimeter) long; the smallest cocci may be only 175 millimicrons (millionths of a millimeter) across. Some exist independently, but others live in pairs, clusters, chains, and so on. They are neither quite plant nor quite animal, and bacterium cells, unlike those of plants and animals, have no nucleus containing a number of chromosomes. Instead, the material holding the bacterium's genetic codes, in just one chromosome, floats freely within the cell.

Bacteria reproduce by dividing themselves into two, sometimes as often as every 20 minutes or so. And they can survive almost anywhere. They have been found thriving at the heart of nuclear reactors as well as on lush grasslands and human skin; some need air to live, while others can survive only in the absence of oxygen. Untold millions of them – some of enormous benefit to us – live in or on every human being. There are more bacteria in or on a single human body than there have ever been people on earth. Perhaps even more astonishing, nine out of 10 of the 1000 million million cells that make up each one of us are bacteria.

Friends and foes

Most bacteria are crucial to the survival of life on the planet. 'Saprophytic' bacteria, for instance, keep the world both clean and green. They consume rotting vegetation and the corpses of animals, and in the process release nitrogen – which is vital to plant life – into the soil. *Staphylococcus epidermis* bacteria live all over human skin – about 150,000 of them per square centimeter (a million per square inch) – filling their niche so effectively that, in the main, other potentially harmful bacteria simply have no room to survive. *Streptococcus viridans* lives in our mouths and, likewise, by sheer force of numbers, keeps infectious invaders at bay. Relatively few bacteria are harmful, but the damage those few can cause can be horrifying, in terms of both the symptoms they produce and the numbers of people they can kill.

The physicians of old were right to believe that illness and disease arose when the natural, normal functions of the body were put out of balance (even if they were wrong about almost everything else in medicine). This is precisely what harmful bacteria do. Earlier we saw both that *Staphylococcus aureus* is a deadly bacterium and that it lives in the human body. At first glance this seems to be a contradiction, but in fact it is not. The staph and the healthy human body are in equilibrium. The bacteria are too few in number for the toxins (poisons) they emit to tax the body's immune system. The trouble starts when the staph become too numerous for the system to handle. This is what happens in toxic shock syndrome, which is caused by a particularly virulent strain of *Staphylococcus aureus*. The bacterium carries a toxic enzyme on the outside of its cell wall that will kill red blood cells, which transport life-sustaining oxygen through the body. This is called an 'exotoxin'. Bacteria that carry poisons within the cell wall are known as 'endotoxins'.

Toxic shock syndrome (TSS) was first noticed and named by doctors in 1977 among a number of children in Denver, Colorado. By October 1980, there had been 408 reported cases in the USA. All but 14 were female, and all but 20 of the women were menstruating. Forty of those infected had died. Scientists at the Centers for Disease Control (CDC) in Atlanta, Georgia, were certain that super-absorbent tampons, which were first marketed in the late 1970s and used by 71 per cent of TSS victims, were responsible. It now seems likely that the way the affected women used tampons also contributed to their affliction.

Super-absorbent tampons are able to take up to 20 times their own weight in fluid, so can be left in place for hours. Besides blood, they also absorb most of the mucus that normally lubricates the vagina. And, if left long enough, they stick to the vaginal walls as they expand. On being removed, some of the tampon may remain behind. Their other disadvantage – as researchers discovered in 1980 – is that they are excellent filters for *Staphylococcus aureus*, which means that the bacteria rest outside them on the walls of the vagina. The warm, damp conditions, in short, are perfect to allow the staph population to concentrate, multiply and survive in unnaturally large numbers. And the toxins are tiny enough to be able to reach the bloodstream through the membrane lining the vagina.

Suicide cells

Once the staph bacteria are present in large enough numbers, the body's immune system will swing into action. White blood cells called macrophages – literally 'large eaters' – stand sentry in tissues throughout the body waiting for just such an invasion. If need be they will migrate through the tissues to help other cells to fight an infection. These 'suicide cells' destroy threatening bacteria by consuming them and their poisons. The cells themselves die as a result, but serious infection is averted. If there is an invasion by huge numbers of bacteria, the macrophages will be overwhelmed; although many will complete their suicide mission, many more *Staphylococcus aureus* will rush past them, and go on to destroy red blood cells. In a full-blown attack, the red blood cells become so depleted that the body is starved of oxygen and begins, in effect, to suffocate from within.

In toxic shock syndrome, the poisonous enzyme carried by the staph bacteria is so virulent that victims go into clinical shock, becoming mentally disoriented and confused while

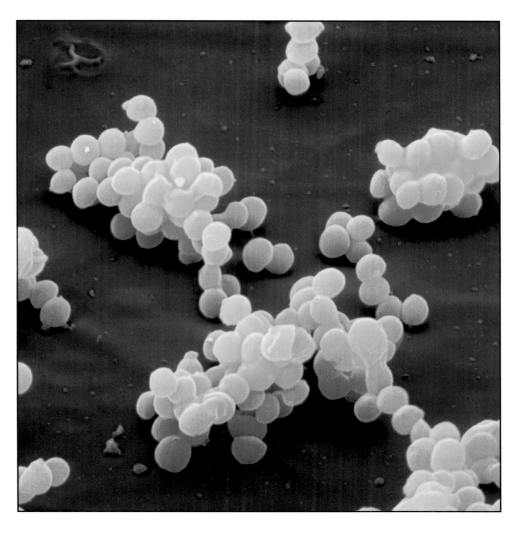

running dangerously high fevers, with drastically lowered blood pressure, diarrhea and vomiting, and kidney or liver malfunction. Once researchers had concluded that a toxic strain of staph was the culprit, they began to realize why the effects of TSS are so violent. The bacteria build up slowly in the vagina toward a catastrophic frenzy of multiplication. In most cases of TSS that the researchers had seen, the women had suffered one or two earlier infections with much milder, flu-like symptoms. This misled their immune systems – some women were actually making antibodies against their own cells – and allowed a residue of staph to remain in place to continue expanding. When the staph popula-

An electron micrograph of Staphylococcus aureus *bacteria, in their characteristic clumps and clusters. 'Staph' has reacted to attack from antibiotics by mutating into ever more virulent forms.*

tion exploded, the immune response was both inappropriate and inadequate, which put the body into shock, sometimes fatally.

Bacterial toxins are essentially chemicals that by one means or another disrupt, alter or wreck the normal chemical balance of the body. That is why and how some bacteria make us ill. For thousands of years humanity had, by and large, lived with the effects of bacterial diseases without knowing where they came from or how to combat them. In the 19th century, the search for true causes and effective cures finally got under way.

Winning a battle

The scientific campaign against bacteria opened in 1865 with Louis Pasteur's recognition that micro-organisms, which he called 'germs', were the cause of infectious diseases. Even before that astute doctors had recognized that cleanliness – or lack of it – had some connection with infections. In 1806 England had witnessed a bizarre scene as a direct result of that insight, when the Member of Parliament for Evesham, Mr Humphrey Howarth, was challenged to a duel by Lord Barry-

more. Few duels with pistols ended in death, but, in any case, Howarth was less concerned about being shot dead than about the possibility of being wounded. He was particularly afraid that pieces of his clothing might be driven into the wound. Howarth had served as a surgeon in the East India Company's private army and had seen the gruesome infections that could result from battlefield injuries filled with dirty fibers. And, being a doctor, he doubtless had no wish to put himself at the mercy of others of his profession, should his wound become septic. Howarth therefore arrived at the appointed time and place for the duel, and proceeded to prepare for the contest by undressing entirely. Lord

Barrymore, confronted by a naked opponent, declared the situation too ridiculous to continue and departed. Honor was apparently satisfied, for the pair never met again.

Similarly, in 1847, the Hungarian-born physician Ignaz Semmelweis noticed that mothers who gave birth in one maternity ward of the Viennese General Hospital in Austria suffered an horrific rate of deaths – between 10 and 30 per cent – from puerperal (childbed)

The Agnew Clinic, *painted by Thomas Eakins in 1889. Then, microbes were barely understood: surgeons and nurses worked without masks, in conditions that would not be tolerated today.*

fever. Only about three per cent of those giving birth in a second ward died from the fever. And women who came to the hospital after having babies rarely contracted the disease. In the first ward, deliveries were made by medical students who often came straight from dissecting cadavers; in the other ward, midwives attended births. Semmelweis reasoned that the students were carrying some kind of poison from the dissecting room into the maternity ward, and he insisted that they rinse their hands in lightly chlorinated water before helping with deliveries. The death rate fell to a mere one per cent, but Semmelweis's innovation infuriated the medical establishment, because it implied that the doctors could have saved the dead women. Semmelweis lost his job in 1850 and died, insane, in 1865, the year that Pasteur conceived his 'germ theory'.

Pasteur's discovery of the existence of microbes and their function in disease made scientific sense of the insights of men like Howarth and Semmelweis. The English surgeon Joseph Lister at once connected Pasteur's theory with infections of wounds. He was already aware that sewage was being successfully treated with carbolic acid, and began to use the acid in solution to clean wounds and as an antiseptic spray during surgery. Within two years he could report that his wards at Glasgow Royal Infirmary had been free of sepsis (blood poisoning from a contaminated wound) for nine months.

Magic bullets

None of these antiseptic measures could treat endemic killers such as scarlet fever, diphtheria or tuberculosis, although they could make it far more

difficult for an epidemic to launch itself and transform into a plague. It was not until the 1880s that the precise 'germs' involved in even a few individual diseases became known, when the brilliant German scientist Robert Koch worked out how to identify bacteria, how to grow them in the laboratory, and how to isolate the microbes responsible for anthrax, septicemia, tuberculosis and cholera (among others). Ten years passed before another German, Paul Ehrlich, coined the phrase 'magic bullets' for his own great aim – to discover specific drugs to kill specific disease-causing microbes without killing the patient as well. In 1909 Ehrlich developed arsphenamine, which he called Salvarsan – the first drug that was lethal to the microbes that cause syphilis. Salvarsan was a compound based on arsenic – a highly toxic element, as many murderers had demonstrated – and, although it could cure syphilis, it could also have grim side-effects.

For nearly a quarter of a century the search for more magic bullets seemed to be stalled. Then, in 1932 another German chemist, Gerhard Domagk, discovered that a compound based on sulfur would kill the deadly *Streptococcus* that caused blood poisoning. It worked on mice, and it worked on his daughter, who was dying of septicemia. Within 10 years doctors could choose, as popular science writer Isaac Asimov put it, 'from a whole platoon' of the new 'sulfa' drugs to treat a huge range of infections, from puerperal fever and pneumonia to gonorrhea and meningitis. Even so, there were sometimes sickening prices to pay for the advantages of these early miracle drugs. One of the most shocking was Lyell's syndrome, in which the skin peels off

the victim's body in sheets. Others included hepatitis, kidney failure, and anemia. More frequently, patients treated with sulfa drugs suffered muscle pain, hallucinations and nightmares, insomnia, vomiting, depression, dizziness, or loss of appetite, among other distressing side-effects. Then, by an amazing accident, came penicillin.

The perfect cure

It is a curious fact that Alexander Fleming noticed the effect of penicillin on a strain of deadly staph bacteria four years before Domagk discovered sulfa drugs. One day in 1928, Fleming had set up some petri dishes of *Staphylococcus aureus* in his lab at St Mary's Hospital in London. He then noticed some specks of green mold in the nutrient on which the bacteria were flourishing – and that around the mold the potentially lethal bacteria had vanished. Intrigued, Fleming isolated the mold and encouraged it to grow, then tested its effect on other disease-causing bacteria. It killed some, but not all. He identified the mold as *Penicillium notatum*, a fungus not very different from the one that grows on stale bread, and named its active ingredient 'penicillin'. Fleming tried more than once to reproduce the result of his initial observation, but failed every time. He really did happen upon penicillin by a lucky accident. Later experiments showed that what he had seen could occur only in very limited circumstances, and they happened in his laboratory purely by chance.

Fleming duly reported his observation in a scientific journal, but neither he nor anyone else followed up penicillin's potential as a mass medication for nearly a dozen years. It was left to the Australian Howard Florey and

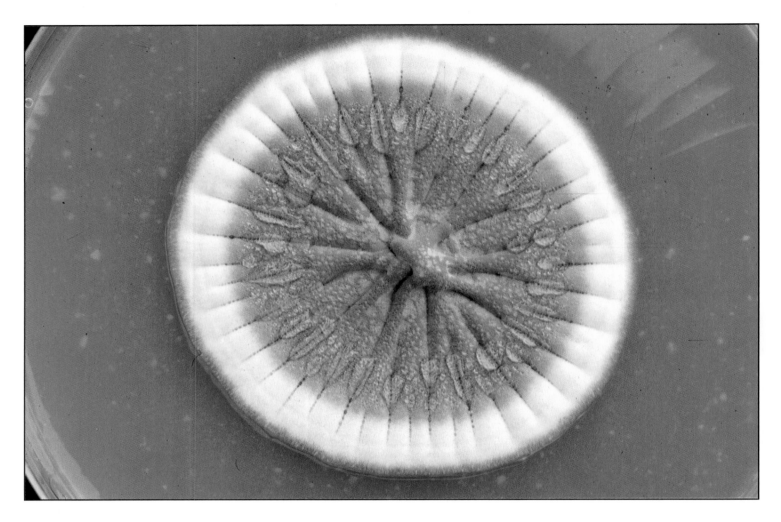

German-born Ernst Chain, both at Oxford University in England, to work out – against considerable odds – how to produce penicillin in large quantities. Their experiments also revealed a crucial quality of the new antibiotic. To be effective the treatment had to be continued until the whole colony of microbes had been mopped up, not just until the symptoms subsided. However, by then World War II had broken out, and because the UK's medical industry was at full stretch, Florey went to the USA to oversee production of the first large batches of penicillin.

Penicillin works by sabotaging the way dangerous bacteria grow: it weakens the cell wall, so that the bug swells, bursts and dies. Many other antibiotics also work by killing bacte-

ria. Some do so by interfering with the function of enzymes within or on the bacterial cell. Some antibiotics do their work differently – for example by attacking the bacterium's single chromosome and interfering with its DNA. This disrupts its ability to reproduce, and stops its rampage through the body in its tracks. In either case it has always been a medical dictum that the key to successful antibiotic treatment is to 'complete the course' – to take enough of the drug to wipe out all the infectious bacteria.

When penicillin first became available in the early 1940s it was rare and costly, and was at once conscripted for the Allied war effort. In 1943, when only 13kg (29lb) of penicillin were made, British Prime Minister Winston

Penicillium notatum growing on a specially prepared gel derived from seaweed. This is the fungus that in 1928 Alexander Fleming found could kill deadly bacteria.

Churchill decreed that the new drug 'must be put to the best military use'. The UK and USA had millions of servicemen strung out across the world. When not caught up in the heat of battle, they were doing what campaigning soldiers have always done, and syphilis and gonorrhea were rife among them. The generals decided to use their meager supplies of penicillin to get VD-ridden soldiers fit to fight, as well as to help combat casualties.

With the end of the war penicillin could be manufactured in commercial quantities, and by 1953 some 400 tonnes a year were being made and prescribed. It really did seem to be a miracle worker. Not only did it cure long-standing and destructive scourges like syphilis and gonorrhea, it vanquished bacterial pneumonia, meningitis, puerperal fever, septicemia, and a whole host of sometimes fatal childhood infections of the ear, nose and throat, including the dreaded 'strep throat'. And it did so with no apparent side-effects. In 1950 Dr Philip Evans, a prominent London pediatrician, gave his opinion that 'one cannot give an overdose' of penicillin, even to children.

The next seemingly magical antibiotic was streptomycin, isolated at the University of New Jersey at Rutgers in 1944 and soon in large-scale production. Its reputation was made when it proved effective against another dread endemic disease: tuberculosis. Like Fleming, Florey and Chain, the pioneers of penicillin, the discoverer of streptomycin, Selman Waksman, was awarded the Nobel prize. Other antibiotics quickly followed. Chloramphenicol arrived in 1947, to sweep through the bacteria behind whooping cough, diphtheria (previously a mass killer of children), gastroenteritis, dysentery, and the plague diseases typhoid, cholera and anthrax, plus a multitude of lesser infections. In 1948 came tetracycline, the first 'broad-spectrum' antibiotic – 'not so much a magic bullet as a magic bomb', in the words of popular medical author Geoffrey Cannon. Tetracycline was (and still is) used to treat acne, bronchitis, cholera, conjunctivitis, ear infections, pneumonia, and typhus, among other afflictions. Tetracycline's huge advantage, it seemed at the time, was that it could be used effectively even when the diagnosis was none too certain. Today it is given to intensively reared livestock as a matter of course, to promote growth and as a preventative treatment ('prophylactic'), simply because it is a 'one-shot stop' for so many potential infections.

Only one new family of antibiotics has been produced since the 1960s – quinolones. Their main use is to treat infections in the urinary tract, although there has been industry pressure to broaden their application – which, as we shall soon see, carries definite risks. Quinolones work by wrecking the chromosomes of bacteria. They appear to have no effect on human chromosomes; if they have, the consequences will be serious, since anyone taking these drugs is likely to

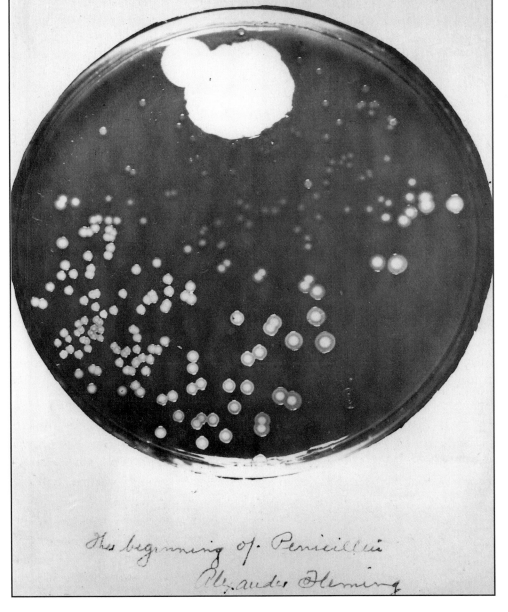

Alexander Fleming's photograph of Penicillium notatum *destroying 'staph' bacteria. Medical science ignored his historic discovery for more than a decade.*

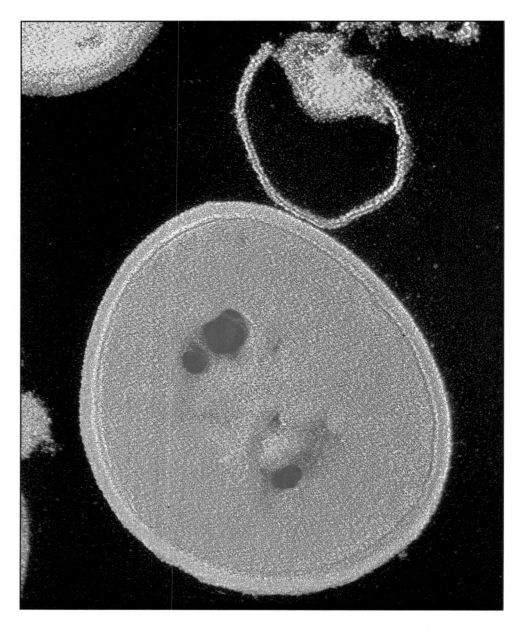

A complete 'staph' bacterium, and one that is breaking apart from the effects of an antibiotic drug, which has destroyed the cell's outer membrane.

produce deformed children. Some microbiologists are uneasy about drugs that work at such a fundamental level. Furthermore, quinolones are synthetic – they have no equivalents in nature – and no one can be entirely sure what their effects on natural organisms will be. Some alarming side-effects have

already been seen. One variant, temafloxacin, caused blood, liver and kidney disorders, shock and occasionally death before it was withdrawn in 1992. Others have been known to bring on skin reactions, disorientation, fits and even psychosis (madness).

Poisoned fruit

Even in the early 1950s it was apparent that, far from being impossible to overdose, the new miracle drugs were capable of producing occasionally devastating side-effects. And, with

family doctors prescribing the drugs for all manner of ailments, even non-bacterial ones, 'just in case', surgeons spraying them around operating rooms, and hospital doctors spraying them around wards to keep infections at bay, resistant strains of bacteria soon began to appear. Both these aspects of the wonder drugs – their side-effects and their all-too-liberal use – have contributed to the development of superbugs and the possible end of the antibiotic era.

The less than miraculous side-effects of penicillin included standard allergic reactions – rashes, nausea, diarrhea. Streptomycin was more vicious, producing fever, numbness, and damage to the kidneys and ears. In extreme cases the latter could lead to deafness and loss of the sense of balance.

In 1952 American researchers found that chloramphenicol could suppress the formation of blood cells in the bone marrow of some patients, so that they died of severe anemia. The effect on babies was particularly catastrophic. In the 1950s premature babies were given chloramphenicol as a prophylactic; hundreds died of a mysterious 'gray baby syndrome' before it was discovered they had been killed by anemia induced by the antibiotic intended to protect them. In the West, chloramphenicol is now reserved for use against typhoid fever and meningitis, and as a drug of last resort, but it is freely used without medical supervision in many developing countries, for ailments as trivial as a simple fever.

Tetracycline had a similar dismal downside. Apart from inducing allergic reactions, it affected kidney function, and the growth of teeth and bones in children, and caused difficulties in swallowing, and soreness of the tongue and anus; some patients produced yellow-green feces. Today, apart from being given to animals in agribusiness, tetracycline too is used more in the developing world than in the West.

Antibiotics may not harm human cells while they damage or kill dangerous bacteria, but their assault on microbes does not stop with those that threaten our health. Broad-spectrum antibiotics especially will also attack and wipe out whole colonies of 'commensal' bacteria – those that live harmlessly in us and, more to the point, often contribute to our health and well-being. One example is *Lactobacillus acidophilus*, which lives in the genital passage of women. It secretes lactic acid, which helps to protect against fungal infection. Another 'friendly' bacterium is *Escherichia coli*, which is a 'facultative anaerobe', meaning it usually lives without air, but will survive in it if need be. It lives in the gut, and mops up air that enters with our food. This is doubly useful. First, it protects the 'anaerobic' bacteria (ones that cannot survive in air) that help to digest food and, like the bacteria on our skin, keep us healthy simply by shutting out other, possibly hazardous, microbes. Second, it keeps air out of the gut that otherwise could let disease-bearing, aerobic microbes flourish.

Some 400–500 species of commensal bacteria live in the mucous membrane that lines the gut (and in the one lining the passages that take air to the lungs, as well). We know little about these bacteria, but they are virtually inseparable from the mucous membrane: the combination has been called 'living wallpaper'. This membrane is also part of the body's defenses. The mucus is a thick fluid that lubricates the passage, moistens tissue and protects it, and is constantly secreted from the membrane along with natural antibiotics. The membrane is continually renewing itself, shedding its own cells, dead bacteria, exhausted mucus and toxins that we take in with air, food and drink.

When a wide-spectrum antibiotic is launched against an invasion of poisonous bacteria, millions of our friendly, commensal bacteria die along with the

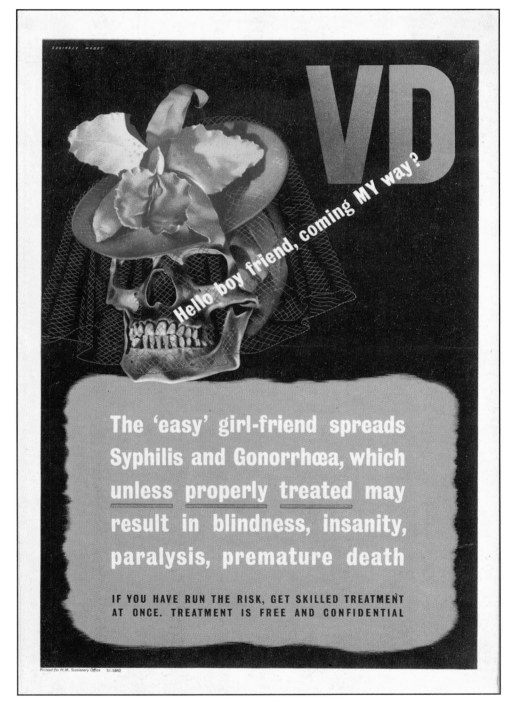

A poster warning of the dangers of venereal disease – real enough in the days before antibiotics. Rather less impressive is the implication that the diseases were somehow spread exclusively by women – how did they get infected in the first place?

ANTIBIOTIC CLASS	DRUGS IN THE CLASS	HOW DRUGS CONTROL BACTERIA	BASIS OF BACTERIAL RESISTANCE
Penicillin	amoxicillin, ampicillin, carbenicillin, penicillin G, penicillin K, ticarcillin, penicillin V, cyclacillin, bacampicillin, azlocillin, mezlocillin, pipercillin	Prevent bacteria from building their protective wall	Plasmids are small particles found in bacteria that consist of a double strand of DNA (protein) that can be quickly transmitted from cell to cell. Plasmids transmit DNA to bacteria, enabling them to make a new protein (such as the penicillinase enzyme) that inactivates the drug. Beta-lactamase is another protein produced by plasmid-infected bacteria: it destroys the beta-lactam part of penicillin
Penicillinase-Resistant Penicillins	methicillin, naficillin, oxacillin, cloxacillin, dicloxacillin	Act in the same way as penicillins	1. Prevent binding of the antibiotic onto the bacteria, by changing the structure of the protein into which the antibiotic attaches itself, just as an old key will not fit into a lock that has been changed 2. Produce penicillinase, ie the plasmid-infected bacteria produce new chemicals that destroy the antibiotics
Cephalosporins	cephalosporin C, cefonicid, cefuroxime, cefaclor, cefoxitin, cefamandole, cephradine, cephalexin, cefazolin, cephapirin	Act by stopping the bacteria from renewing their cell wall	1. Beta-lactamase as before 2. Blockage of antibiotic binding, as when a key will not fit into a lock that already has something in it 3. The bacteria produce new chemicals that break down the antibiotics
Aminoglycosides	kanamycin, gentamicin, netilmicin, amikacin, tobramycin, streptomycin, neomycin	Act by stopping the bacteria from making new proteins that they require to function and multiply	1. Bacteria inactivate the drug by altering its chemical constitution. The change is mediated by a plasmid. 2. A mutation that changes the cell membrane stops the antibiotic getting to the bacteria, just as barbed wire on a wall stops an intruder climbing over
Tetracyclines	chlortetracycline, oxytetracycline, demeclocycline, methacycline, doxycycline, minocycline, tetracycline	Act by stopping the bacteria from making essential proteins	1. Plasmids make the bacterial cell's protein factory less susceptible to the antibiotics 2. Bacteria develop a transport system that pumps the antibiotics back out
Chloramphenicol	chloramphenicol	Acts by stopping the bacteria from making essential proteins by destroying the framework on which they are produced	Plasmids help the bacteria to make chemicals to inactivate the antibiotic
Erythromycin	erythromycin	As chloramphenicol	1. A change in the cell membrane stops the antibiotic getting to the bacteria ('barbed wire on the wall' — see Aminoglycosides) 2. Modification of the framework on which the bacterial proteins are built, so that the proteins can continue to be produced by the bacteria 3. Production of a chemical that destroys the antibiotic
Clindamycin	clindamycin, lincomycin	As chloramphenicol	Modification of the framework on which the proteins are built, so that the proteins can continue to be produced by the bacteria
Vancomycin	vancomycin	Acts by stopping the bacteria from renewing their cell walls	Production of a unique substance that blocks the antibiotic action
Sulfonamides	sulfanilamide, sulfadiazine, sulfamethoxazole, sulfisoxazole, sulfacetamide	Prevent the bacteria producing an essential vitamin-like substance (folic acid) required by the growing and dividing bacteria	1. A plasmid or random change in the bacteria allows them to continue producing the folic acid they need 2. Production of a chemical that destroys the antibiotic
Trimethoprim	trimethoprim, sulfamethoxazole, usually in combination	As sulfonamides	Mutation allows the cell to produce the folic acid it requires by another route
Quinolones	nalidixic acid, cinoxacin, norfloxacin, ciprofloxacin	Act by stopping proper coiling of bacterial DNA	Unclear, suspected to be chromosomally based change
Isoniazid	isoniazid	Kills rapidly dividing mycobacteria, mechanism unknown	Unclear
Rifampin	rifampin	Inhibits RNA polymerase, thus blocking protein synthesis	Alteration of polymerase
Ethambutol	ethambutol	Unclear	Unclear
Streptomycin	streptomycin	Stops the growth of mycobacteria; mechanism unclear	Unclear
Pyrazinamide	pyrazinamide	Unknown	Unknown
Ethionamide	ethionamide	Unclear	Unknown
Aminosalicylic acid	aminosalicylic acid	Similar to sulfonamides	Unknown
Cycloserine	cycloserine	Unclear	Unclear
Sulfones	dapsone, sulfoxone sodium	Similar to sulfonamides	Unclear
Clofazimine	clofazimine	Blocks mycobacterial DNA	Unknown

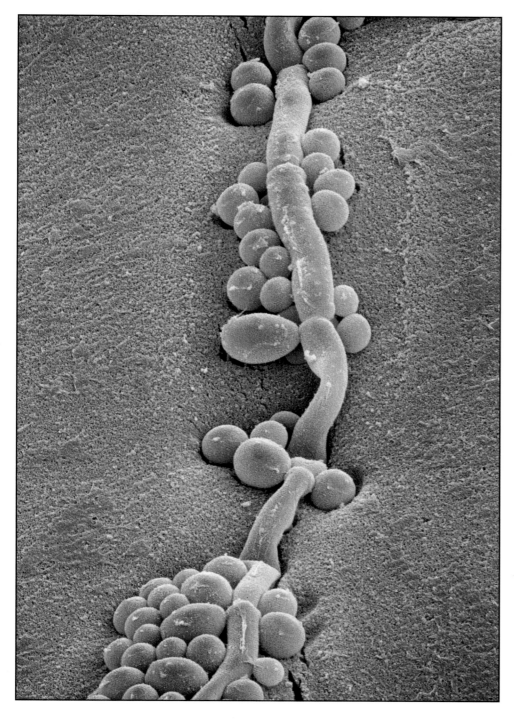

The fungus Candida albicans, *cause of the oral and vaginal infection thrush. Friendly bacteria usually keep it under control, but if they die as a side-effect of a course of antibiotic treatment, the fungus takes the opportunity to expand.*

commensal bacteria that the antibiotic does not affect, fungi, the few naturally resistant members of the infective bacteria, or new and hazardous bacteria from outside that now meet no built-in defenses. Examples of usually harmless commensal microbes are the *Clostridium difficile* bacillus and the *Candida albicans* fungus, whose relatively sparse numbers are usually dominated by bacteria of the 'living wallpaper'. The first can cause a distressing, sometimes fatal, form of colitis, and the second is the cause of thrush. Repeated doses of antibiotics will upset our internal natural balance more and more, and create more and more opportunities for such normally suppressed microbes to flourish. Their suddenly expanding populations make it harder for 'friendly' bacteria to re-establish themselves in the gut – and some of them have also caused new and serious diseases.

This is the phenomenon known as 'superinfection'. To combat it, doctors' natural reaction is to pour more antibiotics, of a different type, into the system. If the superinfection is accurately diagnosed, this second antibiotic treatment – at least in countries where it is available and affordable – will be more specific and very likely effective. In countries where cheap, broad-spectrum antibiotics are the only ones available to all but the wealthy, the superinfection is likely to run its course – and additional antibiotics will not

invaders. At the same time, the mucous membrane reacts to the drug as if it is a poison. So it is not surprising that one very common side-effect of antibiotic treatment is diarrhea. This is actually a healthy, if painful and distressing, reaction. The gut, overloaded with poison, is renewing itself as fast as it can, throwing out the invading

bacteria and trying to get its own bacteria back into balance.

Unfortunately, this doesn't always happen when antibiotics have decimated the gut's natural bacteriological defenses. With the inner ecology disturbed, niches open up for less friendly microbes to multiply and colonize the gut. These may be other

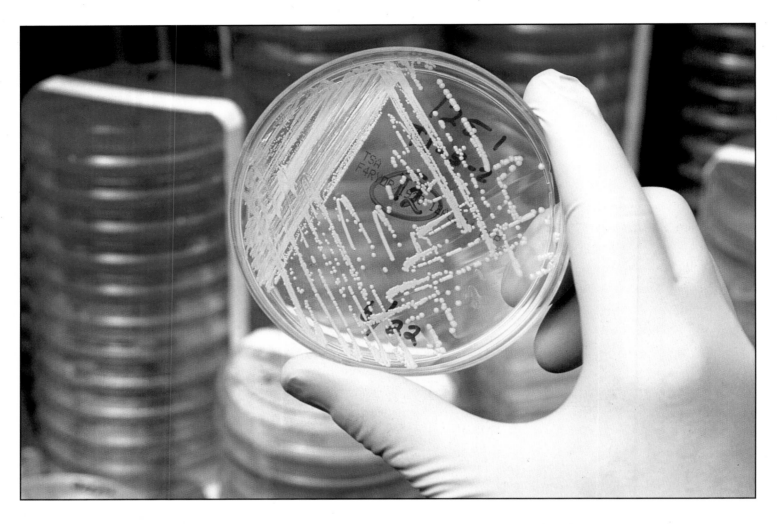

help. In such places the superinfections may include dysentery, cholera, typhoid or other traditional plague diseases, picked up during the initial treatment and blooming in a suddenly friendly environment.

Or something worse may have happened.

Losing the war

Antibiotics, no matter how sharply focused on disease-bearing microbes, don't always halt or kill all the bacteria they target. An infection may be caused by millions of individual organisms, and some species reproduce in less than an hour. This means that one million dangerous bacteria entering the body will shortly produce a second generation of two million – and a third

of four million and a fourth of eight million – and so on. With such huge populations doubling rapidly all the time, it is inevitable that some of these offspring will not be exact replicas of their 'parents'. While they make up only a small proportion of the whole population, such mutants are still multitudinous. As Professor Jacques Monod, former director of the Pasteur Institute in Paris, has explained:

a population of several thousand million [bacterial] cells can develop in a few milliliters of water. In a population of that size, there will be maybe ten, or a hundred, or a thousand examples of any given mutation, and maybe a hundred thousand or a million mutants of all types. In so large a population,

The physician's nightmare: a strain of 'staph' that is impervious to all known antibiotic drugs. It is seen here growing in white colonies on a laboratory medium.

mutation is not the exception: it is the rule.

The biochemical make-up of the mutant cells will be minutely different. In some, perhaps most, cases this may make no difference to either the afflicted host or the bacteria. Antibiotics or natural defenses will wipe them out anyway. But in some instances, the mutant bacteria will be blessed – from their own point of view – with the ability to resist whatever drugs are thrown at them. They will still be poisonous to their human host.

This is the simplest form, the first generation, of superbugs. And they will reproduce just as fast as their forebears.

But, as we have seen, prolonged attack by antibiotics encourages usually harmless microbes to flourish and, by sheer weight of numbers, cause damage. Other antibiotics sent to cope with these outbreaks will also leave behind resistant mutants. So, not only will potentially deadly bacteria have been made less amenable to treatment, but previously harmless micro-organisms may well have been turned into

hostile ones. The response of medical science and the drug industry has been to design ever more powerful antibiotics targeted on resistant strains of bacteria. The response of the bacteria has been to become resistant to an increasing number of drugs.

The classic evolutionary theory derived from the work of Charles Darwin says that, strictly, the bacteria have not responded at all. Natural selection has done the work. Bacteria have simply evolved at unusual, not to say unnatural speed, and the fittest –

those with drug resistance accidentally built-in – have survived. Unfortunately, standard evolutionary theory breaks apart in the sub-microscopic world of bacterial genetics. Bacteria can, it seems, pass on resistance to antimicrobial attack to one another without having to inherit it, and they do so in an astonishing array of ways.

In 1983 the US geneticist Dr Barbara McClintock won the Nobel prize for medicine for her discovery that genes could change position on the chromosomes of maize. She had done this work, battering the plants with X-rays to force the changes, in the 1940s and 1950s; it was only in the early 1980s that its significance became apparent. In the 1950s too, Dr Tomoichiro Akiba of Tokyo University discovered that *Shigella dysenteriae* bacteria in the intestines of victims of bacillary dysentery were resistant to all four antibiotics then used to treat the disease. This flew in the face of all expectations based on the classic Darwinian idea of evolution. Still more extraordinary, Dr Akiba found that the *Escherichia coli* in the patients' guts were also resistant to all four antibiotics. If one assumed one mutation in every million bacteria, the odds of this happening by chance alone were one in 10^{48} (one million followed by 42 zeroes). Further experiments in Japan showed conclusively that, somehow, one species of bacterium was

Nobel prizewinner Dr Barbara McClintock holds a sample of maize from a plant that she forced to mutate under the influence of X-rays. Her work showed that genes could migrate within the plant's chromosomes – a crucial key to the way bacteria develop resistance to antibiotic drugs.

Microbiologist Professor Alexander Tomasz of Rockefeller University, who found that bacteria scavenge free-floating genetic material and use it to develop resistance to drugs. Tomasz warns that antibiotics may soon lose all their effectiveness.

passing its drug resistance to an entirely different species.

In 1963 Dr Tsutomo Watanabe published his solution to the mystery. Bacteria have only one chromosome, made up of genes carrying vital information in the form of chemical codes (segments of deoxyribonucleic acid, or DNA) that ensure the cells reproduce properly. But Dr Watanabe found that, unlike other cells, bacteria also contain free-floating rings of DNA (known today as plasmids). These live and reproduce within the bacterial cell wall; they may, indeed, be separate organisms. They can pass from one bacterium to another when a pair touches – and even from one species of bacterium to another. Crucially, the genetic code of plasmids carries information telling the bacteria how to resist antibiotic attack. By 1980, plasmids were commonly carrying genes that defended bacteria against up to 10 antibiotics. As Dr Richard Novick of the New York Public Health Institute put it: 'The rather frightening clinical implication of this accumula-

tion of resistance genes is that treating a patient with a single drug can promote the selection of an organism that is resistant to everything in sight.'

That, as we shall see, is exactly what happened, but plasmids are not the only means whereby bacteria alter or develop their armory of resistance. What Dr Barbara McClintock forced to happen in maize chromosomes occurred naturally in bacteria: single 'jumping' genes would switch from one part of the chromosome to another within a cell and, like plasmids, could also hop from one bacterium and one species to another. Some of these 'transposons' consisted of whole strings of genes. All could carry codes for resisting antibiotics and, to add to the confusion of microbiologists hoping to counteract all this shape-shifting, it became clear that plasmids too could integrate themselves into the cell's chromosome. Even sections of plasmids could move from one plasmid to another or attach themselves to the chromosome of their own or another bacterium.

Pneumococci bacteria, which cause

numerous infections of the ear, nose, trachea and lungs, including pneumonia, are not too good at taking plasmids on board, so they employ another strategy. All bacteria are great scavengers of potentially useful genetic bits and pieces, but *Pneumococci* are past masters in the art of scrounging. Bacteriologist Alexander Tomasz, of Rockefeller University, New York, actually photographed *Pneumococci* devouring the random strings of DNA that drift through our bodies. As human hoarders and scavengers say, you never know when it might come in handy.

Endless permutations of genetic changes, in fact, are happening all the time among bacteria to ensure their survival, and the busiest traffic is among the very species that the miracle drugs were designed to eradicate. Geoffrey Cannon has summed up the prospect that now confronts us:

Drug resistance caused by random mutation of specific bacterial species can always be overcome by use of a different antibiotic.... But drug resistance that is multiplied and transferred between bacteria, and from one bacterial species to another, is incalculably ominous. For there is no way of knowing how far or fast such drug resistance will spread, or when and where outbreaks...of bacterial infection will prove to be untreatable.

But what *could* be predicted was that highly resistant superbugs would begin

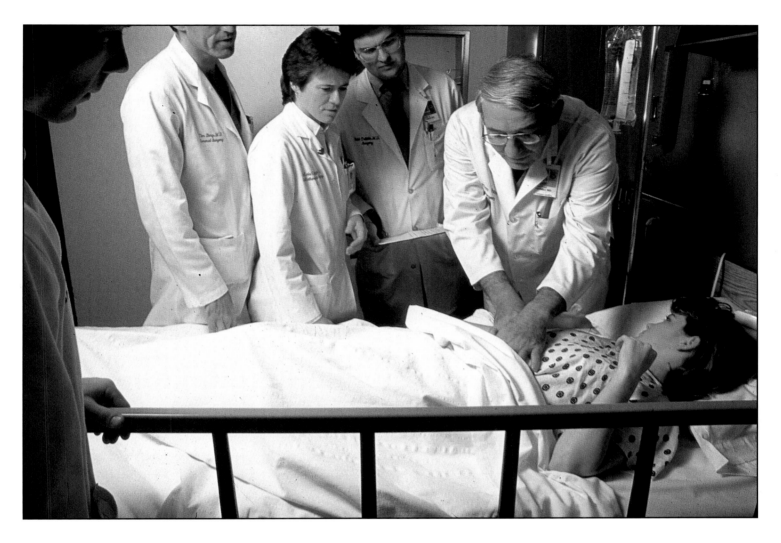

Doctors attend a hospital patient. Their sterile-seeming white coats provide a handy vehicle for bacteria to travel from patient to patient and from ward to ward.

to appear where there was a high concentration of sick people, antibiotics and bacteria together in a restricted space: hospitals.

In superbug heaven

'In May 1982,' medical journalist Laurie Garrett tells us, 'a newborn baby died on the neonatal ward of the University of California at San Francisco's Moffit Hospital of a strain [of *Staphylococcus aureus* bacteria] that was resistant to the penicillins, cephalo-

sporins, and naficillin.' In 1952, *Staphylococcus aureus* bacteria were almost 100 per cent vulnerable to penicillin. Thirty years later that figure had dropped by 90 per cent. The bacteria had, at some stage, adopted a plasmid that produced an enzyme known as a beta-lactamase, and the plasmid had then jumped into the staph's chromosome – to be passed on ever after to succeeding generations. The beta-lactamase enzyme disrupts the active ingredient in penicillin that, in effect, eats a hole in the bacterium's cell wall and makes it explode. The staph that struck in San Francisco had developed the ability to defeat a whole armory of other antibiotics. It was one of the first true superbugs.

At the Moffit Hospital, the immediate source of the killer staph was a nurse, and unwittingly she had also infected two other babies. So alarmed were the hospital authorities by the emergence of the superbug that they treated the ward staff and babies with antibiotics that would kill it, closed the ward, stripped it of rubber fittings, curtains, sheets – anything that could harbor the staph – and scrubbed everything that was left with disinfectants. But even this radical purge could only be a holding action.

Although *Staphylococcus aureus*, as we noted earlier, is everywhere, it is harmless unless it gets into a cut, wound or burn – or someone whose immune system is under stress. Then it

A newborn child in intensive care. When antibiotics are used to protect very young children, they may build up a resistance that weakens the effect of the drugs when they are more urgently needed in later life.

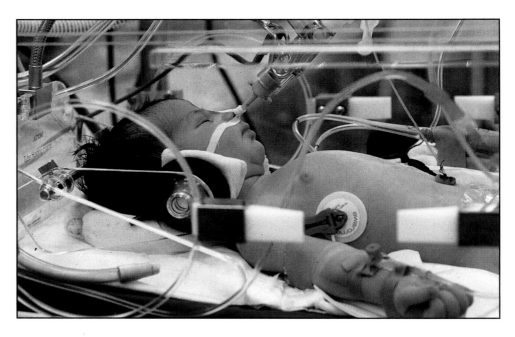

will thrive at its host's enormous expense. Anyone who worked in a hospital – nurses, doctors, lab technicians, cleaning staff, cooks, porters, electricians – could pick up staph, even out of their own garden, and bring it into a hospital at no risk to themselves. Once there, they could easily pass it on to any number of potential, and well-nigh perfect, new habitats. Hospitals are full of people who – accidentally or by the surgeon's knife – are wounded or burned, and of the very young and very old, all of whose immune systems are already working at full stretch.

The growing danger

On top of that, antibiotics are everywhere in hospitals. Particularly at risk are children in intensive care units, with open wounds and immune systems not yet fully formed but at their lowest ebb, lying in a cocoon of powerful antibiotics. Nor are all hospitals gleaming antiseptic havens. A 1982 World Health Organization (WHO) report noted: 'Many surgeons seek to compensate for poor hygienic conditions in their operating theater or wards by employing prophylaxis…. This results in excessive antibiotic use and is certainly counterproductive.' It is self-defeating because it puts massive pressure on staph and other bacteria to adapt any or all of their myriad genetic routines to build increasingly sturdy defenses against the drugs.

In the 1960s doctors had largely abandoned the penicillins in favor of methicillin. The new drug side-stepped the beta-lactamase resistance in staph, but only for a few years. When the staph superbug of the 1980s appeared, it was soon dubbed MRSA – methicillin-resistant *Staphylococcus aureus*; but the name hid a multitude of other defenses. Bacteria that could shrug off methicillin also generally were able to survive attack by all members of the penicillin and 'super-penicillin' classes of antibiotics, as well as all those in the aminoglycoside, tetracycline, cephalosporin, erythromycin and clindamycin classes – which amounted to some 45 generic antibiotics, and many more branded formulations of the drugs.

MRSA soon moved out of hospitals and into the wider community, spreading through kindergartens and day-care centers where it latched onto children with minor cuts and scratches, and through inner cities by drug users who shared needles. In 1992 some 15 per cent of all strains of *Staphylococcus aureus* in the USA were MRSA, as were a staggering 40 per cent of those found in large US hospitals. Put in

human terms the figures are still more striking. Of 23 million Americans who had surgery that year, 920,000 developed post-operative infections, most of them due to MRSA. More expensive and elaborate antibiotics were called on to treat them, creating a further cycle of resistance until by 1993 only one drug, vancomycin, could be relied on to overwhelm MRSA microbes. Even that last hope could fail on occasion.

The price of battling against superbug superinfections was skyrocketing. A 1989 study published in the professional journal *Medical Care* reckoned that having to keep patients longer in hospital and use more costly antibiotics was adding thirty billion dollars a year to hospital expenses. The shift from penicillin to methicillin alone had put up the price of basic treatment by 10 times. As a proportion of the bill for a spell in hospital, most likely paid for by insurance, the extra cost was bearable for most North Americans, Australasians and West Europeans. In the poorest parts of the world, where bacterial diseases did most damage to more people, the difference was prohibitive.

One did not need to be a bleeding-heart liberal to see that the medical fate of people in the developing world had to be a matter of concern to well-off citizens in richer countries. Research into the origins of MRSA published in 1993 made it absolutely clear that even the most heartlessly self-interested individuals in advanced countries should be deeply worried. Scientists in the New York City Health Department used genetic fingerprinting to trace the ancestry of 470 strains of the new highly resistant staph. All threaded back to a single example that was first seen in Cairo, Egypt, in 1961. By 1970 MRSA had winged its way from there to the northeastern USA, Canada, Ireland, the UK, Denmark, Switzerland, Uganda and Kenya. In another decade the superbug was literally everywhere.

Nothing communicates as efficiently in the global village as disease. But in impoverished countries there was neither the money nor the infrastructure – hospitals, pharmacies, highly trained doctors – to handle the threat posed by the now rampant superbugs. In fact in many nations ordinary people depended on just the opposite: village paramedics and 'barefoot doctors' imperfectly trained in diagnosis, with a limited repertoire of drugs – some obtained on the black market – who often believed that antibiotics were the answer to everything. In both rich and poor countries, the use or misuse of antibiotics encouraged the evolution of superbugs, while trade and travel across international boundaries – especially by aircraft – provided ready-made routes for the highly resistant strains to move swiftly from nation to nation.

Staphylococcus aureus was by no means the only superbug threatening the world's health as the 20th century neared its end. Among others, *Streptococcus* bacteria of renewed vigor and virulence were on the rampage again, with all their lethal abilities replenished. 'Strep A', which had once killed thousands of children with scarlet fever, re-emerged in 1989 from the

A ward in Hargeisa Hospital, Somalia. In developing countries, wide-spectrum antibiotics are often applied indiscriminately by quack doctors – leaving professionals with more problems to solve once patients become so ill they are hospitalized.

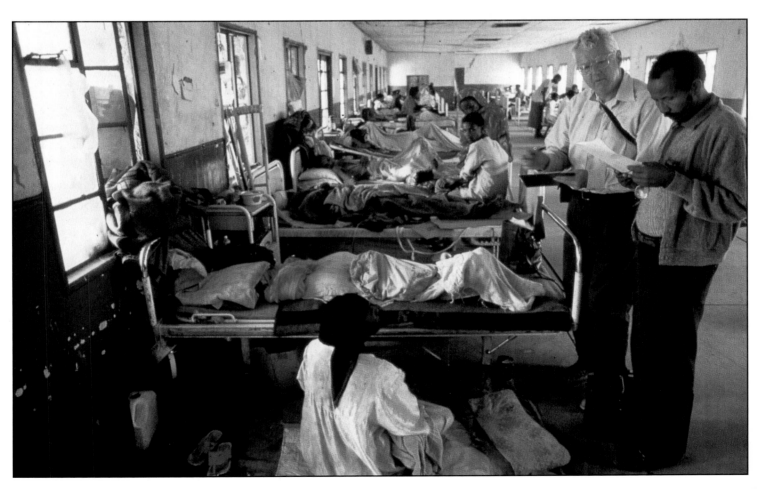

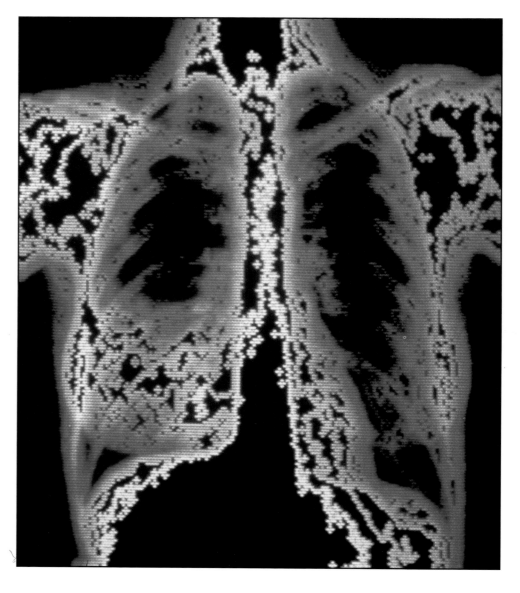

Pneumonia shows up as orange and yellow in this false-color X-ray, revealing how the air sacs in the left lung are blocked with pus. Routed in the West by penicillin after World War II, the strain of 'strep' bacteria responsible for pneumonia had made a comeback by the 1990s.

darkness where the early antibiotics had driven it.

The disappearance and reappearance of strep A is a classic illustration of how an apparent victory over one microbe is really an invitation to another to step forward and spread disease. By the 1960s strep A seemed to have vanished: scarlet fever was unknown in the West. Just how thoroughly it vanished, this writer knows from personal experience. In the 1940s, when antibiotics were still a military secret, my sisters all suffered, and in isolation hospital survived, the disease. When I was a child, a decade later, there were no isolation hospitals left except as names on old maps, and scarlet fever was unheard-of among my contemporaries.

Rise and fall

So much for impressions. The reality was that as strep A receded, strep B – previously kept in check by its close relative – stepped into its place in bacterial ecology. It particularly affected newborn babies, and by 1980 it was killing 75 per cent of infected babies under two months old. Meanwhile, strep A was mutating and multiplying in the background, until it re-emerged with sudden and vicious force in the late 1980s, striking people of all ages and all classes, almost at random. In 1989 it claimed its most famous victim to date – Jim Henson, puppeteer and

inventor of the world-renowned Muppets – and was reported in Canada, the UK, Scandinavia and New Zealand, as well as the USA. The new strep A carried a toxin very like the one that proved lethal in toxic shock syndrome, and resisted all but the most massive doses of penicillin. It seemed inevitable that, sooner or later, the microbe would simply make itself invulnerable to penicillin and, no doubt, to a legion of other antibiotics as well.

In 1982 WHO had stated that the growing menace of resistant bacteria made choosing the right antibiotic for a given infection 'a gamble against

worsening odds'. In 1992, the rising tide of rebellious disease-bearing germs prompted Dr Mitchell Cohen, director of bacterial research at the CDC, to warn: 'Unless currently effective anti-microbial agents can be successfully preserved and the transmission of drug-resistant organisms curtailed, the "post-antimicrobial era" may be rapidly approaching.' He spelled out bluntly what that would mean: hospital wards full of people with infectious diseases that no one could treat.

One of the most feared diseases of the pre-antibiotic centuries was pneumonia, one form of which was caused by another species of strep bacteria, *Streptococcus pneumonia*, also known as *Pneumococcus*. Like staph, it existed as a commensal microbe, living in the human lungs. An individual's immune system geared itself easily enough to keeping its own *Pneumococci* in check, but was not prepared for anyone else's if they were greatly different from its own. An enfeebled immune system – one preoccupied with a violent bout of flu, for example – could be swamped by the opportunistic multiplication of alien *Pneumococci* taken in from even a healthy stranger's breath.

Against the effects of such random attacks, penicillin had proved a boon in its early days. But in the 1980s the *Pneumococci* were back in Western countries, specializing in attacking the middle ear of young children. By 1990 there was growing evidence that about a third of all pediatric ear infections in the USA were being caused by *Pneumococci*, and about half of those – one sixth of all the infections – were generated by penicillin-resistant strains.

Despite these clear warning signals and the known risks of indiscriminate dosing with antibiotics, WHO had decided in the early 1990s to promote the treatment of all cases of pneumonia in children in developing countries with penicillin.

No one could deny that lives would be saved. WHO estimated that in the poorer countries, 800,000 children died each year from *Pneumococci* or similar bacterial infections of the lungs and respiratory tract. Tests in India, Nepal and Papua New Guinea showed a heartening drop of one third in the death rate from respiratory infections, and a still more encouraging drop of 36 per cent in childhood deaths from all other diseases. But the governments

concerned were not impressed by the policy of treating every respiratory infection, regardless of its virulence or danger, with antibiotics. With few qualified doctors outside cities in the countries targeted by WHO, the program would depend on rural paramedics whose rudimentary diagnostic skills and complete absence of laboratory back-up would likely lead them to over-generous use of antibiotics even where they would be ineffective. Highly resistant strains of bacteria were bound to follow close behind.

As early as 1972 it had been recognized that deprived people in impoverished countries were often the ultimate source of resistant strains of bacteria. Lacking skilled medical advice or legal restrictions on the sale of antibiotics, such people tended to prescribe for themselves on the basis of guesswork – as to both diagnosis and required drugs. Taking both rich and poor nations' liberality with antibiotics into account, Laurie Garrett says:

This state of affairs guaranteed that a sizable percentage of the human population were walking petri dishes, providing ideal conditions for accelerated bacterial mutation, natural selection, and evolution.

Whether one looked in Spain, South Africa, the United States, Romania, Pakistan, Brazil, or anywhere else, the basic principle held true: overuse or misuse of antibiotics, particularly in small children and hospitalized patients, prompted emergence of resistant mutant organisms.

So it was that in the 1990s *Pneumococci* bacteria in various strains had acquired an invulnerability to several drugs. Some strains carried protection against six whole classes of antibiotics.

And there was no doubt about the ability of these heavily armored microbes to travel as easily as the MRSA that first emerged in Egypt in 1961. One *Pneumococci* strain, known as type 23F, was traced by genetic analysis to a patient hospitalized in Spain in 1978; it picked up an extra resistance (to erythromycin) in Ohio, went to South Africa, Hungary, the UK, back to Spain and then back to the USA. Another, type 19A, which killed at least half a dozen patients in Durban, South Africa, in 1977 was tracked by Alexander Tomasz back to its very first appearance in 1967 in a village in Papua New Guinea. From South Africa, it spread to Europe, the USA and eventually the world.

In their travels, constantly bombarded by antibiotics, the superbugs have changed out of all recognition. Within the chromosomes of the *Pneumococci* that Tomasz caught swallowing up random DNA, he found sets of genes that were entirely foreign to the textbook versions of the bacteria. What is more, they had 'changed the biochemical composition of their cell walls so radically' that, he said, 'we must actually say...these are new species.'

Against that kind of opposition, thoughtful medical scientists knew, there was very little hope of winning. As Dr Harold Neu of Columbia University once ruefully remarked, 'Bacteria are cleverer than men.'

No hiding place

Introduced with the most noble of intentions, antibiotics, the wonder-working miracle drugs of the 1940s and 1950s, have created monsters for the coming century. The immediate prospect – and the most alarming one for people in the West, who for half a century have regarded disease as fundamentally curable – is a resurgence of untreatable, fatal diseases. They may look only faintly like the scarlet fever, diphtheria or tuberculosis of old, but then the microbes fueling them are not the same either. They will, however, be at least as distressing and debilitating to their victims, and just as disruptive emotionally, physically and financially.

Yet for all the havoc they have wrought, these reincarnated killers do not represent an ultimate peril to humanity. They are more likely to remain draining endemic diseases – some perhaps incurable – than to burst forth in epidemic proportions and then explode into a runaway plague. They are really symptoms of a deeper malaise, and they may be trailblazers and pathfinders for something much worse – and against which we may have little means of defense.

For half a century and more humanity has waged all-out war on the microbes – an assault that now shows every sign of having become bogged down into a debilitating stalemate – like a war of attrition fought from fixed positions, both sides struggling to live long enough in their infested trenches to fight the next battle. As Geoffrey Cannon has pointed out in his book *Superbug*, part of the reason we have reached this sorry condition is that we, and our medical scientists and our physicians, have perceived our relationship with germs in terms of such a *macho* metaphor. Bugs are out there, and out to get us. All we have to do is wipe out the enemy, and we shall be cleansed. But, as we have seen, things are not that simple.

Many of the microbes we have set out to destroy with antibiotics are part of us: most of the time they live in us or

on us and do us no harm. Some of them may even contribute to our welfare in ways we do not know. Likewise, we have seen that when microbes rampage out of control, our vaunted 'élite troops', the antibiotics, do not inflict enormous casualties on just 'the enemy'. In military terms, they also cause massive amounts of 'collateral damage' – they slaughter vast numbers of the civilian population, the 'friendly flora' that keep us functioning and healthy. This damage makes us more susceptible to hostile bacteria. In addition, those same 'enemy' bacteria call on their vast capacity to adapt to new circumstances, by developing phenomenal defenses, and sooner or later come storming back at us. We develop new 'magic bullets' – which really are more like indiscriminate bombs – in response, and fire them off everywhere. The bacteria change again and march on us once more, we create new antibiotics, the germs alter – and so it goes on.

Careless treatment

In 1981, in his book *Germs That Won't Die*, Mark Lappé summed up the way the discovery and enormous promise of antibiotics had backfired – and was charged with exaggeration:

Unfortunately, we played a trick on the natural world by seizing control of these chemicals, making them more perfect in a way that has changed the whole microbial constitution of the developing countries. We have organisms now proliferating that never existed before in nature. We have selected them. We have organisms that probably caused a tenth of a per cent of human disease in the past that now cause twenty, thirty per

cent of the disease that we're seeing. We have changed the whole face of the earth by the use of antibiotics.

Today we can see how right Lappé was. We can see too, if ruefully, that had medical scientists and doctors not viewed bacteria as menacing strangers in our midst, to be exterminated, but as unruly allies that needed nothing more than careful management, we might not have found ourselves today having to confront horrors like toxic shock syndrome, which can so confuse the body's defenses that sufferers develop antibodies to their own cells. Of course, we cannot turn back the clock. We have no choice but to live with the fact that the greatest casualty of this war is the human immune system. And therein lies the real threat to our future.

Our misplaced notion of antibiotics as medical weapons or 'special forces' is not the sole reason our immune systems have been sapped and weakened in recent decades. As we shall see in a later chapter, industrial pollution and domestic waste have played their part. So too has the constant drip of antibiotics into our systems through eating meat from intensively reared animals that have routinely been given the drugs as part of their diet. The upshot is the same: as a species we are now more vulnerable to outbreaks of disease of all kinds, especially 'traditional' plague diseases like cholera, typhoid, anthrax, and bubonic and pneumonic plague, should they choose to emerge from their hiding places. As, from time to time, they do. Latin America and India both saw serious outbreaks of cholera between 1991 and 1994, for example.

As the astonishing wanderlust of bacterial superbugs shows, modern

Back to basics: during an outbreak of bubonic plague in Surat, India, in 1994, a woman sets fire to roadside garbage, to deprive rats of their source of food. The moral: prevention is better than cure.

confined to the monkeys that carried it: the few people who caught the disease survived after a few terrifying and pain-filled days.

That was, after a fashion, a happy accident. But these emerging threats do kill people, and the resources of the West – innate or manufactured – are powerless before them. This is not just a question of weakened immune systems. These diseases are caused by viruses, against which we have only two fundamental defenses: the resilience of our constitutions or the preventive measure of inoculation. There is a third defense – treatment with the blood serum of a previous victim. In the case of the African viruses, there is simply not enough serum to go around if one of them should erupt into a plague, in any country. Essentially, we have only a handful of effective cures for viral infections; we even lack one for a minor distraction such as the common cold.

Still worse, there are hostile viruses against which we have no built-in bulwarks and no vaccine, as well as no certain cure. One of them is ravaging Africa, Asia and the developed world even now. The AIDS virus shows with absolute clarity how an untreatable affliction can spread among people whose immune systems are already in tatters from fighting other infections. The AIDS virus, of course, like any other virus, can take up lodgings in any individual, no matter how healthy, wealthy or wise.

communications and transport can whisk sickness from Indonesia to Indiana in hours aboard a jetliner. This means that incurable and horrific hemorrhagic diseases such as Ebola or Lassa fever, which have flared up across areas of Africa since the 1970s, can literally fly from one continent to another to fasten onto a population

that has no defense against them whatever. This too has happened – almost. In 1989 a strain of Ebola fever reached Reston, Virginia, about 15km (10 miles) from Washington, DC. It came by air from the Philippines via Amsterdam and New York City. By extreme good fortune, the lethal power of that particular strain of Ebola was

CHAPTER THREE

THE INVISIBLE PLAGUE

THE SPREAD OF AIDS THROUGHOUT THE WORLD

AIDS is the most political of all diseases. When first it struck, research and education about it were blocked for political reasons. If it radiates through the developing world in the way current projections suggest, political and economic life everywhere will be affected. Although there is now hope of an effective treatment for the disease, it will be extraordinarily expensive, and the benefits will be felt in rich countries rather than poor ones. Only by looking such disturbing facts in the face can we decide on a rational response to the crisis.

Acquired Immune Deficiency Syndrome, better known as AIDS, is nowadays routinely referred to as a plague. On the face of it, the terminology may seem surprising, even inappropriate. According to estimates from the US National Center for Health Statistics, AIDS accounted for only 1.8 per cent of all deaths in the USA in 1994. It lagged well behind the two chief fatal diseases – heart disease (32 per cent of deaths) and cancer (23.5 per cent). By 1994,

A quarter of a century after the 'Stonewall riot' in 1969, in which New York gays violently proclaimed their liberation, gays mark the anniversary by demonstrating their anger at the leaden pace of progress in AIDS research.

deaths from AIDS in America for all years totaled 284,249, according to the Centers for Disease Control (CDC), which amounted to less than 40 per cent of the number who died of heart disease in 1994 alone.

This is a far cry from the one quarter to one third of the population of Europe who died from bubonic plague in the middle of the 14th century. But, first, we are discussing two entirely different kinds of disease. The Black Death killed its victims within a week of infection. In contrast, the AIDS virus may haunt the human body for years before it destroys the immune system, and allows infections to swarm through the body and kill it. We are also ignoring the totally different picture of AIDS in the rest of the

world – notably in Africa and Asia.

According to the World Health Organization (WHO), by the middle of 1996 some 18 million people worldwide were infected with the AIDS virus (also called the human immunodeficiency virus, HIV). Of those, a quarter had 'converted' from being infected by HIV to full-blown AIDS. Every day 6000 new cases of infection were being added to the toll, and at that rate the world total would reach 30–40 million by the end of the century. While in the USA a huge majority (84 per cent) of AIDS victims are men, the global figure in the year 2000 is projected to include 15 million women and 10 million children.

What that figure may be in a further 10 years depends on one's optimism, or lack of it. If each person carrying the AIDS virus infects another every year, and each of those infects one more person every year, and so on at the same rate, the 40 million cases of AIDS virus infection in the year 2000 will have grown to a monstrous 2.56 billion by 2010, or 36 per cent of the world's likely population. A little less than a fifth of them, or about 460 million people, may have full-blown AIDS. According to WHO, over 90 per cent of these people will be in developing countries.

Before considering these alarming projections further, we should bear in mind that we have already seen how the scope, scale and frequency of international travel and trade have spread drug-resistant bacterial infections from as remote a location as Papua New Guinea to the eastern USA – and beyond. AIDS has spread to virtually every country in the world by way of the same complex network of individual contacts and modern travel routes on which bacteria roam, and will continue to do so. No country on earth can prevent the importation of the AIDS virus without sealing its borders and making its citizens prisoners within them.

Even if that were possible, let alone politically acceptable, the AIDS virus will probably carry on spreading. It will do so within any nation as long as there are people who do not block the virus's routes for moving from one person to another. Drug addicts who persist in sharing needles with other addicts will pass it on. Governments that do not screen or treat their own blood supplies used in transfusions and for treating hemophiliacs will give it a helping hand. And people who continue to have sex with multiple part-

ners and do not practice 'safe' sex will do the same. The most cursory acquaintance with human nature, from its wildest romanticism to its darkest impulses, suggests that the virus would continue to creep through even the most sealed and isolated society. For example: even if every non-commercial sexual encounter in the world could be guaranteed to be a safe one, people will contract and pass on the AIDS virus as long as there is a sex industry, with a clientèle prepared to pay extra for unprotected sex with men or women who are rarely in a position to refuse. The oldest profession is also the most vulnerable to exploitation.

Economic poison

AIDS is thus a world problem. But it is not just a health problem. As WHO explains:

The importance of the HIV/AIDS pandemic cannot be measured solely by the number of infected or ill individuals. Because HIV is transmitted sexually, it mainly strikes adolescents, young adults, and people in early middle age. These are the very people on whom society relies for production and reproduction. These are the men and women who raise the young and care for the old. Yet as they die of AIDS, their elderly relatives are left without support and their children become orphans. They are the ones who grow the crops, work in the mines and factories, run the schools and the hospitals, and even govern the country. Largely because of the lost productivity of this key demographic group, Thailand, for example, has estimated that the HIV pandemic will cost its economy

close to 11 billion US dollars by the year 2000. Thus, for every person with AIDS, countless more people are affected by the impact of HIV and AIDS. Hard-won gains in child survival are being erased. In countries that are not yet industrialized, or are in the process of industrializing, AIDS threatens development itself.

It has long been recognized that worldwide economic interdependence means that it is in the interests of the developed nations for the rest of the world to expand their economies. 'Development' usually means 'industrialization', which brings greater affluence, economic and political stability, and more customers for goods or services from the developed world as well as in the developing countries. Developed economies can also afford better health care, clean water supplies, and a host of other improvements in the quality of life that are not measured by rises in direct income.

AIDS threatens this whole process, for as WHO's statement above implies, the disease attacks the fabric of the whole society in developing countries in a way it has not – so far – in the USA. Even here the statistics are revealing. In mid-1996, 96,613 Hispanics were known to be infected with HIV. This figure represented nearly 18 per cent of all reported cases; and Hispanics make up about 18 per cent of the US population as a whole. This correlation is what one would expect. The 189,004 cases among black people, however, comprised nearly 35 per cent of all HIV cases – nearly three times the proportion (12 per cent) of black people in the population of the USA. A whole segment of the American people, already suffering huge

Users of illegal narcotics who share needles remain a major route for the spread of AIDS. These people are among the most difficult to reach and, as a group, almost impossible to persuade of the risks they run.

social and economic pressures, faces a new threat, with incalculable repercussions on society at large.

Nobody anywhere, however insulated some may feel in their big-city penthouses or their rural retreats, can escape the reach of AIDS. They may avoid the disease, but they cannot escape its consequences, no matter how distant and invisible those actually suffering and dying may be.

The gathering storm

There was a time, as recent as 1982, when no one had heard of AIDS. The CDC first used the term publicly in August that year. The previous acronym for the disease was GRID – which stood for Gay-Related Immunodeficiency Disease. It told more about the fact that, by chance, in the USA it had emerged among gay men, than it did about the real nature of the affliction. By 1982 it had become apparent to medical researchers that the disease was not peculiar to gay men in the USA or anywhere else: it could be caught by anyone, anywhere. In the USA, the minds of the politicians who were then in charge of research and education budgets proved harder to penetrate with mere facts, let alone their frightening implications. The initial association of AIDS with gay men put a brake on understanding the disease and on warning people about it. Such stalling had nothing but prejudice to justify it.

To less jaundiced eyes, the spread of AIDS appeared to be a hideous by-product of a massive outburst of sexual energy and freedom that had begun in the mid-1960s. In both developed and developing countries, more and more young people from rural backgrounds were moving into the cities – often the only places they could find work, and certainly the only places they could explore such a variety of sexual opportunities without reproach. More particularly, in developing countries it was often young men who worked in towns, partying away the weeknights and returning to their wives and families at weekends.

In her book *The Coming Plague*, Laurie Garrett notes that

the scale of multiple-partnering during the late twentieth century was unprecedented. With over five billion people on the planet, an ever-increasing percentage of whom were urban residents; with air travel and mass transit available to allow people from all over the world to go to the cities of their choice; with mass youth movements at their zenith, advocating, among other things, sexual freedom; with a feminist spirit alive in much of the industrialized world, promoting female sexual freedom; and with the entire planet bottom-heavy with people under twenty-

five – there could be no doubt that the size and drama of this world-wide urban sexual energy was unparalleled.

Few celebrated this newfound freedom in the anonymity of the city with greater gusto than gay American men. A police raid on the Stonewall bar in New York City in 1969 crystallized a growing feeling among gays that they were alone in being victimized for celebrating their sexuality; the raid sparked a two-day riot, and in its wake sprouted the gay liberation and gay rights movements. They acted as an advertisement for newly open gay communities, and thousands of young men headed for them. San Francisco, for example, attracted perhaps 30,000

gay men between 1969 and 1978, and 50,000 more in the following decade.

A sometimes staggering promiscuity, with individuals numbering sexual partners in the hundreds each year, was one expression of gay men's sense of release. Whether or not this pattern of behavior was typical, it was widespread enough in the 1970s to make the

A member of the irrepressibly high-spirited Sisters of Perpetual Indulgence with other San Francisco gays. The flamboyance of gay groups like the Sisters produced a backlash of additional prejudice among conservatives – and conservatives held the purse-strings for research when AIDS emerged in the USA.

growth of sexually transmitted diseases (STDs) within this group far outstrip an already worrying increase in the incidence of STDs in the population as a whole. Whereas by 1980 American physicians were concerned that the number of STD cases overall was growing by one per cent a year, it was increasing 12 times as fast among gay men. Some diseases were rampant by any measure: in late 1981, San Francisco health officials estimated that 73 per cent of the city's gay men had, or had already had, the liver disease hepatitis B. Some diseases were peculiar to gay men. In 1980, the National Institutes of Health (NIH) found, more than 20 per cent of gay men in the USA were infected with the *Entamoeba histolytica* parasite, a waterborne organism normally found in developing countries, which creates ulcerous sores in the bowel, and can also invade and infest the liver. Yet in 1975 there had been no locally acquired cases of infection in the USA. By great good fortune, the men were infected by a mild strain of the parasite that produced few if any distressing symptoms. Dubbed 'gay bowel syndrome', this was but one of a string of rare diseases that were turning up in gay men all over the world.

In his book *Surviving AIDS*, New York singer Michael Callen has described the reaction among gays at the time: 'We took each new disease in stride. "Gay bowel syndrome" was, in some quarters, almost a matter of pride; now we even had our own *diseases*, just like we had our own plumbers and tax advisers.' Anal intercourse – among men who moved easily between 'passive' and 'active' roles – was largely responsible for creating what Callen called the 'increasingly polluted micro-

biological sewer' through which gay men moved. Anal sex may be genital, manual or oral. Thus, parts of the body that are havens for germs of all kinds introduce microbes into the rectum, which is not well defended by the immune system. Callen himself calculated that, in his 10 years as an *habitué* of bathhouses, discos and other focal points of gay life, he had had more than 3000 sexual partners, and:

As a consequence, I also had the following sexually transmitted diseases, many more than once: hepatitis A, hepatitis B, hepatitis non-A/non-B; herpes simplex Types I and II; venereal warts; *giardia lamblia* and *entamoeba histolytica*; *shigella flexneri* and salmonella; syphilis; gonorrhea; nonspecific urethritis; chlamydia; cytomegalovirus (CMV), and Epstein-Barr virus (EBV) mononucleosis; and eventually cryptosporidiosis.

For Callen and thousands of others, this was apparently a price worth paying for liberation.

Sharing needles

While US health officials were becoming aware of exotic infections making their way around the gay community, more common infections were working through drug addicts in urban centers, largely by way of shared and far from sterile needles. The needle not only put the drug of choice – usually heroin – directly into the bloodstream; any bugs on or in the needle bypassed the user's usual immune system checkpoints and so enjoyed hugely increased chances of survival and multiplication. Addicts often already had weakened defenses against infection, thanks to the toll taken by the drugs themselves

(few limited their intake just to heroin), poor food, and STDs acquired by peddling their bodies for drugs money. In these transactions, the gay and addict communities touched. Invisibly and anonymously, drug addiction and the wider world met more often and still more intimately through blood transfusions, for one reliable source of income for an addict was to sell blood to a commercial blood bank.

By the late 1970s addicts were suffering increasingly from infections of the heart (endocarditis), attacks by *Staphylococcus* bacteria, hepatitis B, and especially tuberculosis. Much of this information simply did not make its way into the general medical intelligence system, let alone to recipients of blood transfusions, for the world's medical establishment and its scholarly journals had little interest in the problems of what they regarded as the dregs of the earth. In 1980 there was a sign of something deeper and more troubling at work: the CDC were called to investigate an outbreak of hepatitis B among a group of well-off teenagers in North Carolina who had been sharing needles to inject cocaine. Ten of the children died, but what struck the chief CDC investigator was the speed with which victims succumbed to the disease. Some secondary infection seemed to be involved, acting as a catalyst for the hepatitis virus. Samples of the dead teenagers' blood were injected into monkeys, without effect. The mystery remained to frustrate and tantalize. Not surprisingly, no one made any connection with the cluster of strange diseases that were striking homosexuals in the cities of Europe and America.

The medical fraternity was presented with its first hint of the coming

The yellowed eye and skin of a jaundice patient. Jaundice is a symptom of hepatitis B, one of many diseases that were rampant among gays and drug users and were omens of the rise of AIDS in the late 1970s.

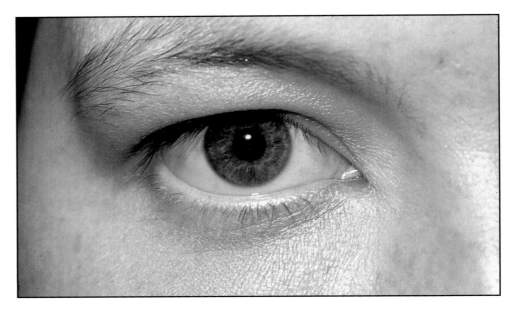

storm on 5 June 1981, in a paper published in the CDC's journal *Morbidity and Mortality Weekly Report* (MMWR). Drs Michael Gottlieb and Wayne Shandera had come across five cases of a rare form of pneumonia in Los Angeles County. *Pneumocystis carinii* usually became virulent in people whose white blood cells had already been severely depleted by some other disease and its treatment. The Los Angeles victims had no such history. They were all young, gay men who, noted Gottlieb and Shandera, 'did not know each other and had no known contacts or knowledge of sexual partners who had had similar illnesses.' What might have remained a minor medical mystery took on more disturbing aspects within a month, when MMWR published a compendium of reports from doctors in New York City and California who had come across 26 unusual cases of a skin cancer – Kaposi's sarcoma – that normally appeared in men over 70 years old and often of Mediterranean descent. These patients were young and homosexual. Four of them were also infected with *Pneumocystis carinii*. Californian doctors had also turned up another 10 cases of *Pneumocystis carinii* – all in homosexual men.

The CDC were sufficiently intrigued to set up a task force to investigate the curious, and alarming, syndrome. Their analysts very soon began to suspect that these infections were attacking people whose immune systems were compromised by some other agent. By the end of August 1981 the CDC had collected 107 reports of individuals suffering from Kaposi's sarcoma or infection by *Pneumocystis carinii*, or the two combined. Ninety-five of the patients were gay men. Of the remainder, six were known to be heterosexual men, and one was female. The key questions were: what was this underlying agent – if, indeed, it existed? And how was it being passed around?

From GRID to AIDS

One of the earliest attempts to answer these questions was made within the gay community itself during the summer of 1981 – months before the public health bureaucracies began active research. A major reason for this lack of co-ordination was that gay communities in centers like New York, Los Angeles and San Francisco patronized so-called 'clap doctors'. These physicians were often themselves gay, did not moralize over a sexually energetic gay lifestyle or the huge burden of STDs that came with it, and were indeed as much a part of the increasingly exclusive and self-reliant gay scene as its plumbers and tax advisers. The 'clap doctors' were far more sensitive to the patterns of disease among gay men than the official bodies, but were not reporting their findings in medical journals. On the other side of the divide, the public health agencies depended for their information on reports from 'straight' doctors (who had only occasional contact with members of the gay community) or on sampling and research taken from the whole population – so that data relating specifically to gays tended to be hidden by sheer strength of numbers.

Dr Joseph Sonnabend, a New York physician with a large gay clientèle, began to suspect in 1981 that the constant battering his patients were taking from STDs was overloading their immune systems. The more microbes they exposed themselves to, the less likely they were able to contend with any one particular infection. Therefore, Sonnabend reasoned, greater promiscuity would mean greater exposure to disease, a greater toll on the immune system, and thus a greater chance that opportunistic infections could avoid detection, take hold and run riot. To test his idea, Sonnabend divided his patients into three groups: the monogamous; those with fewer than 50 sexual partners a year; and those with more (which could number in the hundreds). He had blood samples from them analyzed at the University of Nebraska.

The results not only confirmed his hypothesis, but revealed something more: the most promiscuous men had a startlingly low count of white blood cells called 'T-helpers' or CD4 cells. These acted as fire-watchers or sentries in the immune system, detecting the presence of hostile microbes and calling the appropriate antibodies into action against them. Something in these men, it seemed, was overloading the immune system to the point where it simply collapsed. Sonnabend and some of his patients tried to alert gays in New York to the dangers of promiscuity. They were denounced as 'anti-gay faggots' or fear mongers. Either way, they were ignored.

By the end of the year other studies from larger surveys sponsored by the CDC showed the same pattern emerging. While some researchers concentrated on the role of particular sexual habits and others on the use of amyl nitrites – used to intensify sexual pleasure – among gays, more objective observers noted that exclusively heterosexual men and women were also succumbing to what had been labeled GRID. And that indicated that a sexually transmitted microbe was the culprit. As Michael Gottlieb suggested, it was no coincidence that the illness was first detected among gay men; with their remarkable frequency of sexual contacts, homosexuals were more likely to pass such a disease among themselves than other identifiable groups of people.

Retrospective research was beginning to show, too, that the disease was not new. One check of the medical records threw up the 1979 case of a 30-year-old married woman – with no history of drug abuse or prostitution – from the Dominican Republic who had died of pneumonia, and whose immune system was shattered. In Europe, Belgian virologist Peter Piot had treated a Greek fisherman with similar symptoms who had died in 1978. An autopsy revealed that his internal organs, and even his bones, were infested with bacterial disease, and were in a state of 'pure and complete rot'. Autopsies on gay men with GRID in the USA revealed similar horrors. In many cases, normally harmless bacteria had created the worst havoc.

Prejudice costs lives

By early 1982, 180 people were known to have died of GRID in the USA and Europe since 1978. It was about this point that politics entered the picture. To the analysts at the CDC it was clear that major research and education programs were needed, the first to discover the underlying cause of these deaths and the second to warn those most at risk of the danger they were courting. Since January 1981 a highly conservative administration under President Ronald Reagan had been in office in the USA. One of its most vocal and influential power bases had an unflinching faith in two things: the virtue of reducing taxes and with them the pervasiveness of 'big government', and the defects – not to say wickedness – of deviating from traditional Puritan values, especially in sexual matters. Reagan's appointees at the head of federal health agencies reflected this bias and, while proposing swingeing cuts in the agency's budget, consistently blocked the CDC's appeals for funds to research what was, in the

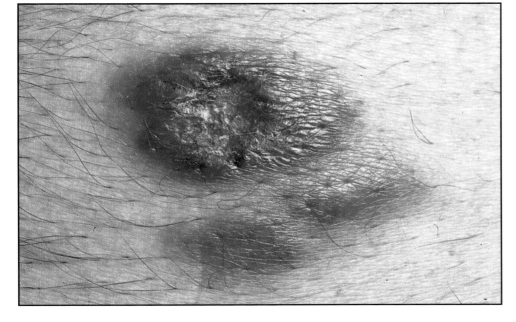

The characteristic purple blotch caused by Kaposi's sarcoma. This is one of the most common diseases to take advantage of the crumbling immune system of someone infected with the AIDS virus.

A few of the 200,000 gays who demonstrated in Washington, DC on 11 October 1987 to honor those who had died of AIDS, and to demand more funds for research.

politicians' eyes, a 'gay disease'. The CDC were reduced to labeling some of their efforts as research into Kaposi's sarcoma – usually an affliction of aging white males not entirely unlike the president and many of his supporters – and to pulling scientists off other projects to track down the origins and causes of GRID.

By summer 1982 the CDC had spent a little less than one million dollars over 13 months looking into GRID which, as history was to prove, potentially affected hundreds of thousands of American men and tens

of thousands of American women. In stark and revealing contrast, in 1976 and 1977 they had spent nine million dollars discovering what lay behind the deaths of 29 men from Legionnaires' Disease. Democratic Congressman Henry Waxman of California drew his conclusions in uncompromising language:

There is no doubt in my mind that if the disease had appeared among Americans of Norwegian descent or among tennis players, rather than gay men, the response of the government would have been different. The victims are not typical mainstream Americans. They are gays mainly from New York, Los Angeles and San Francisco. Legionnaires' Disease hit a group of predominantly

white, heterosexual, middle-aged members of the American Legion. The respectability of the victims brought them a degree of attention and funding for research and treatment far greater than that which has been made available so far to victims of [GRID]. What society judged was not the severity of the disease but the social acceptability of the individuals afflicted with it.

The greatest misjudgment lay in the ostrich-like presumption that the disease could be – or ever had been – contained within the gay community. Nothing in epidemiology suggested that a disease could be limited by sexual orientation. And in the heady atmosphere of the early 1980s, a sexually transmitted disease, whatever its fundamental nature, was no more likely to observe humans' cherished moral codes than any lively superbug would heed manmade borders.

Even in 1983, when the link between AIDS and intravenous drug abuse had become clear, the Alcohol, Drug Abuse and Mental Health Administration and the National Institute on Drug Abuse made no request for federal funds for AIDS research until three quarters of the way through the fiscal year. In April, the NIH proudly announced that they were releasing fully $240,000 for laboratory research into the disease, part of a total commitment of two million dollars for the year. By the standards of most US research budgets, this was a paltry sum. As Laurie Garrett noted, 'AIDS was unique. It touched every nerve that polarized Americans: sex, homosexuality, race (Haitians), Christian family values, drug addiction, and personal versus collective rights and security.'

Albeit rebuffed by central government, the CDC investigators plowed on with their work in 1982, scraping up funds and human resources as best they could – as did others in a similar position. By August 1982, they had pieced together enough information to be sure that GRID was an infectious disease in its own right that respected no obstacle of gender – and the CDC responded by changing the name of the disease to AIDS. And they now knew that, while it was often sexually transmitted, the key media through which it moved from person to person were bodily fluids – especially blood.

Epidemiologist William Darrow of the CDC had steered a remarkable and painstaking detective project that convincingly showed that AIDS was infectious. Called in March 1982 by the male lover of a man dying of AIDS

in a Los Angeles hospital, he was told that two other men, who had also had sex with the dying man, were in the same hospital, also suffering from AIDS. Darrow set out to trace the sexual contacts of all four. At the center of a remarkable web was a handsome French-Canadian flight attendant named Gaetan Dugas.

When Darrow interviewed him, Dugas was already suffering from Kaposi's sarcoma. He estimated that between 1972 and 1982 he had had more than 2500 sex partners. His first signs of AIDS – unrecognized for what they were at the time – appeared in 1979, when his lymph nodes swelled and he had severe flu-like symptoms. He was hospitalized a few months later with *Pneumocystis carinii* pneumonia. Kaposi's sarcoma set in during early 1981. He could remember the names of 68 of his recent sex partners besides the four Darrow had already found in Los Angeles. Darrow was led further afield to a group of men who had partied on Fire Island, New York's gay summer resort, in 1979 and 1980. Finally Darrow was able to draw a map of some 40 men who had contracted AIDS, directly or indirectly, from Dugas. Their interconnections ran from New York to Los Angeles through Atlanta, Houston, Miami and San Francisco. Where Dugas, criss-crossing the world on aircraft, had picked up the disease remained a mystery.

The blood factor

The CDC were also aware that hemophiliacs, and intravenous drug users and Haitians of both sexes, were strangely prone to the disease. Further dogged work allowed them to draw up a tentative explanation for the vulnerability of these three emerging groups

of sufferers. The drug addicts overlapped with the gay community to the extent that some gays abused drugs – later studies found they were two to three times more likely to inject drugs than the population as a whole – and some addicts worked as prostitutes to fund their drug habit. The immune systems of both groups were already under massive pressure because of their ways of life.

Drug addicts also made much-needed cash by selling their blood to store-front blood banks. In the USA it was legal for individuals to sell their blood twice a week up to a maximum of 60 liters (105 pints) a year – four times the maximum recommended by WHO. A donor would receive, on average, $25 on each visit. And, of course, gay men would freely donate blood to the system, if for more altruistic reasons. At the other end of this commercial line, a hemophiliac might, each year, require 65,000 international units of the protein Factor VIII to ensure that his blood would clot normally in case of a cut or even bruise. The Factor VIII was derived from donated blood, and the average hemophiliac's annual intake could include protein from the blood of as many as 3.25 million people. Analysis of the US blood supply showed that as early as 1978 at least one batch of Factor VIII had been AIDS-infected and had been distributed to 2300 hemophiliacs. The response of the US blood industry when approached in 1982 was to balk at requests to test their intake. Not until September 1984 was the US blood supply thoroughly surveyed for contamination. Heat treatment to kill the AIDS virus did not become common practice until 1987.

At the end of 1982 the Haitian

connection with AIDS was only partly unraveled. Haiti had long been a favorite gay vacation resort. In a country where the average wage was as little as $2 a day, sex could be bought for $5. At the same time there was no openly gay community in Haiti, and it seemed quite possible that local 'closet' gays or bisexuals – or men and boys just desperate for money – had been the common gateway between American homosexuals and Haitian women. But there was another, hidden connection with Haiti: Africa.

The same questions about a mysterious immune-deficiency syndrome had been occurring to physicians outside the USA. When Belgian virologist Peter Piot, a veteran of African field research, read the first reports of what was to be dubbed AIDS, bells rang in his mind. He trawled through his case notes and turned up not only the Greek fisherman mentioned earlier but two other men and a woman, who had died from diseases attacking their collapsed immune systems. All four had come to Piot from Zaire, formerly a Belgian colony. And during 1982 fellow-Belgian Dr Nathan Clumeck treated five Zairians who had severe deficiencies in their immune systems. At the Pasteur Institute in Paris, a Zairian woman was treated for the same problem, and died in March 1982. French doctors also noted that of 29 AIDS cases in France, most of the victims had traveled to the USA, Haiti or tropical Africa.

Over the next five years, through reassessments of old, unsolved fatalities, it became apparent that AIDS had probably been in Africa for at least as long as it had been building up in the USA, and possibly for longer. Scandinavian researchers unearthed

the case of Danish surgeon Margrethe Rask, who worked between 1972 and 1975 in rural northern Zaire. She developed enlarged lymph nodes (a typical AIDS symptom) and died in Copenhagen in 1977 of *Pneumocystis carinii* pneumonia. She had treated at least one case of Kaposi's sarcoma in Zaire. She did not abuse drugs and had not been to the USA or Haiti; she was most likely infected through a cut or accidental jab from a hypodermic needle during surgery.

In Norway, retrospective tests on the blood of a sailor, who had often traveled to Africa, and of his wife and one of his children, who had all died of a then-inexplicable immune-system failure, showed they all had antibodies to HIV. The sailor had first shown AIDS symptoms in 1966, as did his wife in 1967 and his child in 1969. All three died in 1976. The earliest AIDS infections yet discovered date back to 1959. Tests of frozen blood samples have found them in David Carr, another sailor with a history of African contacts who died in Manchester, England, in 1959, and in an unnamed patient from Zaire.

By 1984 Clumeck and others published records of 22 Africans of both sexes with AIDS. The earliest had surfaced in 1979, and all but two – one from Chad, and one from Burundi – came from Zaire. None was homosexual, abused drugs or had had a blood transfusion. A still earlier case had occurred in a secretary from Zaire. Having had three healthy children by her first husband, she remarried and had three more children, who developed AIDS symptoms. Two died in Zaire, and she brought the third to Belgium in 1977. While the child was being treated, she herself began to

show symptoms of AIDS; she died in Zaire in 1978.

The Belgians pointed out that all the Zairians they had seen in Brussels were affluent. They probably represented the tip of a vast iceberg of AIDS in the population of Zaire as a whole. No less significant were the facts that these African victims were not gay men, not drug users, and had had neither Factor VIII injections nor blood transfusions. A study in 1983 and 1984 showed that only fractionally more African men than women were suffering from the disease. And, although Zaire seemed to be a focus of the disease, there was a smattering of cases elsewhere.

Slim and Juliana

By 1987 AIDS had been detected in a cluster of countries in Central Africa bordering on Zaire, and also in Mali and Chad, far to the north and west. But it was almost impossible to pin down exactly where it had started. What was called 'slim disease' in Uganda before it was recognized as AIDS began in a fishing village on Lake Victoria and had so spread throughout the district by December 1984 that it was news in the local papers. When government medical investigators arrived the following June, they found the AIDS virus in 110 patients in the district hospital, among them 29 cases of full-blown AIDS. Anne Bayley, a professor of surgery from Lusaka, Zambia, was among the team and later speculated that the disease had come into Uganda either with the Tanzanian army, which had rampaged through the area during its invasion of the country in 1979, or with traders and smugglers who had been slipping between the two

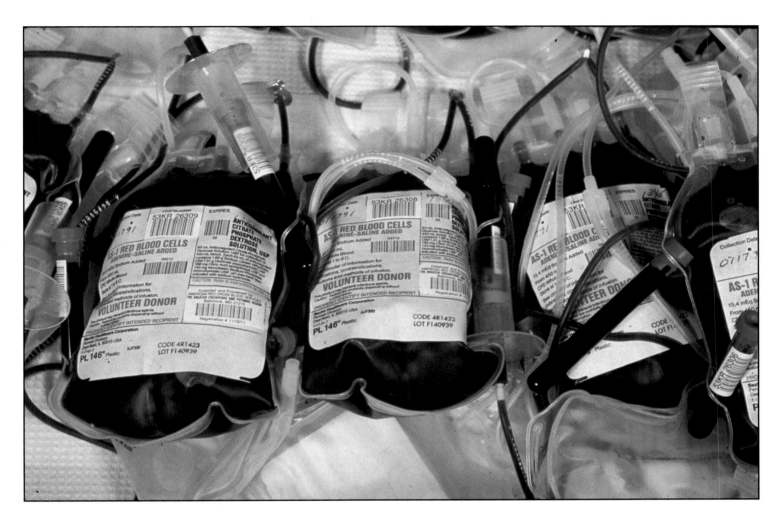

countries for decades. Of 15 traders tested during the investigation, 10 were carrying the AIDS virus. But, asked Bayley: 'If the virus did come from Tanzania, where did Tanzania get it from?'

When AIDS emerged further south along the Lake Victoria coast early in 1983, it was first dubbed 'Juliana's disease'. A number of women had bartered with a Ugandan trader, exchanging sexual favors for cloth attractively patterned with the name Juliana. Within months the women fell ill with terrible diarrhea, wasted away, and died. By the following year cases were appearing at the hospital in the region's major town, Bukoba. In September 1984 two dozen patients, men and women, arrived on one day.

All had caught – directly, or via their husbands – Juliana's disease from one bar girl in their home town. It was not until early 1985 that the CDC confirmed local doctors' fears that the disease was indeed AIDS. The local people were convinced it had come from Uganda.

Quite apart from the folklore of its origins, Tanzanian specialists were struck by the parallel between the spread of AIDS in the USA through drug users' shared needles, and the fact that many of their local victims had for various reasons had a large number of medical injections in recent years. Those needles too had been shared. A doctor or village paramedic in Tanzania simply could not afford to use a hypodermic once only on a single

Containers of donated blood ready for despatch to patients in need. Despite pleas from bodies such as the National Hemophilia Foundation, the American blood supply industry refused for years to screen or treat donated blood for virus infections, on grounds of cost.

patient. Nor could the quack 'injectionists', to whom people turned when they realized that the doctors had no cure for AIDS. Many who consulted the injectionists because they feared they had 'Juliana's disease' were correct in their belief; so AIDS found yet another route by which to spread, through the medical black market.

Possibly the original focus of AIDS was indeed in Zaire. Both southern

Street merchants in the nightclub district of Kinshasa, Zaire, offer condoms for sale – but trade is slow. The disdain for prophylactics has helped to fuel the rapid spread of AIDS throughout Central Africa.

Uganda and northern Tanzania are connected to the main trans-Africa trucking route – the Kinshasa or 'AIDS' Highway that runs from Mombasa on the east coast to Kinshasa and on to Pointe-Noire on the west coast, hundreds of kilometers through Zaire. Besides the truck drivers and the bar girls, the traders and the disruption of war – in which women were regarded as spoils by invaders – throughout the region around Lake Victoria, the deep social background of Zaire, further west, has been a factor in the spread of AIDS. In 1885, King Leopold II of Belgium set up the Congo Free State (which became Zaire), with the declared aim of eradicating slavery in the region. As Christopher Wills explains:

> Leopold, one of history's most venal figures, replaced slavery with something worse, a system of forced labour in which entire villages were destroyed and the surviving men and women were separated and sent to different parts of the country. As a result of forced labour in the rubber plantations, the population of the Congo fell from thirty million in 1890 to eight million in 1924.... It was cheap to move men just once over the long distances from their villages to the mines and plantations, and then jam them together in dormitories and shantytowns. It would have been far more expensive to move their families as well,

for this would have required housing rather than barracks.

The result was a profound and violent alteration in the relations between men and women. For women did, of course, make their way to the labor camps. 'In the gold, diamond and copper producing regions of Africa, companies like De Beers and Union

Minière de Haute Katanga created a new societal pattern based on family disruption and prostitution, a pattern that persisted for decades and involved millions of workers,' says Wills.

A society that has come to regard casual and frequently commercial sexual relations as the norm will, of course, be prime fodder for the AIDS virus, and when the Belgian Congo became independent in 1960 the social fabric of the country was one of the most fragile in Africa. Today, the rate of AIDS infection in Zaire's Katanga copper belt may be as high as 40 per cent. (The region is on the truck route through the Rift Valley directly to Zambia's own rich copper belt.) It is perhaps no accident that Uganda and Rwanda, which have suffered appalling régimes, internal chaos, bloodshed and oppression since independence, also have phenomenally high rates of HIV infection today. Some estimates put the infection rate in Rwanda as high as 30 per cent of all adults. In turn, knowledge of the inescapable consequences of AIDS generates a terrible, contagious sense of futility at every level of society. One can't help but wonder if such widespread hopelessness in the countries around Lake Victoria may not have helped to fuel their murderous frenzies of the mid-1990s.

AIDS became pandemic in Africa during the early 1980s, at much the same time as it did in gay men in the USA. At least two lessons were learned from Africa as the disease there caught the attention of Western researchers. First, AIDS was unmistakably not confined to homosexual males. Second, it was discovered, or remembered, that between 1960 and 1975 some 10,000 short-term contract workers had gone each year from Haiti to Zaire. It seemed likely that the AIDS virus had traveled to Haiti with returning workers, and from there had found its way into the ranks of gay American tourists. But this did not mean that in Zaire lay the ultimate source of AIDS. While trade routes were plainly crucial in spreading the virus, the whole region through which

the so-called 'AIDS Highway' passed was in turmoil from the mid-1960s. War, tribal conflict and brutally dictatorial regimes pushed waves of refugees away from their traditional homes; many ended up in Zaire. Yet the problem remained: if Central Africa was most likely the source of AIDS, how had it begun even there?

When that question was first asked in the early 1980s, no one knew precisely what was causing AIDS in the first place.

Hunting the virus

The scientists concerned with AIDS had early decided that a virus was the most probable cause of the destruction of T-helper cells in its victims. The pattern of infections also suggested that the virus was passing from victim to victim through the bloodstream, not through the air. There was little more to go on. The race to isolate and identify the virus itself was also a race between scientific rivals that became increasingly bitter – but the mystery was still unraveled within two years.

The issues, and the rancorous arguments, were complicated by the fact that – in order to adapt to an individual host – the AIDS virus mutates at an astonishing rate, and it did so even in the laboratory. The main French and American research teams believed they were dealing with different viruses, giving them different names, and each believing 'their' virus was the true cause of AIDS. In fact, they were dealing with slight variations of the same microbes, which had been cultured in the laboratory.

The first step to identifying the virus was taken in January 1982, when the French team at the Pasteur Institute analyzed tissue from the enlarged

lymph node of a patient in the earliest stages of AIDS infection. The key discovery was that 'reverse transcriptase' activity was occurring in the T-helper cells of the infected tissue. Only two viruses were then known to perform this particular trick – the human T-cell leukemia/lymphoma viruses (HTLV-1 and HTLV-2), which cause cancer. Most viruses are essentially lengths of DNA enclosed by a shell of fats and proteins. They use the proteins to latch on to a cell wall, then inject the DNA into the cell, where it enters the genetic nucleus. Like a sparrow that cannot tell a cuckoo's egg from one of its own, the cell then triggers the viral DNA to produce ribonucleic acid (RNA). This makes viral protein, and uses the cell's energy and material to form new viruses. The cell finally becomes so crowded with viruses that they burst out of it – and go looking for new cells to invade.

Viruses like the HTLVs, however, consist of a core of two strings of RNA and a crucial enzyme. In order to reproduce, the virus has to generate DNA. This is done by the enzyme, which – once it has invaded the host cell – allows the RNA to copy itself twice, to create two strands of DNA entwined in its characteristic double helix. The cell then adopts the viral DNA as its own, and production begins as with a 'normal' virus. Because the usual sequence of events (DNA to RNA) is initially reversed, the enzyme is known as reverse transcriptase, and the viruses are called 'retroviruses'.

Ten days after the French team realized that a retrovirus was at work in their sample, they watched new viruses emerging from the T-helper cells. But these brought no response at all from antibodies to the known HTLVs. This

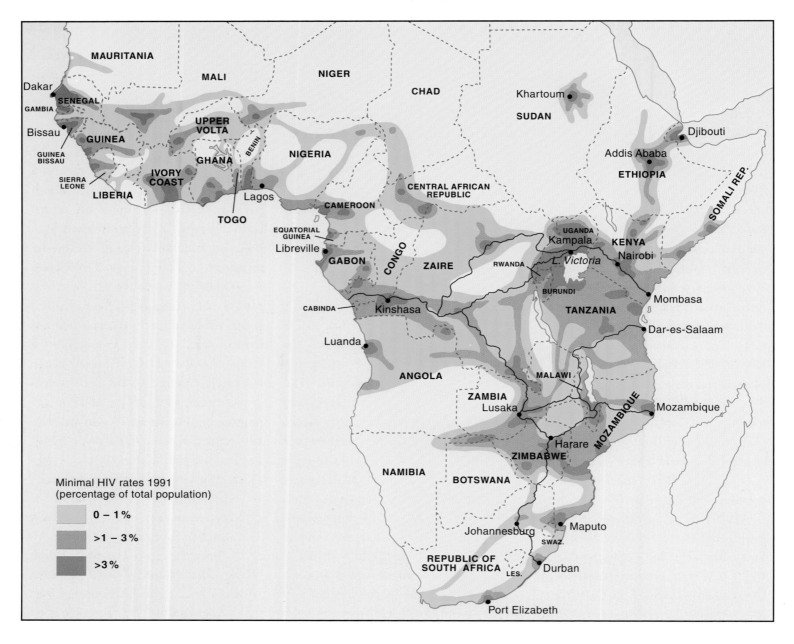

Minimal HIV rates 1991
(percentage of total population)

- 0 – 1%
- >1 – 3%
- >3%

Map of areas in sub-Saharan Africa most affected by AIDS. Significant highways are shown, demonstrating how the disease has moved through the continent. On the main route from Malawi to South Africa, 92 per cent of truck drivers are infected.

virus was something unknown. In spring 1984, while arguing that the 'new' virus was directly related to HTLV, the Americans at the National Cancer Institute found a way to set up a production line that was vastly simpler than their rivals' method of culturing the microbe. This meant that viruses could be produced in bulk and used to test for antibodies in potential victims. (Antibodies are protein molecules that can recognize specific microbes and either kill them or stop them affecting other cells in the body. They are called up by other cells in the immune system and reproduce very rapidly once they recognize the presence of a threat.)

The test for antibodies would detect infection at an early stage, offering the chance of effective treatment. And there was another practical use. Blood donors in the USA and Europe were among the first to be screened, to remove the virus from the medical blood supply.

By the end of the year, British scientists had run immunological tests on the 'rival' viruses and declared them the same, while French and American teams were analyzing the sequence of amino acids in the viruses' DNA to ascertain their genetic 'fingerprint', and thus their fundamental nature.

By February 1985 it was clear that there was a distinct AIDS virus, which was soon dubbed human immuno-deficiency virus (HIV). It was not, after all, related to the HTLVs, but was a close cousin of a group of lentiviruses that caused a similar slow-acting syndrome in horses, cats and goats (the name comes from the Latin for slow, *lentus*). That still left the problem of where, ultimately, the virus had come from, but hinted that like any number of other viral infections (swine flu being but one example) it had some-how crossed from an animal population into people.

In 1985, the CDC and Project SIDA – a joint Zairian, Belgian and US research team based in Kinshasa – began fresh research in Zaire, using the now highly refined blood tests available. Blood samples existed from the 1976 outbreak of Ebola fever in the district around Yambuku, in Zaire, and some of them tested positive for HIV. The task was to compare these results with current levels of infection and, if possible, track down the original HIV-positive subjects and test them again. The research revealed that in 1976 just under one per cent of people in Yambuku had been infected with the AIDS virus – and in 1985, the figure was exactly the same. A second investigation of HIV infection along the vast River Congo showed that the virus was most widespread in urban centers (as might be expected) but rates of infection increased steadily from the rural east to Kinshasa, the capital of Zaire, in the southwest. The researchers concluded:

> The stability of HIV infection in rural Zaire over a long period contrasts sharply with the epidemic spread of the virus in major Af-rican cities. Our findings suggest that traditional village life carries a low risk of HIV infection. The disruption of traditional life styles and the social and behavioral changes that accompany urbanization may be important factors in the spread of AIDS in Central Africa.

Given the savagery that had been raging through the region since the mid-1960s (and before that in Zaire itself), this was highly diplomatic language. But the studies did powerfully suggest that HIV had been buried in rural Africa for a very long time, and recent social changes had given it an outlet to the world beyond.

Hidden in the forest

At about the time these conclusions were published, scientists discovered that African monkeys carried viruses very like HIV, and that a second AIDS virus existed in Africa. Analysis of the DNA of the latter, HIV-2, showed it is very similar to one of the simian viruses; and the present geographical distribution of the sooty mangabey monkeys (in which it probably originated) exactly matches that of HIV-2 in people. The monkeys are not particularly affected by the virus. But people certainly succumb to HIV-2, although it is less virulent than the HIV-1 virus that is now ravaging Central Africa and North America and in the mid-1980s was beginning its deadly pilgrimage across Europe and Asia. There is less correspondence between HIV-1 and its simian equivalent found in green vervet monkeys – the two proved to be about as much alike as the two viruses that affected humans. But there is a distinct similarity between HIV-1 and a simian virus found in chimpanzees in 1990.

Supercomputer analysis of all the viruses found in both people and monkeys suggested to some researchers that their ultimate ancestor had originated in the green monkey.

There are at least three possible means by which the simian viruses jumped into our own species. Monkeys are an important source of food for many traditional African societies. As human beings encroached on the forest habitats of the primates, green monkeys in particular altered their feeding habits to raid garbage, food stores and even houses for sustenance. In either of these cases, a tiny, almost certainly unnoticed, drop of monkey blood could have come in contact with an equally negligible cut on a human hand – and the virus would have jumped species. There are also anthropological reports that some of the peoples living around the lakes in the Great Rift Valley – which today has the highest incidence of AIDS in Africa – would inoculate their genitals, thighs and backs with monkey blood in the belief that this intensified sexual pleasure. Another suggestion is that the huge trade in green monkeys, mainly for medical work in the USA, that grew up after World War II provided endless opportunities for the virus to leap from animal to human – in Africa, America, or somewhere between. But no one really knows when, where, how, or how often such a jump may actually have taken place.

However it happened, the ability of HIV-1 to mutate rapidly in order to take best advantage of its host means that the leap may have occurred quite recently – perhaps during the 1950s. Thereafter, in a population already afflicted with endemic diseases that produce skin lesions and ulcers, which

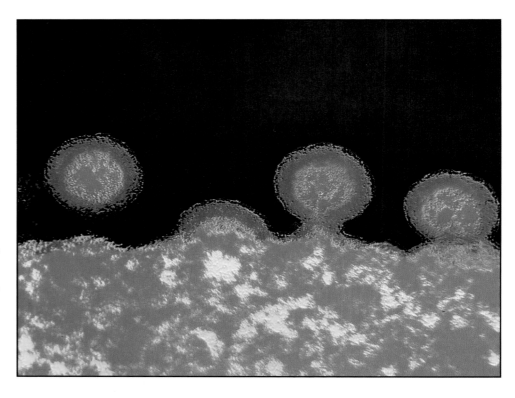

Human immunodeficiency viruses bud out from an infected T-cell, a key part of the body's defenses against disease. At center left, the virus is borrowing its outer coat from the host cell as it emerges, while at left the virus has floated free. It will go on to infect and eventually destroy other cells in the body's immune system.

create a bridge between one person's bloodstream and another's, its spread was inevitable. Add the effects of colonialism, post-colonial wars, urbanization and the development of modern rapid transport, and that spread was sooner or later bound to take the virus into the cities and, from there, to the wider world.

Heads in the sand

'Tell me, Doctor, is it true that Africans have sex with monkeys?' an American journalist brazenly inquired of Zairian AIDS specialist Dr Kapita Bila Minlangu.

'Madam, I don't know what you're talking about,' answered Dr Kapita, seething with fury. 'We don't do these things. But I believe that in Europe they make movies where women have sex with dogs.'

This exchange took place in April 1985 in Atlanta, Georgia, at the first international conference on AIDS, organized by the CDC. The brash naiveté of the New World and the sensitivity of post-colonial Africa were to clash time and again in the coming years in the debate over the extent of AIDS in Africa. Western scientists were rarely as crass as their journalistic counterparts, but still had to find a way through the thorny thickets of politics to get at the truth about the malady. In the USA (but less so in Europe) a

popular misperception that AIDS was limited to the gay community put a bigoted brake on both research and public education about the dangers of the disease. In Africa, decades – and in some places, centuries – of colonial rule and exploitation colored attitudes toward the mounting evidence that AIDS probably originated on the continent, so that it seemed as if Western scientists were blaming Africans for ushering the disease on to the world stage. For Africans, stricken by years of drought, famine, endemic poverty and disease that the public of the world's richest nations routinely ignored and that the Africans themselves lacked the resources to fight, the matter of AIDS only added insult to injury.

The result was a denial that AIDS existed in Africa at all. Speaking for many, Kenya's president Daniel arap Moi declared that 'African AIDS reports are a new form of hate campaign.' African sensibilities were further ruffled when it emerged that a

fault in the early blood tests for AIDS, conducted by Western researchers, had led to a gross exaggeration of the extent of the disease on the continent. No apology for the blunder was ever issued. Partly from pride, partly from habitual discomfort at discussing sexual matters in public, and partly to protect vital international trade links – not least tourism – African governments continued to encourage ignorance of the presence of AIDS within their own countries and to minimize its existence internationally.

One motive that has to be faced without flinching in this context is the almost incomprehensible level, to Western eyes, of corruption in the region. Some African leaders protect their nations' reputations less for the economic good of their fellow citizens than to maintain the flow of hard currency into their own and their cronies' offshore bank accounts. A number have been able to count their looted private wealth in billions of dollars. In the face of AIDS, there developed, according to geographer Peter Gould, a culture of 'officially sponsored ignorance or blatant political lying'.

Gould catalogs the lies, the self-deception and the consequences:

In Kenya, the President spent the first four years of the growing pandemic denying that there was any HIV around.... He threatened to remove the visa and deport any foreign journalist reporting AIDS, and waited until 1986 before allowing the most innocuous 'AIDS guidelines' to be published, meanwhile instructing the Ministry of Health to under-report grossly the known cases on the grounds that many of those with AIDS were 'not Kenyans'. In the meantime, [HIV infections] in Nairobi's large prostitute population went from 17 to almost 100 percent. What the rate was in their customers nobody knows.

In Zimbabwe, a brigadier general was appointed Minister of Health in 1988, and promptly reduced the official death toll from AIDS from 380 to 119, and forbade all references to AIDS on death certificates. In this way the AIDS pandemic is officially abolished since there is no official evidence of it. All blood banks with any testing capabilities at all are forbidden to release HIV rates on the grounds that these are state secrets.

One doctor in the forefront of AIDS care in Uganda was expelled for discovering and responsibly reporting that over 30 percent of the women coming in for pre-natal care to the Kampala hospital were infected. Only in November, 1990, did the President of Uganda permit official endorsement of condoms, by which time more than one million Ugandans were infected. Many doctors with first-hand experience across the continent estimate that actual AIDS cases are 80–90 percent under-reported [in official figures]....

One of the difficulties in assessing the

The life cycle of the human immuno-deficiency virus. This process will go on for years, slowly depleting the immune system until it can no longer deal with even minor hostile microbes when they invade.

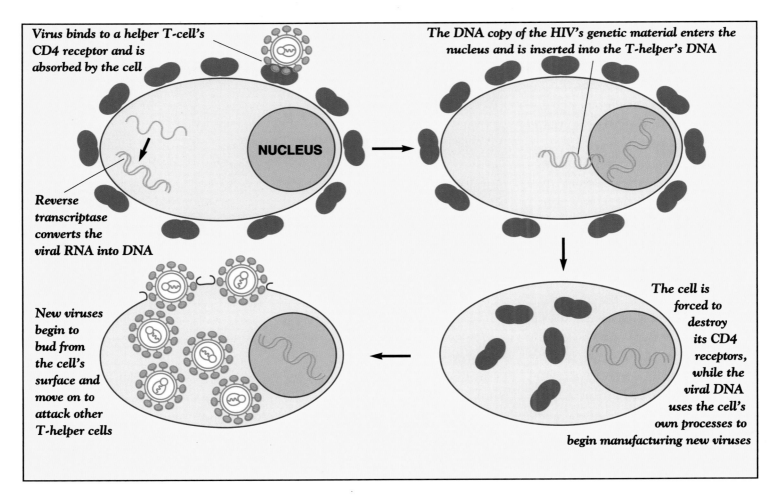

Virus binds to a helper T-cell's CD4 receptor and is absorbed by the cell

Reverse transcriptase converts the viral RNA into DNA

NUCLEUS

The DNA copy of the HIV's genetic material enters the nucleus and is inserted into the T-helper's DNA

The cell is forced to destroy its CD4 receptors, while the viral DNA uses the cell's own processes to begin manufacturing new viruses

New viruses begin to bud from the cell's surface and move on to attack other T-helper cells

The green or vervet monkey, suspected to be the original animal reservoir of the microbe that became the human immunodeficiency virus. Exactly how and when the virus leaped across the species remains a mystery: the effects are all too clear.

true extent of AIDS in Africa is the lack of basic statistics in countries too poor or too chaotic to hold an effective census – at all, let alone regularly. Neither Tanzania nor Uganda has had a reliable census since 1967. The figures on AIDS from Tanzania, for example, have been contradictory: the official rate of infection in 1991 for the country as a whole was 0.2 people in 1000. Yet in 1986, in the capital Dar-es-Salaam, tests on donated blood were already showing an infection rate of 73 people in 1000. Populations in crisis-ridden Africa are neither settled nor stable, as the waves of hundreds of thousands of refugees moving back and forth across the borders of Rwanda in the late fall of 1996 vividly demonstrated. What is actually happening in Tanzania is discovered obliquely:

In areas raped and pillaged by undisciplined and rampaging [Ugandan] troops, over 30 percent of whom were infected at the time, the human presence itself is threatened. Whole areas are evacuated by devastated people, who often carry the virus with them to new locations, and the effects can even be seen on satellite images as villages and towns are abandoned, allowing the bush to grow back over the roads and tracks visible at these resolutions. In the town of Kasensero, over half the people are dead, and nearly all the rest infected. Here, and elsewhere in

Tanzania, the officially reported AIDS cases bear no resemblance to the truth, not because of official lying, but simply because there is no capacity to diagnose and register deaths.

In 1993 there were an estimated – guessed – 800,000 infected people in Tanzania out of a probable population

of 27 million. Uganda had perhaps 1.3 million cases of HIV infection out of perhaps 18 million people. Uganda lost 300,000 people to the savagery of its own soldiers during the 1970s, while its economy collapsed as it was plundered by dictator Idi Amin. Years of political turmoil and civil war followed his downfall; another half million died, and a million more fled the country. Today half the Ugandan armed forces are HIV-positive, with a far higher rate among the officer corps. Ugandans have become fatalistic to the point of death wish: for many young men, reports Gould, AIDS stands for *Acha Iniue Dogedego Siachi*, meaning 'Let it kill me because I will never abandon the young ladies'. In Zaire a related attitude prevails: the French acronym SIDA is laughed off as *Syndrome Imaginaire pour Décourager les Amoureux*, 'Imaginary syndrome to discourage lovers'.

AIDS goes where people go: the major north-south highways and railroads from Zaire and Tanzania meet in Zambia, whose chief industry and hard-currency earner is copper. Half the cases of AIDS reported to WHO were from the copper-mining area. The effects were seen in economic statistics. Between 1990 and 1993, Zambia and Zaire's copper exports fell from 800,000 tonnes to 600,000 tonnes. The road and rail arteries run south toward South Africa through Zimbabwe, with 10,000 estimated AIDS cases in 1993 out of a population of around 10 million, and an infection rate that may be as high as 40 per cent in the capital, Harare.

To the east, the highway runs into Malawi, which has the highest reported rate of AIDS and HIV infection in Africa. Here it is not limited to the cities, where the infection rate is about 30 per cent. Migrants from rural Malawi have long worked in the gold and diamond mines of South Africa. According to one estimate about half the miners returning to Malawi are HIV-positive, and therefore infecting the women of the country, who may not remain monogamous when their partners return to South Africa. Says Peter Gould: 'The truck route [to South Africa] from Malawi is now known as the Highway of Death: 92 per cent of the truck drivers visiting Durban were infected, sleeping with prostitutes there or at stops along the way.' He goes on to describe the heartbreaking prospect facing Malawi:

What the year 2000 will bring no one knows, and it is even difficult

Workers in Malawi watch a video warning of the risks of AIDS. As many as 30 per cent of men and women in the cities of Malawi are HIV-positive.

to speculate. Malawi is essentially agricultural, and as in most Third World countries it is labor-intensive. How do you feed yourself with no one to work the fields, even if you make radical shifts in the crops you raise, away from labor-intensive maize to more flexible and less-demanding bananas?

In these central and southern African nations the infection rate is probably doubling every 12–18 months – and some estimates say every eight months. We can see that, defining a plague as 'usually highly lethal, and spreading fast and far enough to disrupt an entire society', then AIDS is indeed a plague. It is no less so in West Africa, where

the more deadly HIV-1 virus has in six years overtaken the slightly more benign HIV-2, and even in 1989 infection rates were hovering around the 14 per cent mark among women – not prostitutes – coming to hospitals for pre-natal care.

And there is nothing anyone can do to stop it. There is no vaccine and no

AIDS victims occupy one third of all graves in this cemetery in Harare, Zimbabwe. In countries where AIDS statistics are officially suppressed, the real extent of the disease can be gauged only by gathering information from sources like this.

existence of AIDS on the world stage, others have done little or nothing to educate their own people about the threat. In South Africa, where some black communities are more than 20 per cent HIV-positive, condom advertisements are prohibited, and in any case many Africans have long regarded condoms as a surreptitious means of controlling the black population.

Well-meaning Western charities have donated planeloads of condoms to African nations. But rural Africans regard children as social security, providing care in sickness and old age, and as badly needed helping hands on the land. For them contraception is not an easy option, and in some societies, the price of a bride must be repaid if she does not bear children. In Rwanda, the image of a generous flow and exchange of fluids dominates the way people think and behave, from public ritual to personal intimacy. To suggest that Rwandans use condoms, whose function is to block any exchange of fluids, amounts to asking them to repudiate their cultural heritage.

But then, practically, what can African leaders do? Some of the hardest-hit African countries are virtually without effective government; Somalia has none at all. Many have illiteracy rates of over 50 per cent; even radios may be few and far between. Attempts at education are reduced to fleeting visits to remote villages by strangers bearing a handful

of posters and a few condoms. Worse, according to Christopher Wills, a 1992 prediction by epidemiologists that by 2007 the toll from AIDS will cause the Central African population to begin shrinking, has had another effect:

Unfortunately, their prediction seems to have provided a further justification to the governments of some of these countries to discourage birth control and educational measures – for what is the point of embracing the politically embarrassing message of birth control if AIDS is going to do the controlling for you? And what is the point of spending money to educate people if so many of them are going to die anyway?

AIDS today and tomorrow

The only hope for Africa is the discovery in the West of a cure or a vaccine for AIDS. Otherwise, we are likely to witness the 'hollowing out' of the continent – within families, as the number of orphaned children and aging grandparents grows while the 'AIDS generation' dies; within the economy, as workers in key industries and on the land succumb; and geographically, as the center of the continent is emptied of people and productivity. The psychological and social consequences of this husking of whole societies are incalculable, but still more appalling political chaos would seem to be inevitable. The West will not escape unscathed: Africa is a source of metals, gold, diamonds, oil, coffee, tobacco, and a dozen other commodities on which our way of life depends.

Africa is the template for the development of AIDS in other Third World countries. A few other countries, all of them in Asia, face the possibility of

cure. The palliative treatments that do work are phenomenally expensive even by Western standards, while African health-care budgets rarely rise above $10 per person per year – to cover all contingencies. By and large Africans are reticent about sex: it is not easily discussed in public. So, while some African leaders denied the

pandemics of AIDS just as severe. In Thailand, which for a while from 1987 half-openly advertised its enormous sex industry, the HIV infection rate among prostitutes in Chiang Mai province in 1989 was a minuscule 0.4 per cent. Twenty months later, tests showed an infection rate of over 70 per cent. The sex industry in Thailand employs about 500,000 people, but it is not an institution limited to big cities: the brothel is an accepted part of the Thai way of life. Prostitution is also illegal, flourishing by way of kickbacks and bribes – so that those who receive them have a vested interest in maintaining the trade in human flesh.

In an effort to recruit uninfected workers, agents for the industry have reached into the poorest corners of Thailand, buying girls as young as 12 from their parents. Burmese, Laotian and Chinese girls are also bought into slavery. Many of the former are from refugee families escaping repression at home. Some of these women have found their way to Europe. While they may be marketed as 'clean' there is, of course, no guarantee that their first, second or 500th customer will not be infected. At the same time, there is a common misperception – or deliberate self-delusion – in Thailand that AIDS is a disease of the *farangs* – foreigners. Condom use by Thai men is rare, while the women are not in a position to demand it from their foreign clients. Many of these are sex tourists, flown in from Europe, particularly Germany. So the plague reaches across the world by way of an air bridge.

Projections of the cumulative effect of AIDS on Thai society are uniformly shocking. One suggests that by the year 2000 as many as 560,000 Thais may have died of AIDS, creating a loss of up to 8.5 billion dollars within the economy. Another predicts that by 2010, life expectancy will have fallen from 75 to 45 years, with the overall death rate more than tripling from 6 to 22 per 1000.

A similar astonishing rise in AIDS infections occurred in India in the late 1980s, exacerbated in the border province of Manipur by a shift in

In a multi-storey 'massage parlor' in Bangkok, Thailand, girls wait to be chosen by customers. High-class brothels tend to sack HIV-infected girls, but they readily find work in less scrupulous establishments.

neighboring Burma's drug trade. Once the traditional supplier of opium paste, Burma became an exporter of far more profitable heroin, some of which then moved rapidly into the local narcotics market. From 1987 to 1989 in Manipur, former opium smokers became heroin users, and a chronic shortage of syringes pushed their HIV rate up from one per cent to 80 per cent. The addiction was present in all levels of society. By 1990, on the other side of the subcontinent in Bombay, STD clinics were reporting that 40 per cent of prostitutes were HIV-positive.

German researchers estimated in 1993 that India as a whole was seeing one million new HIV infections a year, and that by 2000 there would be 10 million cases in the country. Attempts to educate Indians have been subverted by political leaders and bureaucrats, some of whom refused to cooperate, while others may have pocketed campaign funds. One of the few concrete results of a 120 million dollar grant from WHO and the World Bank for AIDS education in India was the purchase of a billion condoms – just over one per head of population – by the national government. Locally produced, they turned out to be defective. As elsewhere, the economic and social consequences as the AIDS plague spreads in India could be reckoned catastrophic.

If the picture in a highly developed area like Western Europe is less alarming, there is hardly any cause for complacency. In 1995 the region had reported nearly 142,000 HIV cases since 1983, but WHO reckoned the true figure to be nearer 450,000, out of an estimated total of 15 million infections throughout the world. Even Australia had an estimated 20,000

cases. The USA and Canada were estimated to have more than 750,000 infections, and the disease was spreading faster among heterosexual men and women than among gay men.

The likelihood of direct social disruption from AIDS is less in these places than in the developing world for several reasons. There is effective public sanitation, and infinitely better health care. There are fewer virulent opportunistic infections – malaria, gut infections producing lethal diarrhea, tuberculosis, and so on – to leap quickly into the breach in the immune system's defenses. Sufferers receive the best care modern medicine can provide. And so – to put it bluntly – they take longer to die, and do so out of public view. On top of these things, high rates of literacy, greater openness about sexual matters, and determined government education campaigns make it at least fractionally more likely that AIDS will be contained within those groups where it first arose. The West will feel the most devastating effects of the global spread of AIDS when its supplies of cheap raw materials, fuel, foodstuffs and hi-tech goods from overseas begin to dry up. If Central Africa has set the pattern, the West will also face an increasingly lawless and unpredictable Third World as the 21st century gets into its stride.

Two worlds of AIDS

In the West, AIDS in the 1990s has largely stayed within two segments of society – gay men (who represent nearly two thirds of all new cases) and intravenous drug abusers. It is the latter group that accounts for the rise of AIDS cases among heterosexuals in the USA and Canada, as drug abuse increases and addicts contract the dis-

ease and pass it to their partners.

AIDS appears to be thriving among heterosexuals in Africa and Asia because the HIV strain there seems to flourish in cells lining the vaginal wall. In contrast, the virus prevalent in the West has to get direct access to the bloodstream or the mucous membranes. Anal sex and intravenous drug use both create minor wounds and lesions, and this is the reason why they have contributed so heavily to the spread of the virus in the West. The current thinking is that AIDS is likely to expand drastically in the West only if the African and Asian strains take hold among the general population.

Thus, the West has one more reason to be desperately searching for a vaccine or a cure for AIDS. In 1982, when the virus was first isolated and analyzed, many scientists believed such a thing could not be long in coming. That was before they realized how fast the AIDS virus mutates within the human body.

In mechanical terms, this happens because the reverse transcriptase enzyme that triggers the reproduction of the virus's RNA is not very efficient, but at the same time ignores its 'mistakes', making viruses with a huge variety of genetic traits. The result is the very rapid production of a mass of viruses that are so different from one another that they are virtually different sub-strains. This burst of activity seems to occur to ensure that there are enough viruses capable of surviving and reproducing within the host's body. And every virus that breaks out of one cell and goes in search of another to colonize will mutate just as much once it has wormed its way in and begins to reproduce.

This poses a major problem for those

trying to design vaccines against the AIDS virus or drugs to stall the virus once it has taken hold. An AIDS virus that is successful in one person's body will not necessarily succeed at invading another host. People with HIV are most likely to pass it on at the early stage of the infection, when the virus is reproducing and mutating very quickly – and some of its offspring will be better than others at colonizing a new host. There is every chance that the viruses that take hold in anyone else will be markedly different from those that caused the first infection, and so on down the line. This means that a vaccine tailored to deal with one person's HIV is unlikely to create antibodies that work on another's. It may work to an extent, but the infection will continue. There is also a strong chance that the descendants of the viruses that escape the vaccine will also have a built-in resistance to it. So

even if the next person to pick up the virus has been vaccinated, their antibodies may well prove ineffective against the new generation of invaders.

However, one of the most intriguing challenges in AIDS research centers on 40 or so prostitutes who work in the slums on the outskirts of Nairobi, in Kenya. These women seem to be immune to AIDS. For years they have been continually exposed to HIV, yet they remain uninfected by the virus. Tests show that neither the microbe nor any trace of its antibodies is present in their blood.

The women appear to have inherited specialized cells that can kill off the virus before it can inflict any damage. Two of those being studied are sisters who between them have five daughters. All seven women work as prostitutes, and all have remained HIV-negative. Researchers from universities in the UK, North America

Feliciana, a 28-year-old prostitute from Nairobi, Kenya. She is one of a rare group of people who have been exposed to HIV but appear to be naturally resistant to it. Her immune system shows no sign of being disturbed and she has produced no antibodies to the virus.

and Kenya are now mapping the women's genes to try to find out what protects them from infection. The hope is that a vaccine will eventually be engineered from their findings.

Quest for a cure

The search for a comprehensive treatment for AIDS faces the same challenge from the virus's capacity for rapid and radical mutation. There is always the possibility that, over time, an effective drug will simply eliminate all the strains that are sensitive to it. But the virus will have continued mutating as much as it can. The field will then be left open to successful strains of HIV that are out of reach of the drug. In that case we will face the prospect of AIDS superbugs, but with a far grimmer outlook for humanity than that threatened by bacterial superbugs.

Medical scientists and drugs design-ers have developed two strategies to counter this potential hazard. The first involves interfering with the reproduc-tion of the virus in various ways, and at levels that should be unaffected by the plethora of mutations of which the AIDS virus is capable. The idea here is to stop the virus reproducing at all, so the problem of HIV developing a drug-resistant mutation never arises. The second, and more recent, development has involved attacking the virus with several drugs at several levels simulta-neously. At the time of writing, this approach appears to hold enormous promise in defeating the AIDS virus.

The first drug that was really successful in attacking HIV started life as an experimental compound in the fight against cancer. Known variously as Retrovir, zidovudine or AZT, it is an almost exact replica of the nucleoside thymidine, one of the fundamental chemicals that form the backbone of DNA. The difference is that one arm of the AZT molecule contains three nitrogen atoms, whereas the thymidine molecule has none. In all other res-pects, AZT appears to be a thymidine molecule. AZT and drugs like it are therefore known as nucleoside analogs. AZT works like this. When the reverse transcriptase enzyme is rewriting the HIV's RNA into the form of a DNA molecule, the enzyme mistakenly recognizes AZT as a thymidine mole-cule and tacks it on to the end of the forming DNA chain. But AZT, unlike thymidine, has no exposed 'coupling' to which more thymidine can attach itself. In this way, the assembly of the HIV is stopped dead. Other drugs besides AZT, which confuse the re-verse transcriptase but are not analogs of nucleosides, have the same effect, although scientists do not yet fully understand how they work.

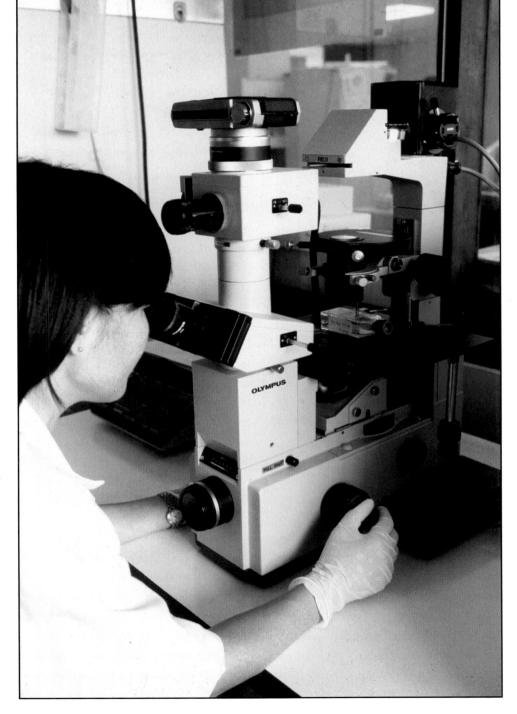

A Thai medical technician checks blood samples for HIV. Limited budgets mean that only a fraction of Thailand's high-risk groups can be effectively screened, and AIDS continues to spread unabated.

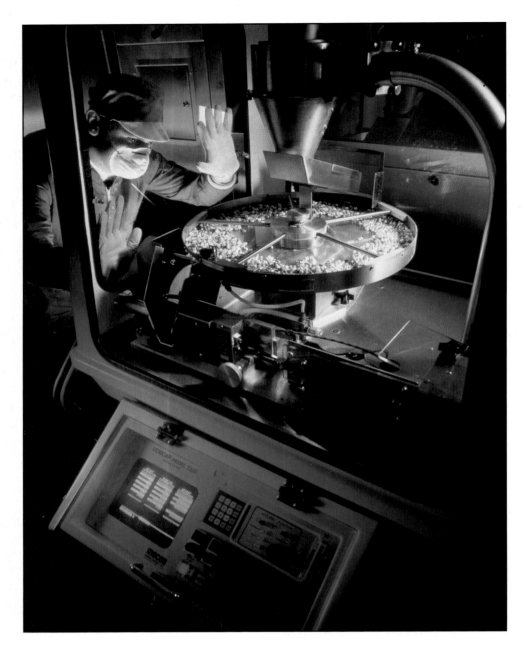

Automatic checking of the weight of doses of Retrovir – the trade name for AZT – at Glaxo Wellcome's UK plant. Trials indicate that, despite sometimes extreme side-effects, AZT in combination with other drugs may prove an effective AIDS treatment.

resulting virus will, purely by chance, have a built-in protection against the drugs. In the hope of reducing the chances of that happening to zero, scientists have tested combinations of AZT, another nucleoside analog and a protease inhibitor on volunteers infected with HIV. The results from trials of these triple combination therapies are extremely promising.

A scent of victory

The success of the trials has been measured in two ways. First, by how few AIDS viruses and how many immune-system cells with CD4 receptors (which act as a biochemical magnet for HIV) are in the patient's bloodstream at the end of the test period. Second, and more revealing if potentially more painful, the long-term clinical trials have shown how many patients have survived and how many have died after receiving this treatment, in comparison to patients who did not have the treatment. The triple combination brought HIV levels so low that they were undetectable by current tests, and led to a huge increase in the number of immune-system (CD4-receptor) cells in those who survived during the trials. And many more survived among those taking the three drugs than among those who did not.

If an AIDS infection is caught at the right time and treated with the triple combination, there is a ray of hope.

Another strategy is to attack the replication of the virus at a slightly later stage. HIV's genetic core is made of RNA. This is copied as DNA (the point at which AZT goes to work), which produces yet another RNA chain to create the final copy of the virus. This last stage is organized by another enzyme, known as a protease (pronounced pro-tee-aize). Drugs such as saquinavir, ritonavir and indinavir interfere with the function of the protease as it assembles the final RNA

chain, so the construction of the HIV virus is never completed.

In practice, both approaches run the risk of encouraging a resistant virus to emerge from the debris of incomplete HIV copies, just because the reverse transcriptase enzyme is so unpredictable in its 'mistakes'. At either stage in a virus's reproduction, it is possible that the reverse transcriptase or the protease will have written out too much of its genetic information for the drugs to interfere, and that the

One computer-assisted study in the USA suggests that if HIV levels can be kept low and CD4 levels kept high for three years, there is actually a chance of a cure – for in that time the body will have naturally replaced any cells in which the virus is lurking out of reach of the drugs. However, no one is yet sure when is the best time to start treatment. And all these drugs have terrible side-effects – few people have been able to tolerate taking AZT for much more than a year.

Nor is there absolute certainty that attacking the virus is actually the most effective approach. Some scientists believe it would be better to find a way to destroy infected cells, which after all provide the machinery and the nourishment for HIV in the first place. It is also possible that people 'catch' HIV through the transmission of infected cells from one person to another, rather than of free-floating viruses. The challenge here is to find a drug that will dispose of infected cells without killing off 'innocent' ones, which remain vital to the functioning of the immune system. One way to do this would be to boost the sensitivity of other cells within the immune system to cells infected with HIV. Instead of attacking the infected cells as a class and risking 'collateral damage', the drugs would encourage natural killer cells to seek out only those that were producing HIV.

The end of AIDS is far from being in sight. Not only do all these scientific problems have to be solved: there is also the ugly question of money. A year of treatment with triple combination drugs can cost between $10,000 and $15,000 at least, and far more if the patient is in hospital at the same time. This price simply cannot be paid even by stable, but still impoverished, Third World countries who have health budgets of $1 to $10 per person per year, and brings little cheer to comparatively rich developing nations such as Thailand, which currently spends about $30 per person a year on health care.

We are left with the bleak, distressing prospect that the appalling projections for the spread of AIDS throughout the world with which we started this chapter may yet come true – and in their train will follow consequences that we can barely imagine.

Freddy Mercury, lead singer of the supergroup Queen. An unabashed bisexual, Mercury flaunted a private life as excessive as any of his stage performances. His death from AIDS in 1991 was one of many among public figures – Rock Hudson, Liberace, and Rudolph Nureyev were others – that helped to deflate some of the irrational attitudes to the disease and to homosexuality.

CHAPTER FOUR

SLEEPING MONSTERS

THE THREAT FROM HIDDEN VIRUSES

In November 1996 an outbreak of Ebola fever in Johannesburg, South Africa, created a wave of fear that this notoriously lethal virus might soon be on its way around the world by ship or plane. Thanks to excellent medical care and detective work, the alarm proved unfounded. But, as this overview of 'emerging' viruses shows, the risk remains that human intrusions into wild places may combine with the efficiency of modern transport – and set off a new round of incurable plagues.

In Libreville, Gabon, on Saturday, 19 October 1996, Dr Clement Mambana was feeling distinctly feverish. He thought he had malaria, and treated himself accordingly. The symptoms went away for a couple of days, but then the fever returned with a vengeance, along with diarrhea. Dr Mambana now feared he had acute viral hepatitis. By 27 October, courtesy of his health insurance, he was on a plane to South Africa, and was admitted to the Morningside Medi-Clinic in Johannesburg the same day. Professor Guy Richards of Johannesburg General Hospital had recently found that steroids had worked 'like magic' on patients with viral chickenpox pneumonia, and decided to try the

A medical worker in full protective gear, during the 1995 outbreak of Ebola fever in Kikwit, Zaire. The epidemic infected 315 people, of whom 244 (77 per cent) died.

treatment on Dr Mambana. Chicken-pox is caused by a herpes virus, and another, the Epstein-Barr virus, is associated with hepatitis.

On Tuesday, 29 October, Morning-side doctors took Dr Mambana into the operating room to insert a deep, 'central line' catheter. It was a messy process, and a lot of blood was spilled. Theater sister Marilyn Lahana had the job of cleaning up afterward. The following Saturday she was at a party with her husband Cyril. The evening was cold and rainy, but Mrs Lahana felt hot, so she took a blanket and sat outside for a while. Next day she felt listless, and by Monday had a constant headache. By Wednesday morning the headache was literally blinding: she couldn't see even to unlock her car. Cyril took her to work at Morningside, but she was sent home immediately. The family doctor referred her to a neurologist who, suspecting that she had encephalitis, booked her into

Sandton Clinic for observation. Tests showed no sign of brain inflammation.

Over the next few days Mrs Lahana developed a rash and diarrhea, which the doctors thought was a reaction to the antibiotics she had been given. By Saturday, 9 November, the Sandton doctors were baffled: their patient's platelet level had dropped by two thirds since she had entered the clinic. This meant that her blood was losing its ability to coagulate, a vital part of controlling bleeding. And she had now developed 'marked leukopenia' – a drastic reduction in white blood cells. It was then that the possibility dawned that Marilyn Lahana could be infected with a hemorrhagic virus.

At once the doctors set up a series of tests at the Special Pathogens Unit at South Africa's National Institute for Virology. The first was a direct, immediate test on Mrs Lahana's blood serum for antibodies to the hemorrhagic viruses – Marburg, Ebola, Rift Valley

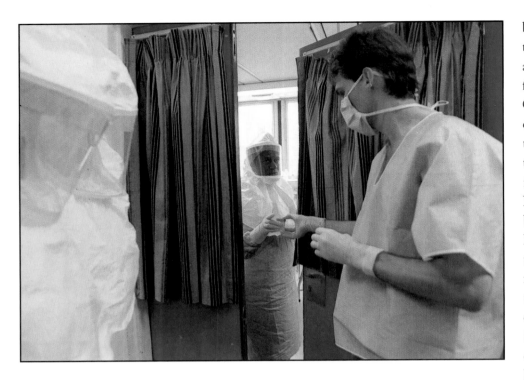

Barrier nursing in operation for South Africa's first Ebola victim, Marilyn Lahana, who lies behind these doors in the intensive-care unit at Johannesburg General Hospital.

fever, Lassa, Crimean-Congo and hantaviruses (known as the 'MERLCH test'). Her serum was also inoculated into laboratory cell cultures and into day-old mice.

The direct serum test revealed no trace of the MERLCH viruses in Lahana's sample, but on Thursday, 14 November the cell cultures were showing a reaction to Ebola antiserum. More blood samples were taken that day – and these showed the presence of Ebola antibodies in the serum.

The prospect of a nightmare opened up before the doctors at once. The Ebola virus is one of the most efficient killers in the world: of those infected in previous outbreaks only one in 10 have survived. The rest have died within a week or so of the first symptoms appearing, bleeding at every

orifice, their internal organs and connective tissue transformed into a grotesque slime by the virus.

This was the first time the Ebola virus had appeared in South Africa, and it was far from its natural habitat. Until now it had been confined to within about 650km (400 miles) north or south of the Equator. Yet here was Ebola in Johannesburg – the hub of southern Africa's transportation systems. It was capable of stepping out on a catastrophic junket – not just across the continent, but to the world beyond. The South Africans had to find where it had come from, and stop it going any further.

Containing the outbreak

By midnight that Thursday Marilyn Lahana had begun to cough up blood, a sign of the internal hemorrhaging characteristic of Ebola fever. Over the next few days, her essential physical systems started to break down. Her kidneys failed, and her lungs began to collapse. The doctors carried on taking

blood samples, running a fresh series of tests using the enzyme-linked immuno-absorbent assay (ELISA) with reagents from both the Centers for Disease Control (CDC) in the USA and their own stocks. The ELISA tests showed that the number of Ebola antibodies in the nurse's blood had increased 16-fold in the six days between 9 and 15 November. On Saturday, 16 November, already on life-support systems, Lahana was moved from Sandton to the intensive-care unit at Johannesburg General Hospital. Here, a team trained in 'barrier nursing' – caring for patients who have to be isolated from all physical contact with others – and already experienced in handling cases of Crimean-Congo hemorrhagic fever, took over.

Meanwhile, as soon as the tests had showed positive, Sandton and Morningside clinics had set up teams to trace all Marilyn Lahana's known contacts over the previous three weeks, and to oversee infection and outbreak control not only at the two hospitals but at the pathology laboratory that had tested samples. On 16 November, when the Ebola infection became unmistakable, the provincial and national Departments of Health took charge of a full-scale crisis management team. Early on, the group decided to hide nothing from the media. Still more effort and urgency was thrown into tracing everyone who had been in contact with Marilyn Lahana. She herself was now too ill to help the medical detectives, but just after 9 p.m. that evening, Dr Mambana was identified as the most likely source of her infection. The nurse had mopped up his blood. And since October an epidemic of Ebola fever had been raging in Booué, 300km (185

Professor Robert Swanepoel of South Africa's National Institute for Virology. He directed the treatment and investigation of Marilyn Lahana's Ebola infection.

miles) east of Mambana's home in Libreville in Gabon.

Dr Mambana had recovered sufficiently to be discharged from Morningside on 11 November, and he had gone to convalesce in a private house nearby. The doctor was now rapidly brought to hospital and interviewed, and blood samples were taken and tested. By midnight the results were ready: he was carrying antibodies to the Ebola virus, and tests on a sample taken during his illness showed the same. More assays were being run to see if he was still carrying the virus itself. Dr Mambana said he had not, as far as he knew, seen any patients with Ebola fever in Gabon. Until that evening he was completely unaware that he himself had contracted the illness. The best guess as to how he had infected Mrs Lahana was that his blood had seeped through a tiny hole in her protective clothing and then somehow – perhaps through a small cut – the virus, or infected cells, had got into her bloodstream. It could have

taken hours to do so: the Ebola virus can remain active and dangerous for at least a month outside a host, even in high temperatures.

Next day Professor Robert Swanepoel of the National Institute for Virology sent the first of several long and detailed 'situation reports' to medical news groups and Web sites on the Internet. By the morning of 18 November, the world knew that South Africa had its first case of Ebola hemorrhagic fever, and that the virus had arrived there on a commercial airline flight nearly a month before. How many more people were now infected? Was an epidemic about to break out in the richest nation in sub-Saharan Africa? And most frightening: had it already begun to spread across the globe on any number of international flights out of Johannesburg? Ebola fever has an incubation period, from the moment the virus enters the bloodstream to the appearance of the first symptoms, of between four and 21 days. Anyone who had

been in contact with Marilyn Lahana since 29 October, the day she cleaned up Dr Mambana's blood, was in theory still at risk of developing the fever. Over the next few days 216 people were traced and screened at yet another hospital, the Rietfontein, which specialized in tropical and infectious diseases. A few were kept in for overnight observation; a few proved to be ill, but not with Ebola fever; and everyone was assigned a health worker who would take their temperature and make other checks twice a day. Staff who were nursing Marilyn Lahana were constantly screened as well. The 10-bed intensive-care unit at Johannesburg General was cleared, just in case further cases emerged.

The specialists reassured everyone that the chances of an epidemic were low – because the virus had to get into a victim's bloodstream to start its lethal work – and a telephone helpline was set up to keep everyone informed of the situation. Despite the doctors' openness, unnervingly inaccurate reports appeared in the international press that over 200 people had been quarantined, and that the public had been advised to wear masks when out on the streets. Rumors flew that the government was lying about the true extent of the outbreak. As these stories went out on the wire, the number of people at any serious risk was reduced to fewer than 100, and by 21 November more than 40 of them were cleared from continuous monitoring.

One place the virus did go, and by

jet, was to the Special Pathogens Branch at the CDC in Atlanta, Georgia. Within 48 hours the 'wizards', as Professor Swanepoel called them, had analyzed the DNA of the virus. It was confirmed as belonging to a type that had previously been seen in Gabon. In the meantime, the Gabonese Ministry of Health had established that in Libreville Dr Mambana had, in fact, been in contact with an Ebola patient from the Booué outbreak. On 20 November the doctor himself was released from hospital in Johannesburg, and flew home to Gabon.

As for Marilyn Lahana, she was now fighting for her life against systemic inflammatory response syndrome (SIRS). The syndrome can set in as a comprehensive reaction after any major infection or injury. SIRS was first named during the Vietnam war when, thanks to medical advances, wounded combat troops survived massive injury, only to succumb to a collapse of the body's regulatory systems. Major organs fail, blood pressure drops, capillary veins leak and other blood vessels go slack. It is as if the foundations of a building have suddenly sagged, or the poles and stays holding up a tent have all broken. Mrs Lahana was now being supported by a kidney dialysis machine, a ventilator to keep her lungs working, drugs to maintain blood pressure, coagulants to control bleeding, and intravenous feeding because her digestive system had failed. With her basic functions in such disarray, there was a real risk that secondary infections, normally taken in stride by her immune system, could take devastating hold. But, as Professor Swanepoel pointed out, there was still hope: the desperately ill nurse had survived longer than most of those

who had been infected in Zaire the previous year.

The hope proved short-lived. First, septicemia set in – Mrs Lahana's body tissues were attacked by hostile bacteria and fungi in her bloodstream. On Friday, 22 November she suffered multiple brain hemorrhages. She finally let go her fragile hold on life at about 8 p.m. on 24 November. 'Marilyn perished in the course of dedicated duty and in an attempt to save someone else's life,' wrote South Africa's president Nelson Mandela to Cyril Lahana. 'Our sorrow is mixed with admiration of her selfless sacrifice.'

Several more anxious days were to pass before the specialists could be sure that the Ebola virus had not settled on anyone else who had been in contact with Dr Mambana or Marilyn Lahana. Gradually, South Africa relaxed, and the rest of the world too. The South Africans set about tightening up their border controls, so that any airline carrying a sick passenger, especially one with a fever, would have to inform the authorities well in advance. Then, if and when another case of Ebola, or any other essentially incurable disease, touched down in the country, they would know about it before it had any chance of spreading through the community, and possibly the world.

Ambushed by microbes

Ebola is one of a handful of somewhat mysterious but exceptionally dangerous African hemorrhagic viruses. As we shall see, these African viruses have broken out of concealment relatively recently. They are devastating to humans, who have generally been responsible for shaking them out of hiding, and they are extremely difficult to control once they have been let loose.

The South Africans knew they had been lucky. Marilyn Lahana had indeed been a sacrifice, whom strangers mourned, feeling that her death might have been their own. What stopped Johannesburg becoming a death zone in November 1996 was, first, the sheer good fortune that no one but Mrs Lahana had come into contact with Dr Mambana's blood, and no one else had picked up the virus from her. Second, the level of medical care and expertise available in Johannesburg had made up for the initial human errors in diagnosis (which were probably inevitable, since Ebola was so unexpected a presence in the country). The resources for barrier nursing the patient were to hand, as were up-to-date immunofluorescence tests to identify the virus, along with direct electronic and airborne communication with American expertise at the CDC in Atlanta. The modern urban setting allowed a rapid and effective trace of all those at risk. It also provided the means to let everyone know the facts about the disease and the day-by-day development of the outbreak, even if nothing could prevent the growth of wild rumor and over-reaction to the news.

People had every reason to be afraid of Ebola. Having fended off potential attack, the virus regards the cells of any tissue or organ in the human body, except bone and skeletal muscle, as fair game. Among the first to be invaded, inevitably, are blood cells. As the virus copies itself inside them they begin to die and clot together. The clots clog the capillaries, cutting off the blood supply throughout the body; dead patches begin to appear in the affected organs. The viral proteins attack collagen, the major protein in the connective tissue that holds organs together, with particular savagery. As the collagen turns to pulp, holes appear in the surface of the organs, including the skin, and blood pours through them. Under the skin hemorrhaging patches appear; liquefied dead skin creates blisters on the surface. At this stage any bodily opening will bleed – victims may weep blood – while the skin and the surface membranes of the muscles begin to break up.

Inside the body, the heart bleeds into itself and into the body cavities around it. The liver bloats and cracks apart, and then putrefies; the kidneys fail, choked with dead cells and blood clots. Dead, coagulated blood cells are everywhere, including the brain, hindering the transfer of oxygen and eventually bringing on dementia and massive epileptic seizures. Meanwhile, the virus has destroyed the ability of the surviving blood to clot, so that the hemorrhaging continues unchecked. Live and dead blood together with dead tissue and sloughed-off membranes, including the linings of the stomach, mouth and intestines, are thrown out of the body through vomiting and diarrhea. Ruined veins, arteries and intestines no longer hold together, so fluids flood into the body. Although awash with liquid, the tissues themselves are dehydrated, cannot function, and begin to die.

A high-security laboratory for handling lethal 'Level 4' viruses at the Centers for Disease Control in Atlanta, Georgia. The researcher wears an air- and fire-proof suit, with its own air supply and communications rig. The lab is bomb-proof and equipped with comprehensive security devices.

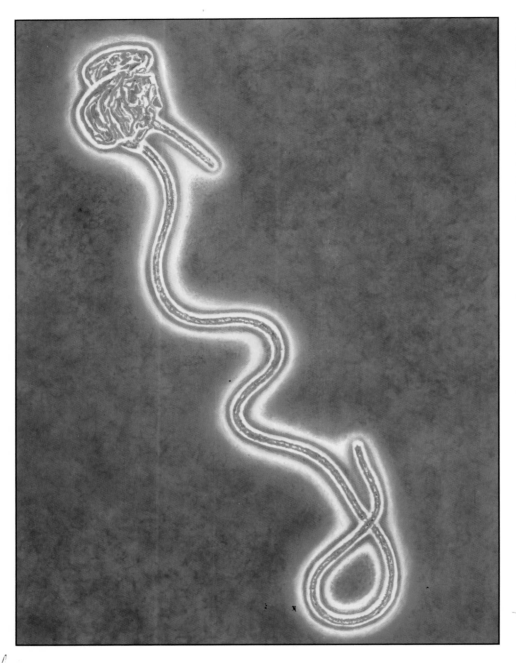

The Ebola virus, as seen by an electron microscope. Just 3/1000ths of a millimeter (8/100,000ths of an inch) long, the virus causes a devastating infection. Only expert, intensive nursing or natural immunity may save the victim.

in to Johannesburg – or Berlin, Bangkok, or San Francisco – soon moving on to relax in some remote, rural village, believing himself healthy while the virus was incubating inside him, surrounded by people with no inkling of how infectious he was or how to deal with the virus when it struck – and then succumbed to the disease, the story could have been entirely different.

Seeking a culprit

In 1996, knowledge of the most destructive hemorrhagic fever viruses was little more than three decades old, and in that time medical scientists had not cracked all their secrets. The first major outbreak of such a virus was detected in 1962 in the isolated village of Orobayaya on the Machupo River in eastern Bolivia. The center of the epidemic was in an equally inaccessible town, San Joaquin. Researchers from the US Middle America Research Unit (MARU), based in Panama, witnessed a fever that could kill in four days flat; it began with agonizing bouts of diarrhea and vomiting blood and ended with the victim bleeding from every aperture.

After 18 months of effort, punctuated by several of the MARU team catching and managing to survive the fever, the field researchers pinpointed the source of the virus to a species of large, gray *Calomys* mice that infested houses and food stores in the town. The accepted theory was that as the mice fed, they urinated, and so deposited the virus on food and grain that the people would later eat. Whatever the exact connection between the mice and humans, the effects on the local population were devastating: between 1962 and 1964, when the

This grotesque process continues until the viruses, replicating exponentially, have so wrecked the internal organs that they cease to function entirely, and the host dies. The organs, already partly or entirely dead when this happens, begin to liquefy. Like the blood, feces and vomit, these fluids are teeming with millions of viruses in every drop.

In close communities whose members live side by side, the scattering and splattering of all these poisoned fluids creates the bridge from one host to the next. Had the primary patient, Dr Mambana, been a vacationer flying

Americans stopped the epidemic in its tracks by setting mousetraps all over town, more than 40 per cent of the area's residents caught the fever, and it killed perhaps half of those infected.

The Machupo fever was, too, a classic instance of an infection that emerged because of a radical change in human behavior – a plague that was, so to speak, caused by human history. Until 1952 San Joaquin had thrived as a river port. Local men tended the beef herds that roamed huge tracts of land belonging to a wealthy Brazilian family, and the distant landlords sent their own refrigerated steamships up the river to collect the carcasses, bringing food and other supplies to San Joaquin in return. In 1952 there was a revolution in Bolivia: the reforming government confiscated the foreigners' herds and land and gave them to the people of San Joaquin. But the dispossessed landowners' steamers stopped coming upriver. Because the villagers now needed to grow corn and other vegetables to fill out their solid beef diet, they cleared areas of jungle – and invaded the natural habitat of the *Calomys* mice. The mice were not that disturbed. They now had a plentiful supply of food, and their population expanded accordingly, finally coming to rest in the houses of San Joaquin. The mice could accommodate the Machupo fever virus; the two-legged inhabitants of the houses could not.

In the optimistic atmosphere of early 1960s medicine, with all manner of afflictions in retreat around the world in the face of vaccines, antibiotics and inoculation campaigns, the Machupo outbreak seemed an aberration. And, to underscore the point, it was successfully contained. Just five years later came a fresh warning that

the microbes were far from defeated. And this time it sounded not in some neglected backyard of the world, but in the clean, efficient heartland of the post-war German economic miracle.

The German connection

Marburg, Germany, is home to a factory producing vaccines for the giant pharmaceutical company Hoechst. During August 1967 three workers at the plant fell ill with what seemed to be a bout of flu. But this was an odd time of year to be catching flu, and the three men were admitted to Marburg University Hospital for observation. The day after they entered the hospital it was apparent that something a good deal nastier than flu was at work. The patients' spleens were swollen and tender, they had strangely bloodshot eyes, they were constantly nauseated, and their mood was sullen and aggressive.

Within a month, the Marburg hospital had 23 cases of the mysterious and destructive sickness, and all worked at the Hoechst plant. In Frankfurt, 80km (50 miles) away, there were six more cases. Four of the Frankfurt patients worked at a government medical institute. The fifth was their doctor, and the sixth was the pathologist who had analyzed their blood and tissue samples. And a veterinarian and his wife had gone down with the same symptoms in Belgrade, Serbia (then Yugoslavia).

The disease followed a gruesome pattern. After the initial flu-like symptoms came signs of a massive viral invasion – besides a swollen spleen, the victims suffered swollen lymph nodes in the neck, a drop in white blood-cell count, and the loss of clotting platelets in the blood. After

six days a red rash appeared, and the patients had to be fed intravenously because their throats were raw; then acute diarrhea followed. After eight days the capillary veins were blocked with dead platelets; red blood cells backed up in the veins, unable to carry oxygen to the body's extremities. Starving nerves sent searing pains through the patients, who were now scarlet from the gridlocked red blood cells just beneath the skin. Next, they began vomiting blood. Those who did not then bleed to death or become demented, then fall into a coma and die, saw their hair drop out in clumps and their skin peel off. These were the survivors. Seven of the 31 people infected with the mystery disease died.

All of those infected, apart from medical staff at the Frankfurt hospital and a morgue attendant at Marburg, had been in contact with vervet monkeys – both the Hoechst plant and the Frankfurt institute created vaccines derived from their kidneys. WHO investigators found that one shipment of 99 monkeys had been sent from Entebbe, Uganda, to Belgrade, and then on to Marburg and Frankfurt. When they arrived in Belgrade, 49 animals were dead; the veterinarian who caught the virus there had performed autopsies on the dead animals, and his wife caught it while nursing him. Two more shipments of infected monkeys had followed the same route. But in Uganda the trail went cold: according to the trader who supplied the monkeys, they had been caught in locations all over central Uganda. Using stored serum samples taken from generations of imported animals, the WHO team was able to reconstruct the Marburg virus's spread through Ugandan monkeys.

It had infected about a third of the

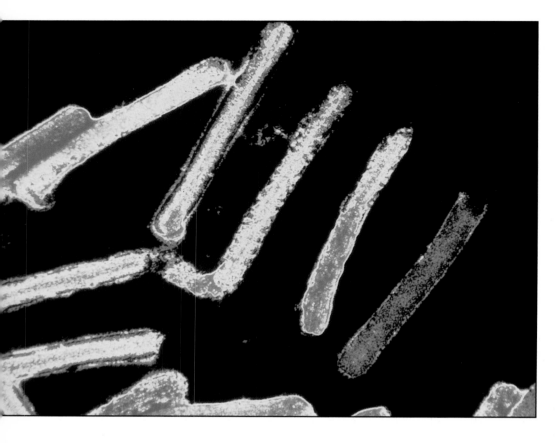

The virus that causes Marburg fever, also known as Green Monkey disease. Its first outbreak in 1967 in Germany was an early warning that virtually untreatable tropical fevers could span continents in the jet age.

population of two species – the vervets and the local red-tailed monkeys – by 1967, and had first infected them only in 1961.

But where had the virus come from before it launched itself on the monkeys? What was its natural reservoir? Clearly not the monkeys, for it killed them too fast to treat them as a long-term host. Did it live in an insect, another mammal, a bird? Repeated searches and examinations of thousands of captured species of animals of all kinds in Central Africa have failed to find the answer. And with this mystery unsolved, it is impossible to say what conditions have to arise to

cause the virus to leap the gap between its natural, commensal host into another animal population – and no way, therefore, to predict where or what that animal victim may be. It could be a human.

A hidden plague

Marburg – named, like other viruses, for the place it first broke out among people – was the first 'filovirus' to reveal itself to medical science. Most viruses are spherical; the Marburg and similar viruses are like threads, and Marburg often curls itself up into a ring – the only virus reported to do so.

The next incurable horror to come out of Africa emerged less than two years later and more than 2500km (1500 miles) from Uganda, in the Yedseram River valley of eastern Nigeria. The first people it struck were Americans.

Laura Wine was a 69-year-old nurse

at the Church of the Brethren Mission Hospital in Lassa. One day in mid-January 1969 she began to feel sharp pains in her back. They went on for a week. Laura Wine thought she must have wrenched her spine inadvertently in the course of her duties. Then she developed a vicious sore throat, which was so painful that she could not swallow. Penicillin injections were no help. She developed a fever of over 38°C (101°F), became acutely dehydrated, and her blood began to clot in a way none of the hospital staff could understand. Her heartbeat became irregular, and she became incoherent as her body began to swell and to show signs of hemorrhaging. On 25 January she was flown to Jos, where she was taken to Bingham Memorial Hospital. The next day she went into convulsions and died.

Three days later at Bingham, nurse Charlotte Shaw fell ill. She had swabbed Laura Wine's mouth with a gauze pad. She had a tiny prick from a rose thorn on her hand, and had not worn surgical gloves while tending her dying fellow-nurse. Within 11 days, Charlotte Shaw too was dead. Dr Jeanette Troup, aided by nurse Lily Pinneo, performed an autopsy on the body and found a scene of appalling carnage: kidneys, liver, spleen, lungs, heart, veins and arteries were clogged with dead blood cells and proteins. Her lymph glands, producers of white blood cells for the immune system, had literally been taxed to the limit: they were entirely empty.

A week later, on 21 February, Lily Pinneo too fell ill. Once again, antibiotics proved useless, and Dr Troup hastily arranged to have Pinneo flown to New York along with blood and tissue samples from Laura Wine and

Charlotte Shaw. After speaking to Dr Troup, Dr John Frame of New York's Columbia University, who was medical adviser to a string of Christian hospitals in the African interior, alerted scientist Jordi Casals at the Rockefeller Institute at Yale University. Dr Casals had charge of a huge bank of viruses that had come from Africa, dozens of them never seen before or since in Westerners who had fallen ill there.

Lily Pinneo and the ice-packed samples were flown to Lagos, the Nigerian capital. There she spent four days in a hellish, mosquito-infested hut, running a 38°C (101°F) temperature while Nigerian bureaucrats and US Embassy officials wrangled over how best to get her to New York. She finally flew out, semi-delirious, with two attendants, the only passengers in the first-class cabin of a Pan Am jetliner. On arrival at Columbia Presbyterian Hospital in New York, Lily Pinneo was isolated in a glass-walled cage, constantly under the eye of intensive-care nursing staff. Over the next few weeks her condition worsened still further – she ran a temperature of 42°C (108°F), her body swelled with fluids, and she also developed malaria, probably the result of sharing a room with thousands of mosquitoes in Lagos. Periods of lucidity alternated with delirium. At the end of March, as the unknown virus attacked her central nervous system, she lost control of her muscles: her eyes jiggled in her head and her body twitched and shuddered. Yet she had already survived the mystery disease longer than her dead colleagues, and by mid-April she began to recover. By 3 May she was able to walk again, and was discharged from hospital.

The doctors thought Lily Pinneo must have survived an attack by the Marburg virus, but Jordi Casals's assays on her and her dead colleagues' blood and tissues said otherwise. Nor did any of his tests show reactions that pointed to any other virus in his huge 'library' of infectious organisms. The Lassa

A patient suffering from Lassa fever is tended by a doctor from the relief organization Merlin. Since Lassa's first appearance in Nigeria in 1969, it has been found in countries all over sub-Saharan Africa.

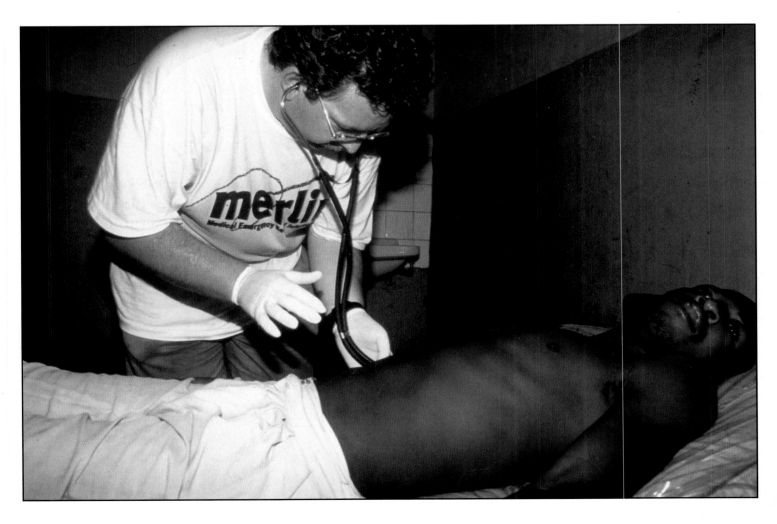

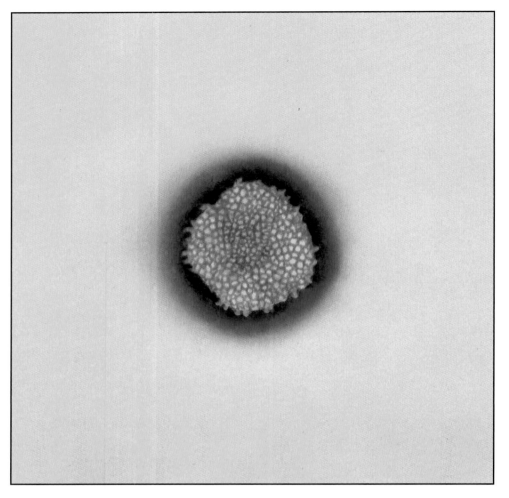

The lethal Lassa fever virus, seen at about 135,000 times its actual size. The microbe is especially infectious as it can travel in microscopic water droplets in the air. However, unlike most hemorrhagic fevers, Lassa can be treated with anti-viral drugs.

designed high-security vaults.) Casals's frustration was not just personal; not knowing precisely how Lassa fever moved from host to host meant that he had no sure idea where it came from, or what potential victims could do to avoid it. At best, his experiments had shown that it did not have a natural reservoir in insects.

The second strike

Lassa hit Jos again at New Year 1970. The Bingham hospital, now renamed Evangel, took in 17 cases within three weeks. On 25 January Dr Troup decided to perform one autopsy to confirm that the virus was to blame. Doing so, she nicked herself through her surgical glove. By 18 February she was dead, two days before Lily Pinneo finally managed to overcome bureaucratic delays and return to Jos with her own potentially life-saving antiserum. Meanwhile, the Lassa outbreak at Evangel continued to claim lives, and spread to the nearby Vom Christian Hospital. By the end of February, 28 people had been infected, and 13 had died. The primary case in the outbreak had been in a bed by an open window in Evangel; investigators concluded the virus had been blown down the ward to infect at least 16 others.

Still no one knew how the primary patient had been infected. Analysis of samples of blood from 712 current and former American missionaries working in West Africa showed that five had

virus even looked unique – with dark spikes poking from the perfect sphere. And the microbe was phenomenally lethal, more so even than Marburg. Just one part of infected blood in 10 million parts of harmless liquid was enough to kill half the cells in a petri dish. Casals carried on sedulously experimenting until 3 June – and then he too succumbed to the disease. Rushed to Columbia Presbyterian, he showed the same implacable symptoms as the nurses. His physician decided the only thing to do was to inject him with Lily Pinneo's blood plasma. The antibodies to the Lassa virus that she had developed might just save him. And they did. Within a week of his first plasma injection, Casals's temperature was back to normal, his mind was clear,

and his heart and blood vessels were functioning healthily.

Once recovered, Casals concentrated on working out how, despite taking the most laborious precautions, he had picked up the virus. He concluded that it could be inhaled, spread by rodent urine, or by direct blood-to-blood contact with an infected person; but he never did find the exact route. He could not explain how it had invaded him or, more tragically, his laboratory technician Juan Roman, who had died of Lassa fever just after Thanksgiving in 1969 without ever, it seemed, having been near even a sealed vial of the microbe. (After that, the Lassa virus samples were shipped out of Yale to the CDC in Atlanta, where they were stored in specially

others at a mission hospital in Zorzor, Liberia, developed the disease. In September there was another epidemic in Sierra Leone, in the diamond-mining region on the Liberian border. In both cases CDC investigators collected hundreds of local animals in the hope of finding the source of the virus. In Sierra Leone the researchers noticed that *Mastomys natalensis* rats were most numerous in villages stricken by Lassa. In the CDC's laboratories in Atlanta, tests on the collected animals showed that only *Mastomys* rats were infected with Lassa, and they all came from villages where humans had contracted the disease. But while the source of the fever virus now seemed fairly certain, the route it took in slipping from animal to man remained obscure.

In the late 1970s another CDC expedition to West Africa uncovered the true extent of Lassa fever in the region. In that part of the world, where lethal fevers are extremely common and analyses of their ultimate causes are extremely rare, it transpired that Lassa had been endemic in the countryside for countless years, camouflaged by the infections around it. (Until its later, hemorrhagic stages, for example, the symptoms are strikingly similar to those of yellow fever.) In some districts in Sierra Leone, up to 40 per cent of the villagers carried Lassa antibodies, and had therefore been exposed to the virus. Over the country as a whole, about one in 10 fevers was caused by

antibodies to Lassa. One had had a long fever in Nigeria in 1952. The others had fallen ill in the mid-1960s in Guinea, at least 2500km (1500 miles) away. The same study showed that two per cent of northern Nigerian villagers had been exposed to Lassa in the 1960s. It seemed that the virus

spent years hiding in some natural animal reservoir between forays into the human population. There was still no clue as to what that reservoir was, but it was clearly distributed all over West Africa. In March 1972, the fact was hammered home as a pregnant woman, her midwife and a dozen

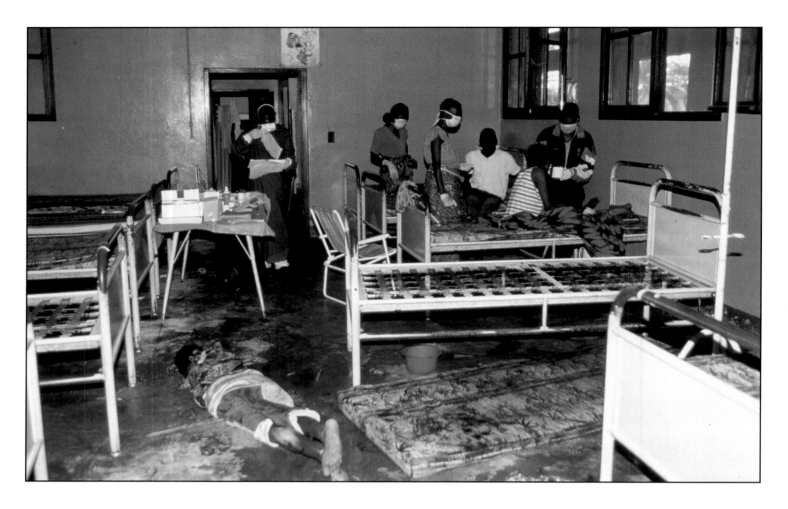

the Lassa virus. A joint Dutch-American study for WHO of all the available data on Lassa throughout Africa revealed that the disease was present in rodents as far south and east as Zimbabwe and Mozambique, and as far north and west as Mali and Senegal. Lassa had not crashed into an urban population and then out of Africa largely because it was a disease of isolated rural communities. It had come to the attention of Western medical science by a paradox – it had turned up in hospitals, and flared to epidemic proportions within them.

The WHO researchers found that in Africa, among people inured for generations to the disease, about 98 per cent of victims actually survived it. But the illness might last for weeks, taking an economic as well as physical toll on those affected. Destroying the *Mastomys* rat was out of the question, and in any case no one understood the exact connection between the rats, the virus, and the people. A campaign of prevention, especially on such a large scale, was simply impossible. And as it had become apparent that serum containing antibodies from the Nigerian outbreaks was useless in Sierra Leone, and still more distinctive strains of the virus had turned up in southern Africa, vaccination – let alone an effective vaccination program – was not practicable. That left a search for a cure. CDC scientists found that ribavirin, an anti-viral drug that is effective against herpes and hepatitis, worked against Lassa fever too, provided it was given in the very early stages of an infection. But impoverished African nations

Inside Pavilion 3 of the hospital at Kikwit, Zaire, during the Ebola epidemic in 1995. The outbreak created chaos: while one patient is being treated, the corpse of another lies unattended nearby.

simply do not have the money to control or cure the disease, even where they are aware of its presence. And that, in an age in which mass intercontinental travel is taken for granted, means that Lassa remains a threat to the people of all nations, rich or poor.

Nightmare in Zaire

Ebola fever first came out into the open in the village of Yambuku in the Bumba Zone of northern Zaire in September 1976. The 120-bed, cinder-block and tin-roofed hospital there was run by 17 Belgian nuns and a priest, and served some 60,000 people in the outlying districts. There was no resident doctor, and only four of the nuns had been trained in nursing and midwifery. They were helped by a female Zairian nurse and four male Zairian medical assistants.

The first person to die was Mabalo 'Antoine' Lokela, one of the mission schoolteachers, on 8 September. Not knowing what had caused his fever, bloody diarrhea and vomiting, and bleeding from the gums, nose and eyes, the nuns had injected him with antibiotics, chloraquine and vitamins, and intravenously given him electrolytic fluids to counter his dehydration. In the following few days, several people who had been patients at the hospital at the beginning of the month also died, showing the same horrific symptoms, in their home villages. Shortly

after Mabalo Lokela's funeral, his mother, wife, and mother-in-law went down with the disease. In all, 21 of his family and friends succumbed. Only three survived, including his wife, but the baby she was carrying was stillborn. On 12 September the first nun, Sister Beata, became feverish; she died a week later, on 19 September.

By then nearly 30 villagers had come to the hospital with the terrible disease, and 14 were already dead. None of the drugs available to the nuns had worked, and they ranged from aspirin and malaria remedies to antibiotics, blood coagulants and caffeine. Some of the patients became utterly demented: four fled the hospital, while others soon failed to recognize members of their family or their friends. Panic, as well as the dreadful bleeding fever, spread into the countryside. Altogether 55 villages were

affected, within a radius of 80km (50 miles) of Yambuku.

Overwhelmed, the nuns radioed for help. Finally, on 23 September, a microbiologist and an epidemiologist from the National University of Zaire arrived, just as another nun started a fever. They were totally unprepared for what they found. Intending to stay for six days, they left after 24 hours, having taken liver samples from the ravaged interiors of the victims. With them in the Land-Rover returning to Bumba were the Yambuku mission's priest, running a high fever, and a very ill nun named Sister Miriam; another

Kikwit, Zaire, 1995: coffins of Ebola fever victims are loaded unceremoniously onto a truck, in a scene reminiscent of collections of the dead during outbreaks of bubonic plague in medieval Europe.

A nun dispenses sterilized gloves to medical workers during the Ebola outbreak in Kikwit, Zaire, in 1995.

nun, Sister Edmonda, went along to nurse them. From Bumba the group was taken by Zairian Air Force jet to the capital, Kinshasa, where the two missionaries were admitted to the Ngaliema Hospital.

Word of the crisis was now spreading to the upper reaches of the Zairian Government, which sealed off the Bumba Zone and put the region under martial law to enforce the quarantine. The CDC were alerted, and another medical investigation team, properly equipped to gather blood and tissue samples, left Kinshasa. On 30 September Sister Miriam died. Her religious order forbade autopsies, but a biopsy of her liver had been taken in her last hours. The tissue and samples of her blood were sent for analysis to Belgium and to the Microbiological Research Establishment at Porton Down in the UK. The latter passed some of their samples on to the CDC.

At about the same time, word reached WHO from N'zara and Maridi in the rain forests of southern Sudan of an outbreak of hemorrhagic fever that sounded ominously similar to the one exploding through the Bumba Zone. Nearly 60 people had died by 9 October. Blood from the victims finally made its way to Geneva and from there to Atlanta and Porton Down.

Then, in mid-October, panic broke out in the Zairian capital. Sister Edmonda, having contracted the disease while caring for Sister Miriam, died. And a young Zairian student nurse, Mayinga N'seka, who had tended both, came down with the disease – having spent two days moving around Kinshasa with a fever, spending hours in government offices and another hospital. Officials managed to track down 37 people who had been in her company and isolated them in the Ngaliema Hospital for three weeks. Another 274 people who had had contact with the dead or dying patients were given blood tests and put under surveillance.

Nurse Mayinga did not survive her infection. Before she died, she had received shots of antiserum from a 1975 South African victim of Marburg fever in the hope that it would overpower whatever was destroying her. The failure of the antiserum confirmed the suspicions of medical scientists that they were dealing with a new and unknown virus. But Mayinga N'seka was the last in the line of infection in Kinshasa. As the quarantined contacts went home and the city relaxed, the epidemic was also receding in Yambuku. The final death toll from the 1976 outbreak in Zaire was eventually put at 318 out of 361 infections, a kill rate of 88 per cent.

Only when the epidemic was over did the microbe gain a name. Rather than brand the already notorious village of Yambuku any further, Dr Karl Johnson at the CDC decided to name the virus after a river flowing nearby. But what was the Ebola virus, and how had it blazed its way through so many people so fast?

Innocent poisoners?

The Yambuku outbreak attracted huge attention in the world's medical research community, and that intensified when it emerged that Mayinga N'seka had carried the infection around Kinshasa for two days. In that time the virus could have run amok among the capital's two million inhabitants – and emigrated out of Africa. By 20 October an international team of virus hunters,

the virus's natural host and method of transmission. Laboratories in the USA, UK, France, Belgium and what was then West Germany had isolated the virus. Like Marburg, it showed up under the electron microscope as a spindly filament. The team had a portable laboratory that would allow them to detect the presence of the virus in human and animal blood and tissue, even if they could not see it directly.

The reason the virus had blasted its way through the district around Yambuku quickly became apparent. Between 300 and 600 patients with a huge range of ailments would pass through the mission hospital on any one day. The nuns treated them with injections of antibiotics or anti-malarial drugs or, most frequently in the case of pregnant women, vitamin B. But the nuns had only five hypodermic syringes, 'cleaned' occasionally in warm water and mild disinfectant, which were used and reused on out-patients and in-patients alike. In dispensing their cures, the nuns had innocently passed the virus from those bedridden in the hospital to out-patients, who had taken it back to their home villages. When the victims died, their bodies were eviscerated before burial by the women of the family, by hand. At once the virus would, if it could, leap into a new host.

How the virus had arrived in Yambuku was less clear. Mabalo 'Antoine' Lokela and his family had eaten fresh antelope meat shortly before he showed his first symptoms. He and another early patient had also handled fresh monkey meat. Two days after that, when Mabalo thought he might have malaria – and was given a quinine shot for it – a stranger came to the hospital with terrible diarrhea and

A monkey poacher arrested in the Ivory Coast in 1993. Monkey hunting and eating infected monkey meat are suspected routes of Ebola infection, but the ultimate reservoir of the virus has yet to be found.

zoologists, epidemiologists and other specialists from Belgium, France, South Africa, the USA and Zaire was assembling in Yambuku, preparing to survey the devastated region and track down

a mysterious bleeding from the nose; he left after a two-night stay. The virus could have entered the hospital along any of these routes – or from a villager standing in line for his jab somewhere in front of the schoolteacher.

A similar chain of events had unfolded in the Sudanese outbreak. The disease had flared out from a single victim in N'zara, and spread east to Maridi; dirty needles were used again and again in the hospital at Maridi; and preparations for burial were similar to those practiced in Yambuku, so that close relatives of the dead came in contact with tissues teeming with the virus. This strain, now known as Ebola-Sudan, was different, and marginally less lethal than the Ebola-Zaire strain that came out of hiding in Yambuku. It remains a mystery why or how the virus insinuated itself into the clerk in the N'zara cotton factory who was its first victim.

And no one has yet discovered the Ebola virus's natural reservoir. Of the thousands upon thousands of mammals, birds and insects trapped and tested, from the Sudan to Cameroon (where tests show that the pigmy forest people have been exposed to the virus), only a few animals have been found with antibodies. None has been carrying the virus. At the time of writing, a small US-Australian-French team funded by WHO working in the Tai Forest in the Ivory Coast had found a Red Colobus monkey that carried Ebola antibodies. The team speculated that the monkeys were catching the virus 'from bats sharing the trees in which they live, or from one of the ground rodents that scamper up these trees and leave droppings on the leaves eaten by the Red Colobus'.

Another study, headed by Robert Swanepoel and published in fall 1996, found that fruit and insect-eating bats could withstand high levels of the Ebola virus without becoming ill. But, warned the authors, that was by no means proof that bats were even the potential reservoir of Ebola. The search for the reservoir is by no means over. To underscore the point, the CDC were still patiently working their way through 18,000 mammal, reptile and bird samples and 30,000 insects collected after the 1995 outbreak around Kikwit, Zaire, in search of a possible key host. And if the true reservoir is ever discovered, there is still the intractable problem of how to control the disease.

Invasion of a body snatcher

As noted, the Ebola virus is a filovirus, a stringy particle of life that can curl and twist into weird shapes; a common one looks like an elaborate shepherd's crook. The Ebola virus consists of seven proteins braided around a single strand of RNA. The proteins, which are still not wholly understood, are what wreak such appalling destruction in the human body. One part of their function seems to be to suppress the immune system of the host, although exactly how is not yet known. They may directly attack immune-system cells, or disrupt the function of receptors on infected cells so that antibodies fail to recognize them and do not go in for the kill.

One reason the outbreaks of Ebola fever have been relatively brief and – so far – relatively self-contained is the sheer malignant power of the virus. It tends to destroy its victims so fast – within about five days – that it has little opportunity to leap to a fresh host. It is transmitted, except in rare circumstances, by direct exchange of body fluids, and eventually runs out of opportunities to find that bridge.

At the same time, the Ebola virus is inefficient, because it is unreliable. Some viruses – such as the influenza virus and, as we have seen, HIV – have evolved in a way that helps them to overcome this hindrance to survival: they mutate very rapidly, which increases their chances of adapting to a new host. Ebola has not gone down this route. A CDC analysis of Ebola genes, published in 1996, revealed that the viruses responsible for the 1976 and 1995 outbreaks in Zaire were virtually identical: the variation in certain genes was only 1.6 per cent. 'The similarity is surprising,' said the authors, 'since more than 18 years and 1000 kilometers [1600 miles] separate the outbreaks caused by these viruses.'

Such stability over time and distance suggests several things. Ebola is remarkably well adapted to its usual host; and that reservoir is extremely widespread (if equally elusive). The virus's settled genetic structure also indicates that it may be very old. And it may be possible to exploit the virus's genetic conservatism and find a vaccine. A bug that hardly changes is open to attack by carefully engineered antibodies. The trick will be first to create them, and second to produce them cheaply enough to protect the huge and yet often inaccessible populations who are vulnerable to Ebola. The first people to be vaccinated ought, in all conscience, to be the few and far-between doctors and nurses who encounter the initial cases in the field. Without their survival, as the original epidemic so vividly demonstrated, there is little hope of containing any outbreak of the disease.

This hard-nosed reflection leads inevitably to others that apply to all outbreaks of these unpredictable and uniquely savage viruses. Even if it was not merely a coincidence that Dr Mambana recovered after he had been given steroids – a subject already slated for research – and even if a vaccine can be developed, the inescapable truth is that fundamentally unsound medical practices caused the original Lassa and Ebola outbreaks to flare out as far as they did. Once more we are looking, on the one hand, at well-meaning and compassionate but ill-trained and ill-equipped medical 'carers' in remote locations and, on the other hand, at countries that cannot afford to provide even these services outside a few cities.

We are also looking at a whole jigsaw of other matters. Humanity is constantly nudging at the edge of the wild, disturbing ancient ecologies. That alone, as the people of San Joaquin discovered, can be enough to awaken a slumbering monster. But then there was the dreadful irony of the original Marburg outbreak. People doing as humanitarian a task as any, creating vaccines to save lives, died because they – or their employers – had broken into age-old jungle habitats to capture monkeys to make those vaccines. Did the monkeys pick up the virus because, in response to the hunters, they moved beyond their traditional limits, even temporarily, and so disturbed and were infected by the commensal host of the Marburg virus? Probably we will never be able to confirm such a conjecture. But such speculations are worth making: history tells us that epidemics, pandemics and plagues arise time and again because, through warfare, commercial adven-

ture or plain accident, questing human beings have upset some delicately balanced corner of the natural world. That is how the Great Dying, the Black Death of the 14th century, began. With only horses, human feet and sailing ships to speed it on its way, the bubonic plague disposed of at least a quarter of the population of Europe and Asia. For all our modern medical knowledge, today's jet transport can outstrip that kind of distribution of disease by several orders of magnitude.

Africa and its people remain among the most exploited in the world. The naked greed of European colonists tore wealth from the land but kept the lid on inter-tribal rivalries. In country after country, nearly four decades of self-rule have seen ordinary Africans crushed by strongmen more engrossed in lining their pockets than in bringing health, wealth, or liberty to the people under their yoke. The exploitation of the land and its resources continues, if often less profitably, and meanwhile the people grow poorer in every respect. In such circumstances, the odds shorten every day on the probability that unknown and incurable diseases will lurch out of the wild to fasten on new and unprepared hosts – and vault around the globe.

Slash and burn: tribal people set fire to forest to clear space for a crop plantation. Traditional agriculture and commercial deforestation both threaten to bring hidden viruses into the open, with unpredictable results.

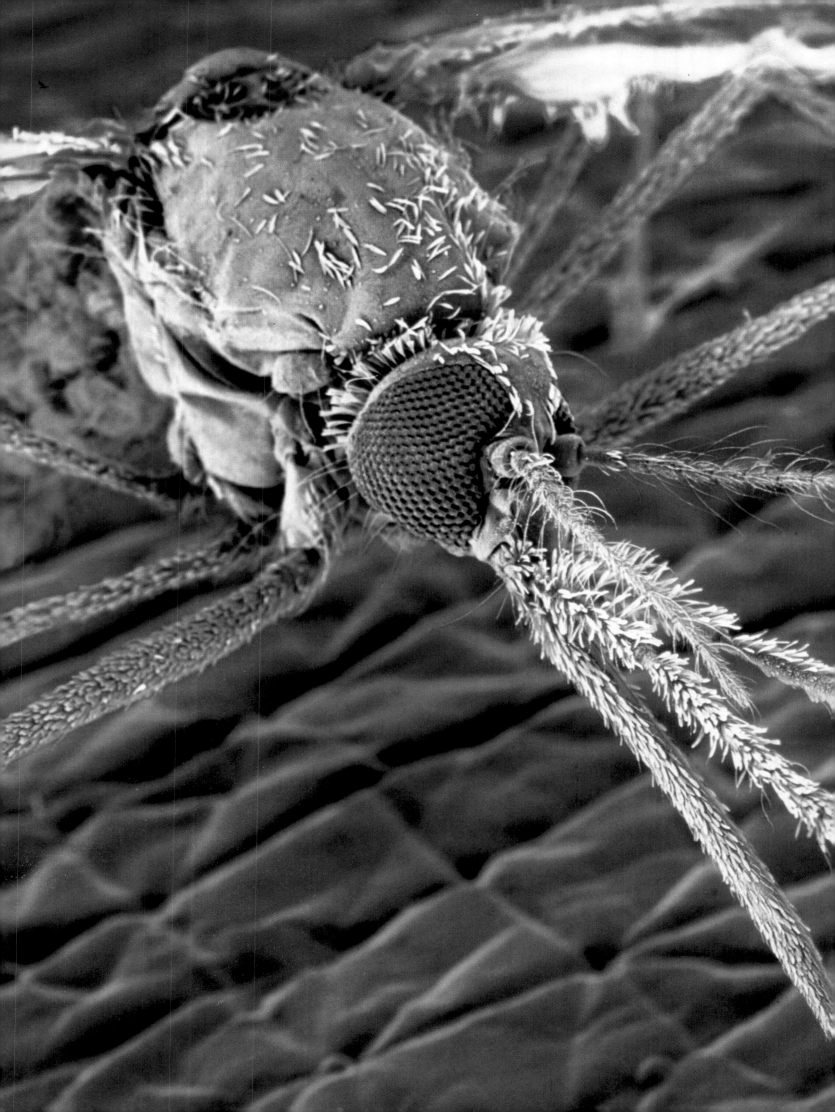

CHAPTER FIVE

ENEMIES IN WAITING

VICTORIES AND DEFEATS IN THE BATTLE AGAINST MALARIA, YELLOW FEVER AND CHOLERA

In some parts of the globe the rapacity of mankind is plain to see – even from space, in satellite pictures of barren lands where tropical hardwood forests once stood in South America and Asia. The 'tiger economies' of Asia have an insatiable demand for raw materials taken from the earth, and their cities have become major hubs in the world's transportation network. Whole tracts of Asia have been fought over without a break for more than half a century, while poverty in South America has brought the rise of chaotic, insanitary shanty towns the size of major cities. Against such a backcloth, Asia and South America, too, have inevitably brought forth their incurable diseases and potential plagues.

Some diseases seem to belong to history, banished into the past. Some appear to be afflictions that occur to other people in other places, horrors that can never happen to 'us'. Those of us who live in highly developed, industrialized countries are not much bothered by malaria, cholera, or yellow fever. Yet it is only recently, in the scheme of things, that malaria has receded from the USA – both presidents Washington and Lincoln sur-

An electron micrograph of an Anopheles *mosquito. Sixty species of these creatures transmit malaria to human beings. Disease-bearing parasites are passed on in the insect's saliva when it feeds on blood.*

vived it – or from Denmark and the British Isles. And only within living memory has malaria been banished from southern Europe – from what are now popular tourist destinations in Mediterranean France, Italy, and Greece. Cholera seemed to appear without warning everywhere in the civilized world in the 1830s, and it continued to run amok in cities from Mecca to New York to Hamburg until about a century ago. Today, anyone venturing from, say, Galveston to the banks of the Ganges takes the simple precaution of being vaccinated first. Yellow fever, still endemic in Africa, was famously banished from Cuba in 1901 thanks to the research of the US Army's Walter Reed, but in 1793 it

had killed over 5000 people in Philadelphia. As late as 1959 there was a resurgence of yellow fever throughout South America, the result of a slow but certain spread of the virus following a major, totally unexpected outbreak in Central America in 1949. In the Americas today it is limited to the tropics, and travelers to affected areas there or in Africa and Asia can take a vaccine to ward it off.

Those who stay at home in suburban comfort should not allow themselves to be too complacent. None of these diseases has been defeated in their original habitats, and in some parts of the world they have actually grown more lethal. A revival of any of these afflictions in plague proportions in the developing world will, as with AIDS, have incalculable effects on developed economies. And it is not inconceivable that they could take hold in the so-called First World again.

They hunt by night

Malaria is a menace to public health in some 90 countries. Over two billion people, or more than 36 per cent of the world's population, are potential victims of the disease. Estimates of the number of people who actually catch malaria each year vary between 300 and 500 million, and more than 90 per cent of these cases occur in countries in tropical Africa. Somewhere between 1.5 and 3.5 million people die of malaria each year, most of them young children in Africa, usually in remote rural areas with little or no access to health services. Other high-risk groups include pregnant women, as well as refugees and displaced persons.

Typically, the symptoms of malaria are bouts of fever alternating with periods when there is no feeling of illness whatever. The beginning of the disease is marked by headache, a general sense of malaise, fatigue, nausea, muscular pains, slight diarrhea and a small increase in body temperature. These rather vague symptoms are often mistaken for flu or a gastro-intestinal infection. But the most severe forms of the disease begin with a galloping fever and develop into delirium, impaired consciousness and convulsions, followed by persistent coma, and death.

The commonest cause of malaria is the bite of an infected anopheline mosquito, which injects *Plasmodium* parasites into the bloodstream as it pierces a blood vessel in order to drink from it. The insects usually feed between dusk and dawn. There are about 400 species of *Anopheles* mosquito throughout the world, but only about 60 transmit malaria. The disease can also be transmitted by blood transfusion, and by contaminated needles and syringes. In congenital malaria, the parasites are passed on from mother to child before or during birth. Human malaria is caused by four species: *Plasmodium falciparum*, *Plasmodium vivax*, *Plasmodium ovale* and *Plasmodium malariae*. Of these the most virulent and dangerous is falciparum, but it is possible to be infected by all of these extraordinary microbes at once,

The British physician Ronald Ross, who from 1890 spent years dissecting mosquitoes and finally found how the malaria parasite was transmitted. For this he was awarded the Nobel prize for medicine in 1902.

should one happen to be in the way of enough mosquitoes. Malaria is by no means limited to people. Of the nearly 120 species of *Plasmodia* currently known, at least 22 infest primates, and 19 others infect rodents, bats and other mammals. A further 70 or so species have been found in birds and reptiles.

It took a century to unravel the complex life cycle of the *Plasmodium* parasite, which (at one stage of its existence, at least) is a transparent, crescent-shaped, single-celled creature known as a protozoon. The first person to recognize that these creatures caused malaria was a French army surgeon, Alphonse Laveran, working in Algiers. That was in 1880. In 1980, the final link in the chain was discovered by the American medical scientist Wojciech Krotoski, working in New Orleans. In the century between came the realization that mosquitoes and malaria were connected, along with a saga of antagonism, bitterness, misunderstanding and misrepresentation among scientists that would rival any soap opera. These human dramas are beyond the scope of this book, but the full story of *Plasmodium*'s transformations in its hosts is startling enough.

Deadlier than the male

The female *Anopheles* mosquito lives on blood. To get a meal, it uses its proboscis like a hypodermic needle, jabbing it through the skin to reach a capillary vein, and at the same time injecting saliva into the bloodstream of its prey. The saliva contains anti-coagulants so that the blood does not clot while the mosquito feeds. An insect that is also infected with *Plasmodium* protozoa simultaneously injects the parasites into the victim's bloodstream. At this stage they have

Malarial parasites encysted on the stomach wall of a mosquito, as seen by an electron microscope. The cysts will eventually burst to release sporozoites, which make their way to the mosquito's salivary glands.

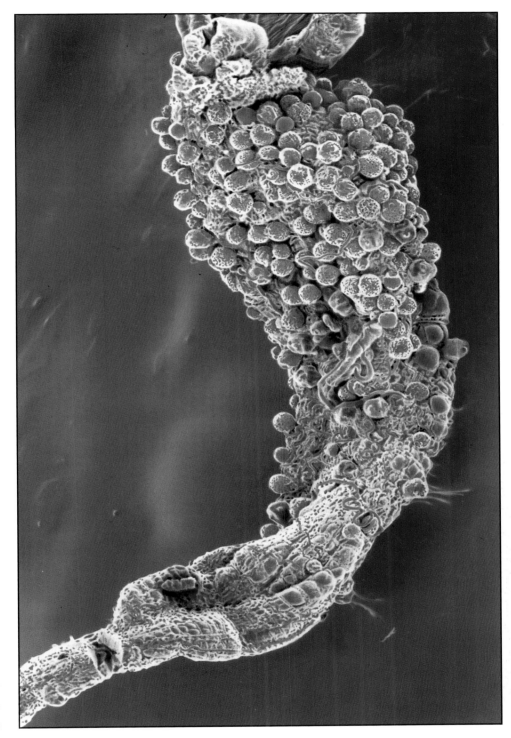

the form of single-celled, rod-shaped 'sporozoites'. In a human host these make their way to the liver, where they transform into 'schizonts'. These then emerge from the liver, and invade red blood cells. There, they mature into 'merozoites', and multiply prodigiously, eventually bursting out of the shattered red corpuscles. This destruction brings on a fever but, more important, deprives the host's body tissues of the oxygen carried by the red cells. Anemia is the least result. In a severe infection that overwhelms the immune system's ability to control the merozoites, the tissues are suffocated, and death eventually follows.

Once they have emerged from the red blood cells, the merozoites – the cells that Laveran saw – swell from time to time and release thrashing, whiplike creatures called 'gametocytes'. These come in two forms – male and female. As the mosquito feeds, passing out sporozoites into the bloodstream with its saliva, it is taking in gametocytes with the blood of its prey. Once in the mosquito's gut, these sexually distinct microbes mate, and produce 'zygotes', which form cysts on the mosquito's stomach wall. Between one and three weeks later, the cysts break open, releasing a new generation of sporozoites that make their way to the mosquito's salivary glands, ready to be injected into a new host's bloodstream and begin the cycle over again.

There is yet another facet to the process when *Plasmodium vivax* and *Plasmodium ovale* enter the human body. These parasites cause forms of malaria that can return and seize their hosts with a new outbreak of illness, sometimes after a lapse of dozens of years. When their sporozoites enter the liver, they do not all transform into schizonts. Some become 'hypnozoites' – 'little sleeping animals' – which remain dormant in the liver, waiting for a signal to catapult them into activity. A sudden shock can set them off, but how or why remains unexplained.

Nor is that the only mystery about the malarias. *Plasmodium malariae* infections can return after many years, too, but no one has yet found hypno-zoites in patients' livers – or anywhere else in their bodies. The reason for the hypnozoites' existence is not hard to find, however. They are the parasites' equivalent of a store of seed potatoes, a way to let the species survive the winter when the mosquitoes, vital to one half of their life cycle, are inactive.

The most virulent form of malaria, falciparum, does not relapse. And because it has – so to speak – no inter-est in keeping human hosts alive as a long-term lodging, it has no interest in their survival. To stay alive itself, it has to keep infecting new hosts, and for this reason it is limited to the tropics where mosquitoes are active all year round. Falciparum parasites reproduce in much larger numbers in the hosts' bloodstream, and the huge amounts of wreckage from exploded red corpuscles can jam capillary veins until they burst. When this happens in the brain, the parasites flood out to cause an horrific cerebral inflammation. In pregnant women it can damage the placenta and cause a spontaneous abortion. The final stages of an esp-ecially severe infection can see the kidneys destroyed, so that blood pours, unfiltered, directly into the urine, to generate new, separate infections.

Breaking the chain

Once it was discovered (in 1898) that *Anopheles* mosquitoes carried malaria, the obvious way to abolish the disease was to stamp out the insects. This was to prove easier said than done and, as we shall see, the attempt at a cure ended by intensifying the problem. The first great success of the strategy came in Cuba in 1901, when the US Army drained or oiled every patch of standing water – where mosquitoes

breed – in Havana. Ironically, this was a byproduct of the campaign to get rid of mosquitoes carrying yellow fever, but deaths from malaria dropped by 90 per cent. A continuing vigilance against the insects has kept Havana virtually free of the disease ever since. An even more ambitious project saw the mosquito-infested Pontine marshes in central Italy drained in the 1930s, and after World War II a massive program of aerial insecticide-spraying in southern Europe and South America shattered the mosquito popu-lations there. Then, in 1958, the US Congress voted huge sums for a world-wide campaign to eradicate malaria everywhere. The spraying was to go hand in hand with global immuniza-tion with chloroquine. The plan was to wipe out malaria by 1963.

The active agent in the spray was DDT. The chemical not only destroyed all manner of other, benign species of animal as well, but allowed resistant strains of *Anopheles* mosquito to flour-ish, along with resistant strains of many other pests. The master plan of 1958–63 was probably always doomed in tropical countries where it was im-possible to deal with every mosquito-friendly pond, pool or puddle that formed in the months-long rainy season. Further, no aerially delivered spray could reach beneath the triple canopy of the world's rain forests.

In practical terms the program was a disaster. When 1963 came, Congress withdrew funding. Some countries had achieved extraordinary success in their campaigns: Sri Lanka, for example, saw one million cases of malaria in 1955, but a mere 17 cases of vivax infection, and none of falciparum, in 1964. The same year saw 10,000 cases, and no deaths, across the entire Indian sub-

continent. But on a global scale, the program was only partly complete when the money ran out. The insects were bound to return, and with new resistances; the people had lost what immunity they had. In 1969, Sri Lanka had half a million cases of malaria; by 1975, India had six million cases. And in both countries, as in others in Asia, deadly falciparum was on the increase, accounting for half Sri Lanka's infec-tions and over a third of India's. Globally, there were nearly three times as many cases of malaria in 1975 as there had been in 1961.

It was clear that malaria would have to be controlled over the vast expanses of tropical Africa and Asia by attack-ing or circumventing the disease itself, not its insect vector. This strategy too was doomed to failure, and in some respects repeated the pattern of events that led from wonder drugs to super-bugs. The traditional defense against malaria was quinine, first isolated by the French chemist Pierre-Joseph Pelletier in 1820 from the bark of the quinchona tree. From the mid-19th century, a reliable supply of quinchona bark came onto the market from the Dutch colony in Java. The British in India mixed it with carbonated water and added gin to obscure its bitter flavor, thus turning a necessity into a pleasure. Quinine not only protected against malaria, it cured it – or at least reduced its symptoms to a tolerable level. British colonials' dependence on the drug, aided perhaps by their gin-and-tonic habit, created a curious side-effect that was long taken to be a disease in its own right – blackwater fever. After repeated bouts of malaria, treated with ever-larger doses of quinine, members of the British Raj would succumb to blackwater fever, so called because of the peculiar darkness of patients' urine. Between a quarter and a half of those afflicted died. The cause, it was eventually discovered, was that after prolonged and heavy doses, quinine would bind onto red blood cells. The immune system reacted as if the oxygen-bearing blood cells were infected, and killed them.

In the case of malaria, politics and war drove forward an improvement of the combined prophylactic (preventative) and treatment. In 1942, the Japanese invaded Java, cutting off the Allies' supply of quinine. In response, the more powerful chloroquine was developed, and for years after World War II it remained the most effective anti-malarial drug available. During the Vietnam war, resistance to chloro-

quine increased, and the US Army developed mefloquine, still in use today. These drugs all work in much the same way. When Alphonse Laveran first spotted malaria merozoites in 1880, he noticed they contained dark granules. These are in fact crystals rich in iron, left-overs from the red blood cells that the parasite has digested. The iron is poisonous to the malaria cell, but the cell contains a specific enzyme that builds up the crystals and seals them off from the rest of the cell. Quinine and related drugs work because they stop that enzyme doing its job. As a result, the iron disperses through the merozoite and kills it.

Merozoites, however, are but one of the four active forms that *Plasmodia*

take in humans, all in the space of a few days. This capacity for shape-shifting makes it extremely difficult to create an effective one-shot vaccine against these parasites. To reduce their impact, people in malarial regions using quinine-related drugs have to keep taking them, to catch the parasites at this specific stage of their development. (Those few who move to less infested places and stop taking anti-malarial drugs then risk the offchance that the fifth form, the

A Thai anti-malaria poster from the era of a global campaign to eradicate the disease by killing mosquitoes. The effort petered out for lack of funds in the 1960s – leaving a tougher breed of mosquito behind.

A researcher inspects trapped mosquitoes. Tracking them provides clues to the likely spread of several diseases. Besides malaria, the insects carry viral encephalitis, yellow fever and dengue fever.

hypnozoites, may come swarming out of the liver.) Each stage of the *Plasmodium* is so different from the others that it displays different proteins on the outside of the cell body. These proteins are what alert the immune system to the presence of a hostile microbe, but in a malarial infection they are not present long enough – before the cell shifts its shape yet again – for the body to build up a concerted attack on them, or to develop a large enough army of antibodies to handle this (or any other) stage of the next

infection. And at each of the eight or nine stages of its life cycle, the parasite is capable of subtly altering itself through random mutations. It is for exactly these reasons that malarial microbes have survived so long – they probably emerged when Africans first cleared the jungle for farming about 10,000 years ago – and why they have remained so destructive all that time.

So it has been inevitable that since quinine and its cousins became widely available, they have been constantly used. The massive intervention of the global anti-malaria campaign of 1958–63, which continued in some countries until they could afford it no longer, reduced such immunity as many communities had been able to establish. At the same time the spraying of DDT muddied the mosquitoes'

gene pool. When the survivors of that onslaught began to multiply again, they were not only more likely to be resistant to insecticides, they – and their parasites – had been subject to a host of other genetic changes too. This factor has to be added to the virtually inevitable build-up of resistance in the parasites themselves to a drug – mainly chloroquine – that was taken constantly as both prophylactic and cure.

The killing fields

Resistance to chloroquine first appeared in southern Asia in the 1950s. Other drug treatments were developed in response. The most widely used were mepacrine, proguanil, and pyrimethamine. By 1962 the *Plasmodium falciparum* parasites – the deadliest – in Cambodia were resistant to the latter pair and chloroquine. The following year, only one of six Cambodian strains of falciparum was still susceptible to chloroquine, and three were resistant to all four leading anti-malarial drugs. Within 10 years, chloroquine was all but useless throughout southern Asia and beyond, from India to Vanuatu and from China to Australia.

The defeat of chloroquine in southern Asia led to a general adoption of the new American drug, mefloquine, in the late 1970s and early 1980s. Yet by 1986 a new strain of falciparum had emerged that resisted mefloquine, too, as well as older treatments including quinine. In Thailand in 1991, tests showed that falciparum microbes had

even developed a resistance to halofantrine, a new anti-malarial drug that had never been used in that country. The following year, this falciparum superstrain was causing half the malaria infections in Cambodia.

Research at Harvard School of Public Health uncovered how the new strain managed to vanquish anti-malarial drugs even before they had been deployed in a particular area. The parasite had evolved a new enzyme within its membrane that reacted to hostile chemicals in the most basic fashion – it simply pumped them out of the cell. 'Once this kind of mechanism occurs,' said one senior scientist, 'it means resistance will emerge even before the drug can be invented.' The new genetic feature probably accounted for the rapid and unprecedented spread of drug-resistant malaria across Asia during the 1980s.

Breeding on the border

The resistant strains tended to come out of the border region between Thailand and Cambodia. In the late 1960s Cambodia's social structure began to fall apart under pressure from US military campaigns on the one hand (including major bombing of the jungle) and the country's own insurgent Khmer Rouge on the other. The victory of the Khmer Rouge in 1975 led to an emptying of the cities, the death of some three million people and the exodus of hundreds of thousands of refugees into Thailand. The remaining

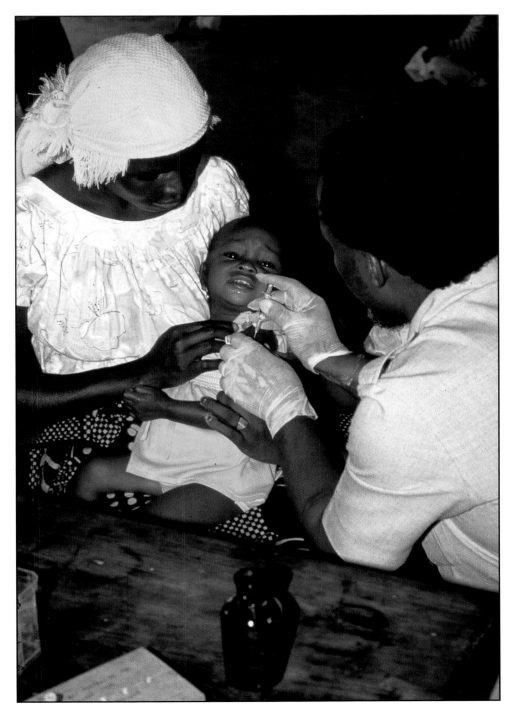

Vaccination against malaria. As attempts to control mosquitoes have proved fruitless, protection against malarial parasites is the next step. In the tropics young children are among their most common victims.

population was transformed into slave labor for an ill-conceived attempt to irrigate the entire country. Since the fall of the Khmer Rouge government in 1979, there has been constant warfare in Cambodia, and there are more than half a million refugees from the conflict in the country and just over the border with Thailand. Some have been herded by the thousand through the jungle to form a human buffer for Khmer Rouge fighters. Human assaults on wildlife habitats tend to awaken previously hidden microbes, and Cambodia has been no exception. To add to the threat, the bomb craters and wrecked vehicles left by the war, the half-finished irrigation works of the revolutionaries, and even the water-filled footprints of the slaves, soldiers and refugees have enormously expanded the malarial mosquitoes' breeding grounds.

The border region between Thailand and Cambodia is singularly rich in raw gemstones. Rubies and emeralds are close to the surface here (as in other parts of Southeast Asia) and can easily be panned out of rivers. The upheaval in the region attracted more and more fortune-seekers, especially during the 1980s; they were heading for an area of dense rain forest where more than a dozen species of mosquito carry the falciparum parasite. While government hospitals and doctors in Cambodia rarely saw anti-malarial drugs, they did find their way onto a flourishing black market. The gem hunters were among the biggest buyers of the illicit drugs. They bought indiscriminately, and rarely applied what they bought properly, adding an extra stimulus to the development of resistant strains of *Plasmodia*.

German epidemiologist Uwe Brink-mann described the conditions in which he found the gem miners working: 'All day long they sit or squat in the streams and rivers zigzagging through the rain forest. It's steaming hot and humid – you can't imagine the heat. They wear no protective clothing, and they stand in mosquito breeding areas all day long sifting the water and mud for gems. At night they sleep in open sheds.'

In this region a chloroquine and pyrimethamine combination cured nearly 97 per cent of malaria infections in 1983. By 1990, it worked against fewer than 21 per cent of cases. The miners came from Laos, Vietnam, China, Thailand, Burma and, of course, Cambodia. When those who survived disease, warfare, border guards and police made it home with their booty they brought with them parasites that were resistant to virtually anything modern medicine could throw at them. And the parasites entered local mosquitoes, just as they had entered mosquitoes everywhere along the long, winding trail homeward.

The price of progress

Against this darkening backcloth there were a few bright spots. In Colombia in the early 1990s, biochemist Dr Manuel Patarroyo combined parts of the genes of three different stages of the *Plasmodium* parasite to create a synthetic protein. This could act as a vaccine, and trials showed that the protein was harmless to humans and could stimulate the body to produce enough antibodies to reduce malarial infections by about 50 per cent. Whether the parasite will evolve a resistance to this strategy before it becomes possible to put the expensive process into mass production remains to be seen.

The speed and unpredictability of malaria's resistance to drugs is nowhere plainer than in the story of qinghaosu. This is the name Chinese scientists gave to the active chemical in sweet wormwood, a plant that has been used for centuries in China to control fevers. The Chinese isolated the chemical in 1972; in the 1980s, WHO and the US Army developed it into an anti-malarial drug. In 1994, trials were successfully completed in Vietnam. But a French traveler in Mali, in West Africa, had already (in 1993) picked up a falciparum infection that no anti-malarial drug, including qinghaosu, could affect. Before long, three more strains of falciparum that resisted qinghaosu were found in Mali. Whether chance mutations were responsible, or the efficiency of modern transport networks connecting Southeast Asia and West Africa, remains unanswered.

Another drug, taxol, which was developed from yew trees of the US Pacific Northwest to treat cancer, has also proved highly effective against the malaria parasite. By 1996 it had had little chance to stimulate any resistance in *Plasmodia* microbes, however, as its price was in the region of six million dollars per kilogram (2.2lb). And there is no reason to suppose that *Plasmodia* will not develop resistance to taxol, even if its use should become an economic proposition in any Third World country.

In the tropics, malaria is winning against all human attempts to defeat it. We saw earlier that its reach once extended into North America (as far north as Montreal) and northern Europe. We shall see in the next chapter why it retreated from northern Europe, and how it could return there and into the USA and Canada. What has happened in the shattered parts of southern Asia to the malarial microbe is of direct interest, then, to the West. For if malaria does come home to roost there, it will be in a form that, for all practical purposes, is incurable.

Yellow jack

Three of the most lethal epidemic diseases in history have been bubonic plague, cholera, and yellow fever. The last has been particularly unkind to colonists. It was a major contributor in giving West Africa its nickname, the 'White Man's Grave', yet it was first recognized in the New World, and was even defeated there decades before its presence in Africa was understood.

The first certain epidemic of yellow fever in the Americas struck the Caribbean islands of St Kitts, Barbados and Martinique in 1648, and reached as far as Cuba and the Yucatan, cutting a swathe through a population that had no immunity to its horrors. When it broke out again in 1664 on St Lucia, there were only 89 survivors in a garrison of 1500 soldiers. Called *el vomito negro* ('the black vomit') as well as yellow fever, it began with a feverish chill. As the fever mounted, the victim felt weak all over, with backache, headache, and increasingly sore limbs. In the severest cases there would be vomiting – and the vomit would be black from the blood of gastric hemorrhages. After two or three days the fever, shaking, and pain would subside. For the more fortunate – about seven

out of every 10 patients – the disease was over, and the survivor was now immune for life. For the rest, there were only another two or three days of relief before the fever and the black vomiting began again. The patients bled from the nose and gums, and became jaundiced as the liver malfunctioned. Victims became delirious, often struggling violently to leave the bed. A few recovered even at this late stage,

but most went into a coma, until convulsions and death put an end to the suffering.

Yellow fever always came as an epidemic, and the worst outbreaks were on board ship, where there was no escape from the raging pestilence. It seemed to move from one victim to the next in completely unpredictable ways. Sometimes it would move up one side of a ship and then down the other,

A wormwood plant sealed in a laboratory growth chamber. Extract of wormwood has been used to treat fevers in China for over 2000 years; Western scientists used it to create an anti-malarial drug in the 1980s.

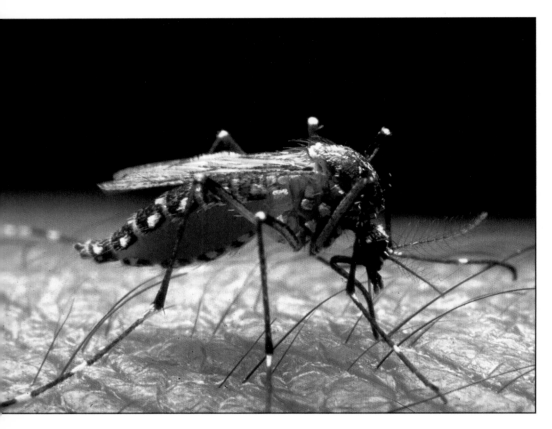

An Aëdes aegypti mosquito, feeding on a human arm. Only female mosquitoes dine on blood. This species carries the yellow fever virus, which was brought to the Americas on slave ships from Africa.

as if hopping from berth to berth. At other times its spread was entirely random. Yet there were a few consistent features. The disease seemed to cling to particular houses and ships, burning itself out there before going on to attack the next set of occupants. The lower floors of houses were worst affected, and houses at lower elevations in a town seemed more likely to harbor the disease. It was a seasonal disease of high summer, but in temperate climates it generally failed to return after one or two outbreaks.

Although the focus of yellow fever long remained the West Indies, by 1668 it reached New York, and savaged the city for an entire summer. Here two other curiosities were observed: the fever seemed to spread in the direction of the wind and, with the onset of the chill New York winter, it died away almost as quickly as it had begun. In 1691 yellow fever was in

Boston, and two years later struck Philadelphia. In the 18th century, 35 American cities suffered outbreaks, and there were virtually annual epidemics in the USA during the following century. One of the worst occurred in New Orleans in 1853. So feared was yellow fever that the city fathers – and the press – conspired to hide the outbreak, until the number of deaths reached 200 a day. In all, 29,020 people succumbed, of whom 8101 died. The toll was even greater in the Mississippi valley in 1878, when over 120,000 people were infected, leaving at least 20,000 dead.

Like most epidemic diseases, yellow fever has had a direct effect on human history. In 1803 the French emperor Napoleon Buonaparte sent an army of 33,000 men across the Atlantic to suppress a rebellion in Haiti. Within a few months of landing on the island, nine out of 10 of the soldiers died of

yellow fever; the insurrectionists defeated the remainder by force of arms. Napoleon abandoned any further thought of developing French power in the New World, and in the same year sold the enormous Louisiana Territory to the USA.

Vector analysis

In 1898 power politics spurred the US Government into making a concerted attempt to solve all the riddles that yellow fever presented. The end of the Spanish-American war in 1898 left Cuba under US protection, with a US Army garrison in place to guarantee the island nation's newfound independence. The island was a deathtrap. Over the previous 50 years some 35,000 people there had died of yellow fever, and thousands more had succumbed to malaria. Here was the opportunity to attack the fever on its home ground, rid American cities of the scourge, and make Cuba decently habitable – and therefore profitable.

The US Army Medical Corps sent a special commission to Cuba to solve the mystery of what caused the disease. The doctors arrived on 25 June 1900 under the command of Major Walter Reed, who had an outstanding record as a medical detective. Reed and his assistants soon disposed of the belief that bacteria caused yellow fever, and then decided to embark on a startling series of experiments: they attempted to infect human volunteers by all conceivable means. They soon came in

contact with the elderly Dr Carlos Finlay of Havana, who for 20 years had been trying to convince anyone who would listen that yellow fever was spread by a common house mosquito, now known as *Aëdes aegypti*. In over 100 experiments, however, Dr Finlay had never managed to cause a yellow fever infection with one of his hand-reared mosquitoes.

The idea of an insect vector for a disease was very new: it was only two years since it had been conclusively proven in India that malaria was carried by mosquitoes, and no other example had been discovered. Reed and his colleagues hatched some of Dr Finlay's mosquitoes, let them feed on a yellow fever patient (there was an

epidemic in full swing among the US Army garrison), and then let them bite the nine brave souls who had volunteered to risk their lives in the experiment. At the first attempt, not one of the volunteers showed a single symptom. At the second, one doctor fell ill, as did a Seventh Cavalry trooper. But the doctor had been exposed to infection from many other potential routes; and the trooper had such a mild illness it might not have been yellow fever. Both survived.

Then, by chance, a wild mosquito bit another member of the commission, Dr Jesse Lazear, as he made a round of the fever wards. Five days later he was in the grip of a fever, and 10 days after that he was dead. Reed

Dean Cornwell's painting of the US Army medical commission sent to Cuba in 1900 to find the cause of yellow fever. One doctor, Jesse Lazear, died for the cause, but the disease was defeated within a year.

was convinced Dr Finlay had been right first time, but he had yet to prove it in a properly controlled experiment. The team set up a new series of tests whose results were beyond question. From these it also became clear that freshly hatched mosquitoes would pick up the infection from a patient only in the first few days of the fever – and then would pass it on only after another nine to 16 days. (The volunteers who became sick all survived.)

Further experiments confirmed that the mosquito was the only possible cause of the infection: for example, Reed and his team were satisfied that linen and clothing from yellow fever victims could not pass on the disease.

The discovery of the mosquito vector solved many mysteries of yellow fever – its seasonal nature, its susceptibility to wind, weather and elevation, and its unpredictable spread from person to person. The following year further experiment showed that the microbe ultimately responsible was a virus, then a newly discovered form of life. In Havana in 1901, Surgeon-Major William Gorgas did not wait for that final piece of evidence before putting mosquito-proof screens in fever sickrooms to break the chain of infection, fumigating infected houses, and detailing squads to drain or oil every patch of standing water they could find. Water containers in houses were scrupulously covered to deny the insects a breeding ground indoors. Within three months of this campaign, Havana was free of yellow fever. In 1900 in Cuba, 311 people had died of the disease; only six died in 1901, and none the following year.

In 1904 Gorgas was sent to Panama, where years before work had ground to a halt on an ambitious French scheme to build a canal linking the Atlantic and Pacific Oceans. A major reason for the project's failure had been yellow fever, which claimed the lives of 20 per cent of the workforce. By 1903 the USA was in a position to complete the canal. Gorgas's successful onslaught against the mosquitoes of Panama meant that when the canal opened in 1914, only 1.7 per cent of the workforce had died of the fever during seven years of construction.

In 1927 the animal reservoir of the yellow fever virus was discovered: capuchin and rhesus monkeys. This allowed work to start on finding a vaccine without using human subjects. At about the same time, scientists realized that yellow fever was endemic in tropical Africa, and was resident in the monkey population there too. So, far from being originally a Caribbean disease, the fever had most likely been imported to the West Indies in slave ships. In 1937, the South African microbiologist Max Theiler, working at Harvard, bred a mutant form of the virus that produced only mild symptoms in humans. When administered as a vaccine, it gave complete immunity to the disease.

The fever fights back

The discovery of a vaccine was some comfort to those who could afford it for, as more was learned about the virus, thoughts of eradicating yellow fever began to crumble. More and more species of mosquito were found to carry the fever virus. In 1949 an epidemic hit Panama again, and spread throughout Central America. Ten years later, yellow fever was cropping up in previously sanitized parts of South America.

By then, there was a further complication. Researchers had found there were two types of yellow fever – one found in cities and carried by *Aëdes aegypti*, the other a forest or jungle variety, carried by several species of mosquito and resident in several species of monkey. The 1959 epidemics had largely begun in classic fashion: with people disturbing a natural habitat, in this case farmers or loggers working at – and into – the edges of the tropical rain forests. While the

urban fever virus and its insect vector could be controlled by covering potential mosquito breeding waters and a massive vaccination campaign, it was plainly impossible to vaccinate the monkeys in the rain forest or destroy all the insects there.

A huge vaccination and DDT-spraying campaign from the late 1940s until 1960 did, however, drastically reduce the *Aëdes aegypti* population in South America. By 1972, worldwide, three quarters of the mosquitoes' habitats, in 19 countries, had been cleared of the insects. Estimates of the cost of continuing the task to eliminate the remainder in the Americas varied from an affordable 326 million dollars to in excess of one billion dollars. (The latter figure included the expected cost of defeating lawsuits brought by outraged US citizens who objected to compulsory spraying. During the anti-fever campaign of the early 1960s many Americans, newly alerted to the ecological impact of insecticides, had refused to allow their land to be sprayed.) Cynical observers were not surprised when the proposal faded into oblivion. While verbally supporting the earlier sanitation campaigns south of the border, the US Congress never voted funds for a similar exercise at home. It merely called on the Centers for Disease Control (CDC) in Atlanta to 'attempt' to eradicate *Aëdes aegypti* from the USA. Given the funds available, one disillusioned CDC scientist said, the demand was 'equivalent to instructions to fly across the Atlantic with half a tank of gas'.

Today, therefore, the USA remains a reservoir of *Aëdes aegypti* while the nations beyond its southern border have at least kept the insect in check with sprays, and held yellow fever at bay through immunization. The closely related dengue fever is on the rise in Latin America, while public health officials there are not convinced that yellow fever vaccine is reaching all the people it should. The risk that yellow fever could explode in South America is exacerbated by the continuous assault on the tropical rain forest on the one hand – by everyone from loggers to coca farmers and gold seekers – and by 'urbanization' in the shape of filthy, sprawling shanty towns on the other. The forest virus could well make the leap from the trees to the cities; the slums, besieging the cities and enjoying the minimum of medical supervision, could become a focus for both forms of yellow fever.

There is little comfort in the thought that – just a plane ride away – in the USA the *Aëdes aegypti* mosquito carries only the urban form of yellow fever. Since the 1970s numerous other insects have been found to harbor the virus. In the modern world, it is not just insects, either, that spread yellow fever. The CDC found that in Nigeria it was being spread by the local quack 'injectionists' operating openly in markets and bazaars. The equivalent in the Americas is far less visible: it is the shared syringe among drug addicts who live in a twilight zone overlooked or unreached by public health agencies most of the time. If either or both forms of yellow fever were to flare uncontrollably in Latin America, and come burning north along the highways and airlanes, the USA could face a series of epidemics to rival those of one or two centuries ago.

Whether or not the country could afford an exercise in mass vaccination as a last-ditch defense against such an invasion, it is at least questionable whether a yellow fever epidemic would be detected soon enough to make mass vaccination effective. A 1993 survey by the CDC of disease surveillance in the USA found that through budget cuts, reduced tax income and economic recession, 'only a skeletal staff exists in many state and local health departments' and that many diseases, which were required by law to be notified to state agencies, were going unreported. Still more disheartening was a survey of international disease

Insecticides are sprayed in an area of New Delhi, India, infested with mosquitoes carrying dengue fever, during an outbreak in fall 1996. Reaction to disease, not prevention, is now the rule in most countries.

detection laboratories, carried out by WHO in the same year, which discovered that half of the labs could not reliably diagnose yellow fever (and figures were worse for other epidemic diseases). The makings, at least, of a medical disaster are in place.

As biologist Christopher Wills has said: 'Yellow fever may be another epidemiological time bomb.'

Out of the Ganges

Next to bubonic plague, cholera is the quintessential plague disease, swift to fall upon its prey, dreadful in its effects, and universally feared. The collective memory of the healthy, wealthy West is very long. Bubonic plague has not been a serious threat as a pandemic

since the 17th century, and cholera was so well understood that a vaccine had been developed by 1893, barely more than six decades after it first fell upon Europe. Yet outbreaks in South America, Africa and India in the 1990s caused alarm and swift reaction in the West.

Cholera first came out of the Ganges river delta in 1817 and fastened on Calcutta, already a teeming, insanitary, polluted city. Cholera killed 5000 British soldiers stationed there, and spread out in all directions from that key diplomatic, military and trading center. Six years later this first pandemic died away, having reached Asia, eastern Africa and the Arabian peninsula. In 1826 the second pandemic

began, spreading north and west through Afghanistan and in 1830 striking Moscow, where half those infected died. It reached through Poland into Germany and Scandinavia, and arrived in Paris and London, where 7000 died, in 1832. From Europe it crossed the Atlantic and struck Manhattan, killing 50,000. In spring 1833 the disease faded again. But it returned in 1847, when it killed 15,000 Moslem residents and pilgrims

A New York magazine illustration depicts the fear engendered by the cholera pandemic of 1892 – even though new public health measures ensured that its impact on the city was reduced to the minimum.

A PROPHETIC PICTURE—THE WORLD'S FAIR WILL BE CLOSED BY THE CHOLERA.
The cholera has broken out again in Hamburg—an emigrant-ship lately landed over twenty-two hundred emigrants in New York.

in Mecca, and 53,000 people in London. When it reached the USA in 1849, it felled one in 10 of the population of St Louis.

The disease smoldered in eastern Europe, then burst out across the continent again in 1853. In London's Soho district it went to work with unexampled savagery at the end of August, and within two weeks 700 people had died in just that one small parish. And then the epidemic stopped. It did so because one Dr John Snow – then making his reputation as a pioneer of anesthetics – had persuaded the parish authorities to remove the handle from the common pump in Broad Street, at the heart of the outbreak. Flying in the face of conventional medical wisdom, Snow had rejected the idea that cholera sprang as

a poisonous 'miasma' from the soil, and concluded that some minute organism in the pump water must be responsible. There was a strict boundary line in the area of the pump, beyond which the disease did not seem to move – except for the occasional household who made a point of going to Broad Street for their water. Within the boundary, houses or workplaces with their own water supplies avoided the disease.

Cholera begins with a sudden feeling of faintness, sweating, and stomach flutters – followed by a prodigious attack of diarrhea. The attacks continue, and after a few hours the motions become an odorless white fluid – the 'rice-water stool' that confirms the diagnosis of cholera. The already agonized patient becomes desperately thirsty, although vomiting

Hindus take a ritual morning bath in the River Ganges in India. The river's delta region has long been heavily populated, and conditions were soon ripe for epidemic disease. Cholera first arose there in 1817.

and retching make drinking extremely difficult. Dehydration brings on spasms, and severe pain in the limbs. As the body throws out its fluids, it loses weight so fast that the skin begins to hang in folds off the flesh. (In Snow's day, doctors who tried to bleed their patients found the blood had turned thick and dark, so violent is the dehydration.) The victim's complexion begins to turn blue, finally darkening almost to black. Coma and death follow. The whole terrible process may last no more than 24 hours.

Snow reasoned that as the disease started in the intestine, whatever poison caused it had to be swallowed. The rice-water stool became virtually invisible as it dried on bedding and clothes; nurses and relatives could easily soil their hands without knowing it and, if they did not wash, take the poison in with food or drink. The final step in Snow's thinking was that, therefore, the water flowing to the Broad Street pump had to be contaminated by a sewer or a drain from a privy. Laborious investigation by a parish board of inquiry eventually bore out Snow's theory. The medical profession took longer to accept the evidence, and it was only in 1866, under threat of the fourth cholera pandemic (which arrived in 1868), that the pump itself was removed.

By then Snow was dead, but London's water supply had been vastly improved, and closed sewers now took effluent to the Thames. Not surprisingly, after these reforms, deaths in London from cholera in 1868 were far fewer than before, but tended to cluster in the capital's East End, which took its drinking water downstream from the rest of the city. Mecca, less fortunate in its public health system, suffered 30,000 dead.

Vibrio cholerae, the comma-shaped bacterium responsible for cholera, was identified during the fifth pandemic in 1883 by the pioneer microbiologist Robert Koch. Public sanitation continued to improve in the light of the new 'germ theory'. When the sixth cholera pandemic circled the world in 1892, cities in Europe and the USA – which had rapidly copied London's example – were barely touched. In 1893 a vaccine became available, and a decade later the Egyptian authorities, who controlled the flow of the Moslem *hajj* from North Africa to Mecca, made inoculation against cholera compulsory for all pilgrims. The disease was effectively banished from Mecca.

Cholera remained, however, in India, and especially in what is now Bangladesh, around the Mouths of the Ganges, but it was largely reduced to an endemic disease. Through the 20th century there were occasional outbreaks in Africa and China and other parts of Asia. But so effective were public health programs in most of cholera's old haunts that it was not

A scene in the slum of Belem, Brazil. Shanty towns like this, with little or no sanitation or supplies of clean water, make ideal breeding grounds for cholera, which is soon exported by modern transportation.

until 1961 that a new pandemic began. The *Vibrio* was also a new strain, and it was dubbed El Tor. Compared with the lightning strikes of the previous century, its progress around the globe was positively leisurely. It first broke out in the islands of Sulawesi in Indonesia. It slowly affected coastal cities in Asia and eastern Africa, and avoided health-conscious developed countries altogether. It did not reach South America until January 1991, when it broke out in Lima, Peru.

Poison on tap

El Tor arrived in Lima to find ideal conditions for generating an epidemic. The city had abandoned the practice of chlorinating its fresh water supply, probably because of the expense but officially in response to a US Environmental Agency report that linked chlorine to cancer. The water system was built in the first two decades of the 20th century, when Lima's population was just 230,000. It now stands at seven million, and the creaking system cannot supply all of those people adequately. Still worse, as a CDC investigation into the cholera outbreak was to show, the system was leaking flushed-away *Vibrio* into the tapwater. Most cases of cholera in Peru started with contaminated water.

In other major cities the situation was even worse. Chimbote, 350km (220 miles) north of the capital, has no municipal water system at all. Raw sewage is dumped straight into the river, and tapwater is piped out of it. Once cholera got into the river water, it was inevitable that it would be taken out and drunk. Trujillo, some 500km (310 miles) from Lima, has no river but a series of wells, from which some official and many unofficial pipes take

water. The ground water in the wells was easily contaminated by sewage.

According to the official figures, 336,554 people in Peru caught cholera in 1991, of whom 3538 died. The epidemic spread through Latin America, finally burning itself out in 1994. By September that year, 1,041,422 infections and 9643 deaths had been reported to WHO from Central and South America, but the agency estimated that only some two per cent of cases found their way onto the record. If that is so, then 52 million people, or nearly 12 per cent of the continent's population, were made sick, and more than 482,000 died.

In Peru, the number of deaths was at least kept low by the foresight of the national minister of health. He was aware of the level of severe diarrheal

Rehydration therapy at work in Bangladesh. A cheap, simple mix of salts and sugar dissolved in water will often provide all the body needs to help it to recover from devastating diarrheal diseases like cholera.

diseases already at work in the country, and also of the rehydration therapy newly being used on cholera patients in Bangladesh. Doses of vital electrolytic salts, which the diseases purge from the system, and glucose to make the salts acceptable to the gut, were called *bolsitas salvadoras* – 'little packets of salvation' – and distributed by the million. The doses were simply dissolved into water being given to a patient, and had already cut deaths from diarrheal diseases by 40 per cent when El Tor hit Peru.

In December 1992, while the seventh pandemic was moving across South America, yet another new, and this time very strange strain of cholera emerged in Bengal. Known as *Vibrio cholerae* 0139, it claimed over 2000 lives within six months and infected 100 times as many people. By then it had also turned up in Bangkok. The eighth pandemic appeared to have started. Why it was strange, how it traveled, and what it implied for the rest of the world we shall see in the next chapter.

CHAPTER SIX

THE RUIN OF NATURE

HOW HUMAN ACTIVITY IS CREATING NEW OPPORTUNITIES FOR ANCIENT AFFLICTIONS

The warnings of ecologists and 'green' campaigners about the effects of global warming, the destruction of the ozone layer and the tide of pollution in our rivers, lakes and seas often make a shameless appeal to our affection for creatures of the wild. Polar bears, seals, magnificent birds of prey and many other kinds of wildlife are indeed threatened – but it is less often noted that environmental decay has already begun to have an impact on human health. Some of the repercussions are all too plain to see, such as the two pandemics of cholera currently circling the globe, even if the underlying causes became apparent only through remarkable detective work and a good deal of lateral thinking. Other consequences are both more subtle and more sinister – the constant gnawing away at our capacity to resist infection, for example, or the possibility that global warming will bring a flush of fearsome tropical diseases to the populous, affluent but ill-prepared nations of the temperate zones.

The flutter of a butterfly's wings in the Andes may cause a hurricane in Bombay, says a popular summary of chaos theory – the mathematical description of the way a mosaic of tiny, almost unnoticeable incidents may culminate in a major, even cataclysmic

An oil refinery belches smoke near Baton Rouge, Louisiana, USA. The use of fossil fuels like oil, coal and gas since the Industrial Revolution lies behind global warming and its less-publicized health hazards.

event. In the world of diseases, a tiny random alteration at the molecular level of a microbe's genetic make-up is like the flutter of the butterfly's wings; the pandemic that can result is the hurricane that can destroy lives and dislocate societies on a grand scale. Ecologists and environmentalists have long argued that we have to view our connection with the natural world in the same way. Even the smallest disturbance in the infinitely complex web of relationships among plants, animals and human beings may have unfore-

seen and possibly disastrous effects. We deliberately interfere with the natural world at our peril: we may not only witness the direct and visible consequences – the extinction of a species, say – but we ourselves may also suffer as subtler forces come into play and affect our health and well-being.

Not all interactions between people and the rest of the world's living things are harmful, although as often as not the benefits have arisen by accident. The retreat of malaria from northern Europe is a case in point. It was the byproduct of changes that were not at all calculated to control disease. The forms of malarial parasite that plagued these temperate climates survive through the long winters by nesting – in effect hibernating – in the human liver. Here they await a trigger – perhaps a change in temperature, perhaps a chemical signal; no one knows – that revives them and sets them on their way through the human body toward a feeding mosquito and the resumption of their life cycle. The parasites can be eradicated only by making it impossible for them to complete their life cycle – which means severing the connection between humans and mosquitoes. In Denmark in the first half of the 19th century malaria ravaged agricultural communities, notably on the islands in the Kattegat, the narrow channel that links the North Sea with the Baltic. In 1831 the disease took such a toll that it was feared that the islands would be depopulated. And then, after a severe epidemic in 1862, malaria vanished from Denmark over a generation or two. There were only 10 cases between 1889 and 1900, and none has been recorded since 1900.

The reason lay in a change in farming methods and the peculiar tastes of the mosquitoes that carried the malaria parasite. In the second half of the 19th century Danish farmers began to cultivate the land as well as keep animals on it. Wild stretches of countryside went under the plow, and the cows, sheep and pigs that had once roamed freely there were brought under cover at night. The malarial mosquitoes now had an alternative, and equally captive, source of food on their nocturnal forays and, as it happened, they preferred cows' blood

to human blood for nourishment. The malarial parasites, however, could not survive in the bovine bloodstream and died out.

In Britain a similar change in farming methods had had the same effect – in a rather warmer climate – nearly two centuries earlier. From the late 17th century on, the practice of letting one arable field in three lie fallow every year – plowed and harrowed, but not sown – as a way of maintaining fertility and controlling weeds and pests, began to give way to a system of planting crops such as turnips and alfalfa. These were used as feed for cattle and sheep, supplementing their grazing on the common pastures, which meant that more animals could be kept on the available acreage. Thus, malarial mosquitoes already had better access to the bovine blood they preferred when British landowners began fencing off traditional open grazing lands into fields. The great 'enclosures' that began in the 18th century forced many people off the land and into the cities, but the reform made for more productive management of both land and livestock, and further concentrated cattle herds. The attention of the mosquitoes was concentrated too, and they abandoned feasts of human blood in favor of the more attractive cows' blood.

The revolution in agriculture that Britain saw between 1675 and 1845 included improvements in farm machinery, fertilizers, land management, crop storage and seed development. It also most probably led to a more general improvement in the nation's health, and underwrote the population explosion that provided the manpower for the Industrial Revolution. The historian William H.

McNeill explains:

Other complex ecological results flowed from the spread of the new style of agriculture. More animals meant more meat and milk in human diet, and an enlarged supply of protein. This may well have increased human capacities to manufacture antibodies against infection of any and every kind, since such antibodies are themselves proteins and can only be produced from the chemical building blocks proteins supply. Generalized levels of resistance to infectious diseases may therefore have risen significantly among wide segments of the population.

A curse in disguise

More often, diseases have been tackled head-on with cures, vaccines or vector controls and, as we have seen, at least partly defeated; and changes in the human way of life have tended to release previously hidden microbes or have carried them from one part of the world to another. The story of the modern spread of cholera, and especially its sudden outbreak in 1991 in Lima, Peru, shows how a confluence of apparently unrelated human activities added up, in the end, to an alarming pandemic, with a perhaps worse one on its heels. To understand how that came about, we need to explore what led to the deaths of tens of thousands of marine mammals in the North Sea and the Gulf of Mexico just a few years before.

A key strand in this web of circumstances is the chlorine industry. Since the early 1960s ecologists and 'green' campaigners have been targeting chlorine as a source of many ills in the world's wildlife. In 1962 Rachel

Carson's landmark book *Silent Spring* alerted the world to the hazards of chlorine-derived pesticides such as DDT. But this was just one of a whole family of such compounds known collectively as organochlorines, which since the 1930s have been used in a huge range of industrial and domestic products. Besides a variety of pesticides, organochlorines form the basis of solvents, propellants, coolants, fast-food packaging and insulating foam (all these involve chlorofluorocarbons, or CFCs), of plastics such as polyvinyl chloride (PVC), which are used to make insulating materials, clothing, building materials and containers of all

shapes, sizes and uses, and of additives such as polychlorinated biphenyls (PCBs) whose heat, flame and electrical resistance have found them employment in items as diverse as neon lights, hydraulic systems and, most widely, electrical transformer insulating fluids.

While the dangers of organochlorines have been recognized and some of these substances are no longer made, they have still found their way into the oceans, the atmosphere and the soil. For example, of the estimated 1.2 million tonnes of PCBs ever produced, 31 per cent was believed to have found its way into the sea and the soil by

Over-packaging causes unsightly litter, wastes resources, and uses masses of material made from organochlorines. These leak into the atmosphere and attack the ozone layer, exposing us to the sun's harmful ultraviolet rays.

1990. The rest was in use, in storage, or dumped in landfills – and it was leaching out of the latter at an estimated rate of 600 tonnes a year in the UK alone. When organochlorine products were first developed, they were regarded as 'wonder materials' because they were chemically inert – they did not react with other chemicals and for this reason were regarded as especially safe. That inertness means that they persist unchanged in the environment for very long periods.

One of their unforeseen qualities, however, is their affinity for the body fat of living beings, in which they dissolve easily. This means that once released into the environment they build up through food chains – starting

An Inuit woman guides a sled as her husband leads his dog team onto the frozen sea to go hunting. Although thousands of miles from any industry, these people are exposed to organochlorine pollution that has accumulated in the fish and seals that form much of their diet.

off lodged in tiny quantities in plankton in the sea, for instance, they are passed on unchanged to the fish that eat the plankton, to larger fish that prey on them, and to the mammals that eat the fish. At each link in the food chain the concentrations are hugely magnified. Fish have been found with 159,000 times greater concentrations of some organochlorines than the water in which they live, while the accumulation in a polar bear may be three billion times the level in its environment. Thus a family of Inuit Indians, living a traditional way of life far from any industry, may accumulate phenomenal amounts of chlorine derivatives in their body tissues – for in their respective life-

times a single fish may eat millions of plankton, a seal may eat tens of thousands of fish, and the members of the Inuit family may consume thousands of seals, relishing the blubber in which the pollutants lurk. As well as passing up the food chain, organochlorines are passed directly from parents to their offspring. Human children are first exposed to them in the womb, and subsequently take them with their mother's milk.

PCBs are increasingly being identified as hormone disrupters in animals as different as herring gulls, dolphins and mink, and are the likely cause of various cancers, deficiencies in the immune system, disruptions of sexual development and differentiation, and

damage to the nervous system, liver and kidneys. Some of these effects occur because the compounds interfere with the way genes function. In 1992, in a document on organochlorines prepared for an international intergovernmental conference on pollution in the northeast Atlantic, Greenpeace summarized the effects of these chemicals on people. Minus its many references to the scientific literature, the report read:

Given the wide variety of effects upon animals, it is inevitable that humans, too, are vulnerable to the effects of organochlorines: the progressive contamination of aquatic environments has exposed humans to these chemicals through the food chain.

It is now well established that PCBs can be readily detected in fatty tissues of humans in industrialized countries. Research in the Netherlands indicates that in humans PCB levels, unlike those of other organochlorines, do not decrease over time. PCBs are reported to be present in human fatty tissues from all regions of the United States. In the Great Lakes, in particular, contamination of fish with PCBs and other organochlorines poses a hazard to humans. Tests on sport-fish anglers in Wisconsin have shown a strong link between high levels of fish consumption and high PCB levels in the blood. In general, it has been found that in people who ate large quantities of contaminated fish – approximately one meal per month (3–10kg [6–20lb] per year) – PCB levels increased in direct relation to consumption and length of exposure. The women affected tended to suffer from unusually high rates of anaemia, oedema and infectious disease.

Although still the subject of some controversy, the balance of evidence now strongly suggests that dioxins are powerful human carcinogens. Studies of chemical workers in Germany, confirming earlier studies in the US, show that exposure to TCDD [2,3,7,8-tetrachlorodibenzo-p-dioxin] increases the risk of cancer developing in humans. Preliminary results from a recent study suggest that some organochlorines also play a role in promoting breast cancer in women. Levels of DDE [a toxic product that is produced when DDT breaks down] and PCBs were found to be 50–60 percent higher in breast fat samples from women with cancerous tissue compared to those with benign growths.

Exposure before birth
Children born to women who ate Lake Michigan fish contaminated with PCBs and a number of other organochlorines were found to weigh less at birth, have smaller head circumference and poor coordination compared to children whose mothers did not eat Great Lakes fish. Tests conducted after 5–7 months showed that these infants performed poorly in visual recognition tasks.

From mother's milk
Although exposure to PCBs within the womb is considered particularly harmful, the mobilization of PCBs into human breast milk also poses a potential risk to the health of the child. Such mobilization has been widely reported.

A Canadian study compared PCB concentrations in breast milk of Inuit mothers with Caucasians, and found that they were about four times higher, probably due to the Inuits' high consumption of marine mammals and fish. It is thought that the exposure to toxic substances through the food chain may be linked to abnormalities in the immune system, resulting in higher infection rates, especially among Inuit children.

Failing fertility
Increasingly, studies are evaluating the effects of organochlorines on the ability of men to reproduce. There are some reports of abnormalities in male reproductive systems being linked to elevated PCB levels in the blood. Israeli males with fertility problems generally had higher blood organochlorine levels, including PCBs, than those without such problems. Low sperm counts have also been related to the presence of PCBs in semen.

The Greenpeace document was aptly titled *Death in Small Doses*. What it demonstrated, as did other studies, was a generalized and inescapable lowering of levels of immunity to disease in people all over the world. The implicit conclusion is that should any pandemic of an exceptionally virulent or infectious disease, on the scale of the 14th-century Black Death, launch itself on the world once more, it would meet even less resistance today than it did six centuries ago.

By the time the Greenpeace report was written, environmental scientists had built up an intricate picture of the reasons behind the catastrophes that had struck two different populations of marine mammals between 1988 and 1990. Early in 1988, harbor seals in the northern sector of the North Sea began to die; for two years dead seals were found along coasts from Northern Ireland to the Baltic Sea. Altogether 18,000 animals died, or more than 60 per cent of the region's harbor seals. They were infected with a morbillivirus, soon to be named PDV-1, but it was an entirely new variant of the type. (Morbilliviruses cause measles, rinderpest, and canine distemper; they are named for the medical term for measles.) The seals had high levels of organochlorine compounds, including PCBs, in their bodies, and their immune systems were impaired. Unable to cope with the unusual virus, they had died in huge numbers.

In 1990, a morbillivirus struck again. The bodies of bottlenose dolphins, beluga whales, Atlantic harbor seals and porpoises were coming ashore on the east coast of North America, notably in the Gulf of Mexico, into which the mighty Mississippi debouches. These creatures displayed the same morbillivirus infection, the same high levels of organochlorine pollution, and the same failure of the immune system as the North Sea seals.

The scientific consensus was that both the North Sea seals and the marine mammals in the Gulf of Mexico had become vulnerable to infection because of their exposure to organochlorines. Marine biologists believe today that overfishing in Arctic waters may have been the driving force behind the morbillivirus that killed the North Sea seals. Ring seals in the Arctic, deprived of their food by the

fishing industry, moved south in search of nourishment and came in contact with the community of harbor seals in the North Sea. And then, the theory goes, a morbillivirus carried by the ring

A dead seal washed up on the coast of Norfolk, UK, during the great die-off of the late 1980s. The virus killed about 18,000 seals, whose immune systems were weakened by pollution in the North Sea.

seals, and to which they were immune, jumped species to the harbor seals – whose immune systems were compromised – and burned through them. But in the Gulf of Mexico, a different force was at work exploiting the effects of organochlorines. And it was this that was to provide the clue to the outbreak of cholera in Lima.

The Midwest and the Mississippi valley had seen phenomenally high levels of rainfall in 1990, and the swollen rivers feeding into the Gulf of Mexico had dumped massive quantities of pesticides, chemicals and human and animal sewage into the sea. That accounted for the organochlorines in the dead animals on the American coast, just as notoriously high levels of pollution in the North Sea explained their presence in the victims of the die-off there. It very probably explained their lack of immunity too. The unanswered question was: where had the morbillivirus come from?

Death on the ocean wave

Off the coast of the Carolinas, it was discovered, a gigantic colony of red algae had appeared in 1990. Communities of these tiny not-quite-plant, not-quite-animal creatures are natural and normal in all oceans, but pollution – especially from sewage and from nitrogen- and phosphorus-based fertilizers – has had the effect known as 'eutrophication' on them. Literally meaning 'happy feeding', eutrophica-tion defines what happens when any plant or animal population becomes unusually well nourished – it expands tremendously, often to the detriment of the plants and animals with which it co-exists in the somewhat precarious 'balance of nature'. Algae are no exception. A 'bloom' of algae may consume enormous amounts of the oxygen in the water, leaving precious little for other living things in its

An Atlantic bottlenose dolphin, photographed in the Bahamas. In 1990, thousands of these creatures, along with whales, porpoises and seals, died on the eastern coast of North America due to a combination of pollution and disease.

vicinity; if this happens during a breeding season, both fish fry and the tiny creatures on which they feed can be severely depleted. Some algae also produce powerful toxins – possibly to ward off the plankton that feed on them – which themselves can kill or sicken marine life. For example, a huge algal bloom, one of the biggest the world has ever seen, had appeared in the North Sea in early May 1988. Eventually it covered over 1000km (625 miles) of coastline, from north of Stavanger, Norway, to southern Denmark. On one day, already a thick soup containing tens of millions of algae cells per liter, it grew by 50km (30 miles). Zoologist Dr Malcolm Mac-Garvin has described the devastation it and its poison wrought:

By the time the bloom died away at the beginning of June, the seabed was littered with dead lobsters and crabs. Strong-swimming fish, such as adult cod, ling and herring, had been able to flee, but young cod and whiting, too small to escape, died in their thousands. Others, such as wrasse and gobies, were forced to seek refuge beneath rocks or in crevices on the seabed, and there they perished. In coastal waters, huge numbers of organisms – delicate red seaweeds, cat worms, whelks, topshells, periwinkles, limpets, starfish, sea-urchins – were damaged or destroyed. Around 600 tonnes of farmed fish in Norway and Sweden were killed, and

many more would have suffered had not fish farmers taken the unprecedented step of towing the huge pens into the fresher and safer waters of the fjords.

The realization that runaway algal blooms could contribute to marine mammal die-offs owed much to the work of marine biologist Rita Colwell of the University of Maryland. Since the 1970s she had been amassing evidence that communities of algae harbored all manner of exotic viruses.

Dead fish, victims of poison released by algae, float in the River Seine in France. Wildlife show the most dramatic effects of contamination of the environment, while subtler problems descend upon humans.

A toxic 'red tide' caused by a massive bloom of microscopic algae comes into shore at Whangarei Heads, North Island, New Zealand. The algae are now known to support, and transport over great distances, billions of potentially dangerous viruses.

these interminglings were further complicated by the presence of bacteria and, more to the point, by viruses and bacteria that were flooding into the world's oceans in human and animal fecal matter. The sewage of more than two billion people flows into the sea without being treated at all, let alone being given the sophisticated filtering that would remove organisms as small and elusive as a virus. Human and animal wastes were thus both feeding the algae with nutrients and contributing to the interbreeding and multiplication of the microbes that existed within it.

Recipe for a plague

All this circumstantial evidence would suggest that the die-off in the Gulf of Mexico in 1990 could reasonably be ascribed to several factors working together: a probable weakening of the animals' immune systems through the action of organochlorine pollutants in their food supply, and the emergence of new mutations of virus from the soup of algal blooms – themselves encouraged by other forms of pollution. None of this boded well for human health, but the cycle of causes and effects did not end there. Organochlorine pollution also infests the atmosphere, especially in the form of CFCs and other fluorocarbons. As these rise into the stratosphere, they break down under the influence of radiation from the sun. Unattached

And she had discovered that, as the algae multiplied in the warm summer months, so did the viruses. In Maryland's Chesapeake Bay, she found, a milliliter of water in January might contain 10,000 viruses; by October, the number might have risen to as many as one billion – a pattern repeated worldwide. There was evidence too that the relationship between algae and viruses was far from static. Colwell strongly suspected that the two forms of microbial life were exchanging genetic material by way of free-floating particles of DNA such as plasmids and transposons. The potential results of

chlorine atoms then react with the modified, three-atom oxygen molecules (O_3) known as ozone that exist at this level, stripping away one of the ozone molecule's atoms to form chlorine oxide and leave regular oxygen (O_2) behind. Ozone, however, acts as a vital filter of sunlight. Without it, ultraviolet rays penetrate to the earth's surface, where they can cause all manner of damage to living things, ranging from the death of plankton, on which all fish, birds and mammals in the oceans ultimately depend, to skin cancers in humans and mutations of plant life. Because ultraviolet light disturbs living things at the genetic level, it amplifies the already feverish levels of mutation and genetic interchange occurring among the microbes in algal communities.

In the 1970s Rita Colwell had found cholera bacteria (*Vibrio cholerae*) living in algae colonies. The *Vibrio* were dormant, encysted inside the algae. When the El Tor cholera pandemic was in full flood in southern Asia and eastern Africa in the early 1980s, Colwell and her co-workers examined the new strain and found that it had an extraordinary affinity with marine algae. To begin with, the bacteria would shrivel up when dunked in cold seawater, shrinking to one three-hundredth their 'normal' size and becoming dormant. After the water was freshened and warmed, and nitrogen was added, the *Vibrio* returned to their normal, active state. The equivalent conditions would be met in real life when the algae reached brackish or fresh water at a river mouth or estuary, in summer, and were bathed in nitrogen released from coastal sewage discharges and fertilizer run-off in the river water. The El Tor bacteria were

entirely adapted for survival at sea – and specifically in the company of algae. The researchers discovered that the microbes, even when shrunken and dormant, fed off the egg sacs in the algal cells. A single algal cell could support up to a million bacteria.

Colwell argued that if the movements of colonies of algae were tracked – particularly from the coastal waters of Bengal, where cholera was endemic – then epidemiologists would be well placed to forecast the locations of cholera outbreaks and help the potential victims to defend themselves. Yet, ironically, it was not a microbial soup drifting on lazy ocean currents that brought the El Tor cholera to Lima, Peru, in January 1991.

The stowaway virus

The disease arrived as so many others had on the shores of South America – by boat. A Chinese freighter dropped anchor in Callao harbor, just outside Lima, and pumped out the bilge water it had taken aboard in the cholera-infested seas of Asia. In the middle of an exceptionally hot summer the microbes hit an unusually warm sea that was (as we saw in the previous chapter) fouled by Lima's raw sewage – which was nourishing an algal bloom. The algae and their new bacterial passengers found themselves particularly well fed as they moved up the coast with tides and currents, contaminating fish and their human consumers as the infection spread in parallel on land. (A summertime specialty in Peru is ceviche, a mixture of fish and shellfish, with a dash of lime juice, eaten raw – a perfect vehicle for seaborne bacteria.) Short of inventing the bacteria, there was little more that human activity could have done to

bring about the South American cholera epidemic.

Nearly two years after that outbreak, cholera 0139 appeared in Bengal, and within six months had infected 200,000 people and killed 2000. The Mouths of the Ganges, where it emerged, embraces the border between India and Bangladesh. Besides containing the packed cities of Dhaka and Calcutta, this is one of the most densely populated areas in the world, and one of the most intensively farmed, mainly for rice and jute. Bangladesh supports over 125 million people, with a population density of around 875 individuals per square kilometer (2250 per square mile) – making the country about three times as crowded as the State of Massachusetts. The whole region is liable to flooding, and the vast Ganges delta has both a constant interaction with the sea and precious little modern sanitation, while soil erosion upriver sends yet more nutrients into the sea. Once, mangrove swamps in the delta acted as a natural sewage filter, but the trees have been harvested for fuel, and new growth is thwarted as the land is taken over for commercial shrimp and fish ponds, and living space for the region's landless peasants. That it is the cradle of cholera and a prime site for algal blooms comes as little surprise. And within months of its emergence in Bengal, cholera 0139 had reached cities in southern India.

Cholera 0139 had all the marks of an organism that had mutated among the algae. It had El Tor's capacity for survival at sea, combined with the extreme virulence of the classic cholera strain. Researchers from the International Centre for Diarrhoeal Disease in Dhaka found cholera 0139

in all the waters they tested in Bangladesh. Rita Colwell commented: 'There is no explanation for its emergence and spread but ecology.'

The great warming

The Mouths of the Ganges are one of many areas of the world that will be stricken over the next half-century or so if the predicted effects of global warming turn out to be accurate. It is hardly in question that some alterations in the world's climate will occur in response to our astonishing consumption of fossil fuels over the last two or three centuries. Whether or not the worst forebodings of the experts are fulfilled, burning coal, oil and gas has undoubtedly added a massive burden of carbon dioxide to the atmosphere. Generated naturally by plants, this gas, along with methane – emitted by rotting vegetation and animals' digestive systems – traps heat from the sun that would otherwise be reflected back into space in the form of infra-red light. Natural 'greenhouse gases' have maintained the earth's temperature at an average 15°C (59°F) and have helped make life on the planet possible. Since the Industrial Revolution carbon dioxide and nitrous oxide have also been generated by smokestack industries, with the internal combustion engine dumping an ever-increasing load during the 20th century. And

A traffic policeman in Thailand wears a mask to protect himself from exhaust fumes. Ever-increasing urbanization in the developing world threatens to add to the 'greenhouse effect' that creates global warming.

since the 1930s these gases have been augmented by CFCs, which also corrode the ozone layer. Global temperatures have been gently rising since the mid-17th century, with a sharpening rise in the last 100 years of about 0.75°C (1.4°F).

Like a kettle coming to the boil, the additional heat caught within the earth's atmosphere would be expected to make itself felt gradually at first, and then rapidly reach a crisis point. In the UK in 1996 scientists were noting that since records began in 1659, three of the five warmest summers had occurred since 1989, with the warmest ever happening as recently as 1976. (Globally, 1990, 1991, 1994 and 1995 are the four warmest years on record.) Within 25 years, a UK Government report stated, the southern British climate will be like that of central France today. British agriculture will have to change to suit the new conditions, which will not bring simply warmer, drier summers. There will be warmer but wetter winters in the north, more storms everywhere, and regular summer droughts in the south –

the most heavily populated and most intensively farmed part of the country. Wildlife habitats will change and soil erosion increase. With a predicted rise in sea level of around 30cm (12in), low-lying areas, wetlands and beaches would disappear. In Europe, the prognosis is no less radical: Spain will become a desert, and France will take on the hot, dry climate of present-day Spain. All this will happen with an increase of only 0.9°C (1.6°F) in average regional temperatures – but that will still represent a climb, in 25 years, 120 per cent greater than the increase over the whole of the previous century.

The predictions for the end of the 21st century inevitably vary, but a

1995 draft report from the International Panel on Climate Change (IPCC) offered the following worst-case scenario:

Sea levels will rise by up to 2m (6.5ft) as glaciers and parts of the polar ice caps melt and the ocean waters expand as they warm up. That will submerge vast areas of low-lying coastal land, including major river deltas such as the Nile, Ganges, and

Floods in the Mississippi valley strike St Louis in 1993. Natural disasters like this will increase as the world warms up, while rising sea levels will deprive many nations of vast tracts of productive land.

Mississippi, most of the beaches on America's Atlantic coast, parts of China and the island nations of the Maldives, the Seychelles and the Cook and Marshall Islands. More than 100 million people will be displaced – and perhaps very many more. Even today, about 1.75 billion people live within 65km (40 miles) of the sea. In the Mediterranean, for example, about 135 million people live in a coastal strip that is rarely wider than 40km (25 miles). In the USA, even a 1m (3ft) rise in sea level will inundate 18,000sq km (7000sq miles) of land – roughly the area of Massachusetts. In southern Asia, the picture is bleak. According to a Greenpeace summary:

In India, 5700 square km [2200sq miles] of coastal land is at risk of inundation, with the subsequent displacement of 7.1 million people. In Vietnam, where coastal inundation would displace 6.9 million, the report suggests that flood damage could be minimised by the construction or upgrading of 4700km [3000 miles] of dykes, at a cost of $1 billion. In coastal regions of Indonesia, 3.3 million people could be displaced from 3.4 million hectares [8.4 million acres] lost along 81,000 kilometres [50,000 miles] of coast by 2070, with urban housing, offices, ports, roads and railways destroyed. Fishing communities, agriculture and tourism could also be seriously affected. Parts of Jakarta are already subsiding due to removal of ground water and tectonic movement. In Bangladesh, about 15 percent of the population and 20 percent of the nation's land surface will be inundated, with an annual loss of GDP of $5 billion by the year 2070. In Malaysia, the sea is predicted to advance 2.5km [1.5 miles] inland in some areas, disrupting coastal tourism, mangrove products and fisheries. Heavy flooding is expected in Pakistan, impacting heavily on agricultural crops such as cotton, while in the Philippines, typhoons, storms, floods and droughts are expected to increase. Increased flooding and storm damage are also expected in Sri Lanka.

The effects will be exacerbated by developing industry in the region. Says Greenpeace: 'Rapid economic and population growth means this region will also become the largest source of greenhouse emissions on earth, according to At Qureshi of the Climate Institute in Washington, DC. India and China in particular are proposing vast energy generation programmes.'

Rainfall will increase over the next century – but not uniformly across the globe. Areas that are already prone to flooding, such as the Ganges delta, will flood more often and more severely. Water will evaporate more easily in an altogether warmer world, so that drought-prone regions and deserts will become even drier. Hurricanes draw their energy from warm oceans and will become even stronger as their waters become warmer still.

Turbulent times

Temperature and rainfall patterns will shift in unpredictable ways. Farmers will have to change their crops and patterns of irrigation. Natural ecosystems that have to adapt on their own, however, will be devastated. Perhaps a third of the world's forests will be affected. Rises in temperature will not be uniform; winters will be warmer near the poles than elsewhere.

The warming may have some built-in checks and balances. For example, as the world warms up, it should get cloudier, and the clouds' shadows should counter the warming effect. But no one knows how the deep ocean currents – which play a major but little-understood role in channeling heat from one part of the globe to another – will react to the combination of a warmer but more turbulent atmosphere, the input of ice from the poles, and other factors.

Even if the effects are not as drastic as this, scientists agree that global warming is occurring now, and will get worse, even if no more greenhouse gases are added to the atmosphere's existing burden. And no comprehensive international framework exists to control them. It is clear enough what action needs to be taken – but persuading people to stop using coal and oil and to curb automobile use is much easier said than done.

As Michael D. Lemonick wrote in a 1995 *Time* magazine article, to defeat global warming,

people in the developed world would have to completely transform their society, and rich countries like the U.S. would have to subsidize poor but fast-developing nations like China. And that's just to roll CO_2 emissions back to 1990 levels, the goal most environmentalists endorse. To stave off global warming completely, Richard Lindzen [an atmospheric scientist at Massachusetts Institute of Technology] maintains, 'you would have to reduce emissions to where they were in 1920.' Despite noble proclamations issuing from

Mexico City suffers a smog. Air pollution directly damages health and buildings, but less visible effects include contributing to global warming and long-term harm to the human immune system.

Harvard University's Working Group on New and Resurgent Diseases, has noted that plants are following this shift, and moving higher up on mountains all over the world. The shift is best documented in the European Alps, but can be seen in the Americas and in New Zealand as well. 'This,' he says, 'is consistent with seeing glaciers in the mountains along the tropics melting.' As warmer conditions move up the mountains, the environment at higher altitudes also becomes more favorable for organisms such as mosquitoes and the parasites they carry.

Aëdes aegypti mosquitoes, which carry dengue and yellow fever, have been limited around the world to altitudes no higher than 1000m (3300ft), but they are now being found in Colombia and India, for example, at elevations above 2200m (7200ft); scientists have found similar types of upward migrations in Central America and in East Africa. In 1994 Michael E. Loevinsohn, of the Institute of Agronomic Science in Rwanda, reported in *The Lancet* that malarial *Anopheles* mosquitoes had established themselves at high altitudes in Rwanda where they had previously been absent or at least rare. Erwin Jackson, climate impacts specialist for Greenpeace International, has noted that dengue has also appeared at higher altitudes than previously reported in Costa Rica, at 1250m (4100ft); in Mexico, where transmission of dengue was unknown above 1200m (3950ft) before 1986, the

meetings like the 1992 Earth Summit in Rio, that is virtually inconceivable. As economist Henry Jacoby of M.I.T.'s Sloan School of Management puts it, 'If you said, "Let's design a problem that human institutions can't deal with," you wouldn't find one better than global warming.'

Global warming, then, is here to stay, and responses to it are likely to be last-minute and haphazard, as well as unco-ordinated. The forced movement of so many people will not just be from the coasts, but from areas whose economies collapse as climatic shift alters patterns of grazing and agriculture, forest exploitation and management. These migrations alone, if history is any guide, would be a golden opportunity for diseases of all kinds to flourish. But

what may come to be known as the Great Warming will spread disease even without that additional boost.

Death on the wing

As warmer, wetter winters and hotter, drier summers creep steadily further north and south, the shift of weather patterns across the horizon will be matched by 'vertical' changes: alterations in climate will spread upward as well as outward.

Indonesia's Carstensz Mountain (also known as Puncak Jaya Kesum) is the only mountain in the Asian tropics that retains an ice cap throughout the year. But the mountain's glaciers have receded dramatically over the last few centuries. As a result, the snow line has risen up the mountain about 100m (330ft). Paul Epstein, a member of

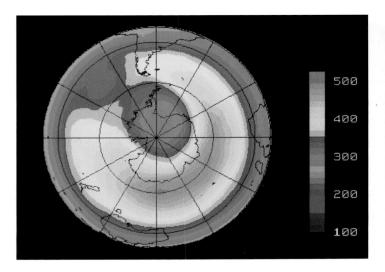

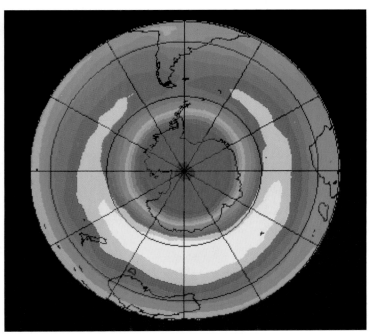

The growth in the seasonal ozone 'hole' over Antarctica – as seen by satellite – from October 1979 (above) to October 1990 (right). The colors depict Dobson units (measures of atmospheric ozone).

dengue vector (the *Aëdes aegypti* mosquito) has been detected at 1600m (5250ft). Meanwhile, epidemic malaria has occurred at high altitudes since 1985 in Rwanda, Zambia, Ethiopia, Swaziland, and Madagascar. One outbreak in highland Madagascar in 1988 killed more than 100,000 people. Jackson believes that increased temperatures and/or rainfall, sometimes in concert with increased drug resistance, have promoted these epidemics.

Climate is a key factor in the outward, as well as upward, spread of vector-borne diseases such as malaria, yellow fever and dengue, because it affects both where the disease-carrying insects will settle and the infectiousness of the disease itself. The *Anopheles* mosquitoes that transmit malaria generally require mean winter temperatures above 15.5°C (60°F) to survive. For the parasite to be actively infectious, temperatures need to be above 17.75°C (64°F). In warmer conditions, the life cycle of the parasite speeds up and infectiousness increases – for instance, an increase of 2.5–3.75°C

(5–7°F) in average temperature doubles the rate of transmission of the dengue virus. In Rwanda, Loevinsohn attributed the spread of malaria to a large increase in mean temperatures over at least three decades, and to heavy rains in 1987 and 1988. Malaria epidemics also occurred in other parts of East Africa during the late 1980s, and Loevinsohn suggests that these too were driven in part by heavy rains and warmer temperatures. One model reviewed by the IPCC estimates that in response to a global mean temperature rise of about 0.6°C (1°F) – predicted to occur before 2025 – the zone of potential malaria outbreaks could increase from one containing 45 per cent of the world's population to an area encompassing 60 per cent of the world's population. This would amount to between 50 and 80 million extra cases of malaria annually. The estimate does not, of course, take account of the statistical likelihood that the expansion of the parasite-and-mosquito population will lead to further mutations for resistance to

drugs and insecticides, or the probability that social chaos and refugee populations will create countless fresh habitats for the insects. Some epidemiologists suggest that an additional 620 million people in developing countries could be at risk from malaria by 2050.

Malaria will not be the only disease to migrate further north and south. The *Aëdes aegypti* mosquito, which carries yellow fever and dengue, is currently limited to about 35° of latitude either side of the Equator. Global warming could stretch its reach by another 5–7°. In plain geographical terms, its range in the northern hemisphere would leap from the present east-west line linking Memphis, Tennessee, Osaka, Baghdad, and Casablanca, to one running from New York City through Chicago and on to Beijing, Istanbul and Madrid. The British Isles, already warmed by the Atlantic's Gulf Stream running up from the Caribbean, can certainly expect a new incursion of malaria, and may become prey to yellow fever and dengue as well.

Aëdes albopictus or the Asian Tiger mosquito, another carrier of the dengue fever virus, is believed to have arrived in the USA at Houston, Texas, in 1985, in a shipment of used, water-logged Japanese automobile tires. Within two years it had appeared in 17 states, and in the cities of Baltimore and St Louis, and even as far north as Chicago. Medical entomologist and Asian Tiger expert George Craig has said that, since the mosquito vector is already well established in the USA, 'all that might be necessary is for enough people to import the disease itself from places like Puerto Rico, the Virgin Islands and Jamaica to set the epidemic wheels in motion. And with the immigrant population swelling, the wheels are already greased.'

Insects in waiting

The prospect that dengue, and in particular its severe hemorrhagic forms, dengue hemorrhagic fever (DHF) and dengue shock syndrome (DSS), may arrive in strength among the close-packed populations of the northern hemisphere is not to be taken lightly. In humans, dengue causes a spectrum of illness ranging from mild, flu-like symptoms to severe hemorrhagic disease and death. The classic form of the disease – known as 'breakbone fever' because of the agonizing pain it brought on in the joints – was rarely fatal. But in the 1950s a new and more lethal strain of the virus appeared in the Philippines and spread throughout Asia. In October 1982, a massive epidemic hit New Delhi, India, in which one in five of the city's 5.6 million people became ill. Eighteen months before, Havana, Cuba, saw the beginning of a six-month epidemic that caused 344,000 illnesses and 158

deaths among a population of two million people. In both these outbreaks the death toll was relatively low, but medical facilities were stretched beyond their limits: the disruption and economic damage brought by dengue is intensified by the need for a long period of recovery and convalescence.

The incubation period for DHF/DSS can be as short as three days or as long as 14, with an average of four to six days. Although infected individuals are never infectious to other people, they remain infectious to mosquitoes for about six days, so the potential for epidemic spread is high unless patients can be isolated from the insects.

DHF/DSS begins with a sudden onset of fever, usually lasting from two to seven days. During this acute phase, it is difficult to tell DHF/DSS from 'regular' dengue fever and other viral illnesses. Temperature then falls to normal or below, and the critical stage of DHF/DSS begins: the symptoms include skin hemorrhages, nosebleeds, bleeding gums, gastrointestinal bleeding and blood in the urine, as the virus destroys the platelets that are vital to control bleeding. If not corrected with fluid replacement therapy, this may cause an overall loss of blood volume, shock and death. There is no therapeutic cure or vaccine currently available.

There are several other environmental factors that account for the recent increase in DHF/DSS and other insect-borne epidemics. First, the world has experienced unprecedented population growth since World War II, most of it in developing tropical countries. Unplanned and uncontrolled urbanization in those countries in turn has resulted in deteriorating housing and inadequate water, sewage and waste management. Consequently,

bigger populations of mosquitoes are living intimately with swarms of people in overcrowded conditions. Second, the loss of traditional ways of life and the spread of consumerism in the Third World have contributed to the spread of *Aëdes aegypti* mosquitoes and an increase in their populations. For example, most consumer goods are packaged in nonbiodegradable plastic, which is discarded indiscriminately. By holding pockets of water this litter creates ideal habitats for *Aëdes aegypti* larvae. There has been a dramatic increase in the number of trucks and cars in developing countries, and used tires are dumped everywhere; they too make ideal breeding grounds for mosquitoes. Third, increased commercial air travel has provided a perfect mechanism for moving dengue viruses in infected travelers from one population center to another in the tropics. Finally, since 1970 attempts at controlling mosquito populations have failed to reduce them to levels where transmission of the disease is interrupted. The result has been the repeated introduction and migration of new strains of the virus into and among urban centers. Taken together, these factors have led to the emergence of a virtual epidemic of dengue and DHF/DSS in the tropics since 1980. The packed urban societies of the northern hemisphere, with their endless scope for offering *Aëdes aegypti* and *Aëdes albopictus* mosquitoes places to breed, now face the same future.

As early as September 1991, a warning of other possible insect-borne epidemics – within the USA, not the Third World – was being sounded. The *Los Angeles Times* reported:

The USA may also be prone to another mosquito-transmitted tropical disease – encephalitis, or sleeping sickness. In [the winter of 1990–91], there was an outbreak of encephalitis in Florida, with 280 confirmed cases statewide. According to University of Florida entomologist, Jonathon Day, the outbreak was connected to an unusually light rainfall during the winter dry season, providing plenty of puddle breeding grounds.

Enrique Bucher from Argentina's University of Cordoba Center for Applied Zoology warns of other diseases, such as leishmaniasis and Chagas disease, spreading northward into America in conjunction with warming air temperatures. 'Generally speaking, increased temperatures would raise the reproductive rates of disease vectors, adding to vector-control difficulties. As a consequence, the shorter generation times for these vectors could favor the emergence of strains resistant to pesticides'. Leishmaniasis can cause horrendous facial disfigurations; there is no vaccine and treatment is...painful. There is no vaccine or cure for Chagas disease, caused by a parasite which invades and debilitates the muscles, including the heart muscle.

An increase in skin diseases might also be expected, according to David Taplin, professor at the department of dermatology at the University of Miami School of Medicine. And Cornell University's Thomas Eisner warns 'It is folly for anyone to tell you that we can cope with spreading insect populations. I'm anxious about

People pick over garbage on Manila Smokey Mountain, the Philippines. This vast mound of rubbish is a perfect breeding ground for disease-bearing mosquitoes, yet has become a township for the poorest Filipinos.

that kind of technological optimism. We tried to wipe out malaria, and what have we got? DDT-resistant insects, drug-resistant plasmodium and a vaccine that's not working.'

Good intentions

As Thomas Eisner implicitly recognizes, the spread of cruel and unusual diseases through environmental factors has largely been encouraged by human activity that was, in the first place, entirely well intentioned. The organochlorines from insecticides, pesticides and packaging that pollute our bloodstreams, reduce our fertility and threaten our children with congenital horrors; the internal combustion engine and the coal-fired furnace that have contributed to global warming; the belief that industrialization would cure all the ills of the developing world – all these seemed boons when first conceived. Even something as obviously beneficial as air conditioning – without which such cities as Phoenix and Las Vegas could scarcely exist, and jetliners would be reduced to snails in the sky – can turn out to have a dark side. In this case, it is not so much a mistaken intention that brings ill in its wake as a (perfectly natural) desire not to give up the advantages that technological progress has brought.

When the USA was self-sufficient in oil and gasoline was 10 cents a gallon, the cost of central heating and air conditioning was a negligible item in the minds of architects and aircraft designers. With the massive hike in oil prices after the defeat of the Arabs in the Yom Kippur War of 1973, such costs became critical. Buildings were now designed to keep people warm or cool, depending on the season, with a

minimal inflow or outflow or air. It is simply cheaper – if one persists in using oil as an energy source – to recirculate the same air, which is already near the desired temperature, than it is to bring in fresh air, change its temperature, expel it, and start the whole process over again. Frequently, buildings were designed with windows that could not be opened, to ensure 'energy savings'. The best known result of this policy was sick building syndrome, which was finally identified as the effects on people of inhaling formaldehyde, radon, and other poisons that building materials exude and that were being recycled along with the air. At the same time, an interesting *mélange* of the occupants' viruses and bacteria were on the same merry-go-round. While direct fuel bills fell, indirect costs in terms of reduced efficiency, health insurance payments and lost workdays soared.

Jet transport has been targeted in these pages several times as a prime mover of disease within and among continents. In addition, the closed environment of the aircraft itself always offered microbes, should they be present, the opportunity to amplify their effects locally, in the course of a flight. The 1973 oil crisis led aircraft designers to a fuel-saving solution not unlike that adopted by architects, and they at least had the excuse that wind and solar power were not practicable options for passenger airliners. The temperature of the air outside a jetliner cruising at 10,000m (33,000ft) may be as low as –45°C (–50°F), and to warm it to breathable temperature clearly consumes considerable energy. Before 1985, most commercial airliners' ventilation systems refreshed the air every three minutes. After 1985, the fre-

quency of the cycle was reduced so that a mixture of 'old' and fresh air recirculated every seven minutes, and a complete change of air would take up to half an hour.

Savings in fuel were enormous, but flight crews increasingly complained of dizziness, colds, flu, headaches and nausea while passengers came to accept that a long-haul flight usually brought a mild viral infection (easily ascribed to jet-lag) in its wake. Objective studies of aircraft cabins revealed that carbon dioxide was present at levels of up to 50 per cent above legal standards set in the USA, while air quality in general was well below the level set for workplaces – where an American office might have 0.57cu m (20cu ft) of fresh air injected into it every minute, an airliner could have as little as 0.25cu m (9cu ft) of fresh air pass through it every minute. Scientific measures backed anecdotal evidence: aircraft were potential incubators of disease.

So now imagine a conference of American industrial executives in newly fashionable Cape Town, where one of them picks up an exotic, airborne virus, and flies home across the Atlantic with his or her colleagues. On a wide-body jet literally hundreds of others could be infected, and they in turn would be dispersing to sealed, air-conditioned office buildings across the USA in which thousands of others work – and breathe the same, half-stale, recycled air. And, very likely, members of their families live and breathe in similar buildings. In the global village and the modern workplace, epidemics of alien diseases are openly being invited to break out.

A dependence on oil – a fossil fuel that contributes to global warming –

that leads to false solutions to energy problems naturally attracts the wrath of environmentalists. For while solar-powered airliners may forever remain an impossible dream, there are alternative sources of power to warm or cool buildings. Yet 'green' campaigners and even official watchdogs have paid remarkably little attention, publicly at least, to the opportunities that environmental degradation has opened up for infectious diseases.

Engineering disaster

Ecologists and others have certainly made us all aware that well meaning public works may have disastrous results, often the exact opposite of those intended. Dam projects are a favorite example, and few have achieved fewer of their stated aims than the Aswan High Dam in Egypt.

The environmentalists' objections to this enormously expensive project, first planned by the British in the 1950s and finally completed with Soviet money in 1971, are straightforward. While its hydroelectric generators have provided cheap power to Egypt and removed the uncertainties brought by the annual flood of the Nile river, the dam has over-controlled the flow of water. Silt and nutrients no longer spread across the Nile valley, but sink to the bottom of the enormous Lake Nasser, the dam's man-made reservoir. Consequently, Egyptian farmers now work a smaller area of fertile land than they once did, and

The departures board on a typical day at Manchester airport in the UK. Air routes form a complex network through which infections can travel, while aircraft themselves can be incubators of disease.

137

have to boost its productivity with fertilizers, pesticides and herbicides, which bring environmental and health problems of their own. Nutrients that nourished the plankton on which fish and their fry fed in the Mediterranean no longer reach the sea. The sardine fishery that once regularly landed 18,000 tonnes of fish each year col-lapsed catastrophically, harvesting only about 600 tonnes for some years, and recovering only because of more aggressive fishing and the effect of artificial nutrients in the sea.

These effects are bad enough, but they are compounded by a shift in human infection of which less is heard. Bilharzia, also known as schistomiasis, is caused by schistosome parasites that spend part of their lives in snails and part in people. The parasite larvae

The Aswan High Dam (at top of picture) and the northern reaches of Lake Nasser in Egypt. Since the dam was built, disease patterns in the region have altered for the worse.

excreted by the snails into river water will pass directly through human skin, and eventually make their way to major internal organs, where they grow into worms. These lay eggs, which in turn are excreted and infest snails. Anemia, the formation of scar tissue in the intestine, chronic diarrhea and dysentery, cirrhosis of the liver, cystitis and cancer of the bladder are all possible outcomes of bilharzia. Before the Aswan High Dam was built, the prevailing schistosome parasite mainly

attacked children and resulted in fairly minor urinary disorders. After the dam came into operation, the slower flow of the Nile's current fostered the growth of a different species of parasite whose target was young adults, and that brought a full panoply of disorders with it. Similar changes in the bilharzia parasite occurred after the Sennar Dam in the Sudan and the Akosombo Dam in Ghana were built.

Probably the least expected source of actual and potential new epidemics

is one of the most rejoiced-over events of modern times: the fall of the Soviet empire and the end of the Cold War in 1989–90. Despite its manifold evils, Soviet rule kept in check numerous ethnic and religious rivalries in Europe and Asia – just as the European colonial powers had done in other parts of the world. Small, local wars were still fought in Asia and Africa, but were controlled by the patronage of the superpowers, who were themselves ultimately restrained by the threat of mutual nuclear extinction. Once that threat and the influence of the Soviet (essentially Russian) system were removed, those ancient resentments boiled over into actual fighting – nowhere more obviously than in the former Yugoslavia. Other insurrections, guerrilla campaigns and full-scale conflicts have broken out in the former Soviet Union's Asian republics, while the possibility of yet another major regional war looms in the Middle East.

Whether actual or potential, these clashes bring in their train death, refugee migrations, and the collapse of basic health services, transport and communication – the chaos on which microbes thrive. And there is another especially unnerving aspect to these local rivalries. That is the possibility, and in some cases the virtual certainty, that nations seeking to dominate others will turn to biological weapons of mass destruction with which to blackmail or bully their neighbors.

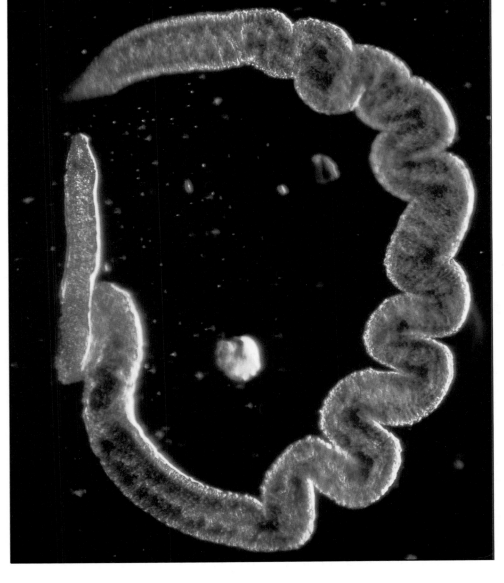

A full-grown female fluke of the schistosome parasite that causes bilharzia. The microbe's larval form hatches out in snails then, to become an adult, leaves and burrows into humans who enter infected water.

CHAPTER SEVEN

SOWING THE WIND

THE MULTIPLE THREAT
OF BIOLOGICAL WEAPONS

Warriors have always sought to gain an edge over their enemies,
whether by more cunning strategy or through technological
advantage. Since the revolutions in biotechnology in the 1970s
and 1980s made it possible to breed and manipulate microbes as
never before, the skills, knowledge and equipment required to
produce super-deadly biological weapons have been within the
competence of any biology graduate. Any nation, rich or poor,
can now afford to arm itself with weapons of mass destruction.
Simple to create and easily disguised, they also make ideal
instruments of terror for psychopaths and political extremists.

There can be few things more grotesque and terrifying than a plague deliberately unleashed on the innocent by one's fellow human beings. But there do exist weapons designed to accomplish just that. They use two basic classes of 'agent', or active ingredient. First, there are living, organic microorganisms, such as the anthrax bacillus, yellow fever virus, or plague bacteria. Second are toxins – naturally occurring poisons, produced by living creatures. A favorite toxin among weapons designers is the one that causes botulism; it is produced by growing *Clostridium botulinum* bacteria.

The US troops involved in the Gulf War's Operation Desert Shield lacked the capacity to detect biological weapons on the battlefield. The first real indication of any biological attacks was ill and dying soldiers.

Besides infecting soldiers or civilians with lethal or incapacitating diseases, biological warfare can be waged against an adversary's crops or livestock. The agents may be delivered to their targets by aerial spraying, bombs, missiles or even small-arms fire.

Biological weapons hold many attractions for terrorists, be they renegade groups or nation states, and it is extraordinarily difficult to control their development, manufacture and delivery. Although biological weapons are probably proliferating throughout the world, they have been outlawed internationally – or, more accurately, many countries have agreed not to develop or use them. Despite that, Russia and Iraq, who were parties to the 1972 Biological Weapons Convention (BWC), are known to have stockpiled them. And many others have chosen not to be bound by any

such convention. Some, like Israel and her Arab neighbor Syria, probably possess biological weapons and, in the atmosphere of mutual distrust that prevails in the Middle East, prefer not to sign an agreement they may not be able to keep. It is very likely that all those who have ignored the BWC find these weapons an inexpensive and easily manufactured alternative to nuclear weapons as a deterrent to potential enemies. According to experts, the countries besides Russia and Iraq that are likely to have offensive biological weapons include North Korea (rumored to have kept samples of smallpox virus for military use), Libya, Iran, India, Israel, Syria, China, Taiwan, and South Africa. Many more nations are said to want them.

However, it is possible to retain some degree of order among nations – whether through pressure of diplomatic opinion, trade sanctions or, ultimately, waging war. Such constraints are ineffective against terrorists. A fundamental tenet of terrorist doctrine is the merit of outraging human decency. No holds are barred and no quarter is given. The idea is to exhaust the enemy, who will accede to one's demands, however unprincipled, for the sake of peace. Some nations have endorsed this strategy – if not directly, then by arming and paying clandestine groups of activists. Terrorists would find biological weapons hugely attractive. They are highly lethal, ideal for surprise attacks, cheap to make, have tremendous psychological impact and, in cunning hands, will drain the resources of even the most powerful and prosperous society.

Bugs not bombs

Whether we like it or not, modern warfare is not limited to the battlefield. In a full-scale conflict it is as important to reach beyond the combat zone and disrupt or destroy an enemy's supporting social structure as it is to win battles at the front. Biological weapons – in theory, at least – give military commanders the ability both to put soldiers out of action on the battlefield and, at one blow, to kill or cripple vast numbers of civilians, whose wealth and industry sustain the enemy's fighting forces. Biological munitions have unique advantages over other weapons in their capacity to deprive an enemy of basic resources such as food, and to bring chaos to essential services. A handful of well placed bioactive agents can spread infections among livestock or ruin huge areas of crops in a way that no amount of conventional bombing could hope to achieve.

Another application of this kind of behind-the-lines biological warfare is not much mentioned in the literature. That is the use of bioactive agents in peace time, against a political enemy's key cash crops or livestock. This can be done out of sheer vindictiveness, to destabilize a country and topple its ideologically unsound leaders, or to undermine its economy so that it cannot afford to undertake a fighting war. If the agent is intelligently delivered, it is almost impossible for the victim to know whether natural misfortune or covert action has made his crops fail and his animals die. In 1971, several diseases flashed across the Communist-ruled island of Cuba. One was African swine fever, which broke out simultaneously in two sites that were a considerable distance apart; 500,000 hogs were slaughtered to halt the epidemic. Blue mold broke out in Cuba's valuable tobacco plantations, cane smut struck the sugar crop, and the human population reeled before an outbreak of the hemorrhagic strain of dengue fever. President Fidel Castro accused the CIA of releasing the diseases. Whether the agency did or not, the Cuban economy and people took an expensive battering, and the cluster of epidemics demonstrates how a nation can be radically disrupted when just a few pathogens run wild.

There are not many biological agents that are really suitable for direct use on or beyond the battlefield, any more than there are many general types of artillery. Generally speaking, it is a more effective tactic to disable both combat troops and civilians than it is to kill them. A corpse can be buried and forgotten; but one wounded or thoroughly sick person will tie up a whole train of others and distract them from the battle, whether that is

military or economic. Whether meant to kill or only to incapacitate, the ideal biological weapon will:

- be consistent and reliable in its intended effect
- need only a low dose in order to be effective
- have a short and predictable incubation period
- be used against a target not previously exposed to the agent
- have no treatment that is available to the target
- be readily mass-produced
- be easy to deliver and disseminate
- be stable (i.e. safe) to store and transport

From the user's point of view, it is also essential to have full protection available to friendly troops and civilians.

Another consideration has traditionally been post-delivery controllability and contamination. There is little point in scattering fleas carrying the bubonic plague over an enemy town, watching the citizens drop like flies, then marching in triumphantly only to have one's own troops promptly fall fatally ill. Such an agent is of military use only if one has no intention to occupy the ground gained – which contradicts virtually all tactical and strategic thinking. The history of epidemics suggests that it would be unwise to unleash deliberately any disease that has a vector as unpredictable as an insect.

Problems like these have made most military strategists extremely wary of actually deploying bioactive weapons. Like nuclear weapons, whose potency needed to be demonstrated only once, they may be more useful as a deterrent to a potential aggressor than as a practical tactical or strategic option. Unlike nuclear weapons, they do not call for a costly and elaborate development program. The basic materials, unlike the basis of weapons-grade plutonium, are both inexpensive and available on the open market – Saddam Hussein's scientists bought the anthrax for Iraq's massive biological warfare program by mail order from the USA. The finished munitions are lightweight, and pack more casualties per gram than any nuclear device. A single aircraft, a remote-controlled drone, a special forces squad or a missile can thus deliver a compact device that will kill more people over a wider area than any nuclear warhead, with the additional advantage that the enemy's property will remain intact whatever the casualty rate.

Some direct comparisons make the attractions of biological over nuclear weapons alarmingly clear. In 1993, the US Office of Technology Assessment (OTA) compared the effects of the two kinds of weapon on a city with 3000–10,000 people per square kilometer (0.4sq mile). It calculated that a 12.5-kilotonne nuclear-armed missile would create a circle of destruction of 7.8sq km (3sq miles) and leave 23,000–80,000 people dead. On an overcast day or night with moderate wind the same missile carrying 30kg (65lb) of anthrax spores would result in 30,000–100,000 people dying within a cigar-shaped area of 10sq km (3.85sq miles).

The OTA then took a specific urban area – Washington, DC – and compared the results of attacks under three different sets of weather conditions. In each case an aircraft would follow a 100km (60-mile) line upwind of the city, releasing 100kg (220lb) of anthrax spores. In less than perfect conditions – a clear sunny day with a light breeze (both would reduce the effectiveness of the agent) – an area of 46sq km (17.75sq miles) would be affected, killing 130,000–460,000 people. On an overcast day or night with moderate wind, 140sq km (55sq miles) would be affected and 420,000–1.4 million people would die. Under ideal conditions – a calm, clear night – the anthrax spores would cover 300sq km (115sq miles) and kill between one million and three million people. In all cases the vastly cheaper anthrax was more lethal – and absolutely less destructive – than the nuclear option.

Biological weapons are nothing if not cost effective – a detail unlikely to be lost on terrorist groups or nations operating on pinched defense budgets. To 'affect' one square kilometer (0.4sq mile) of ground, it costs around $2000 using artillery, bombs or missiles armed with high explosives. A nuclear weapon will complete the task for about $800, and chemical weapons come only slightly cheaper at $600. A biological weapon will do the same job for precisely one dollar.

At this point we have to bear in mind that the countries with the greatest expertise and resources in biological warfare – the USA, the UK and the former Soviet Union – officially gave up the development of offensive biological agents in 1972, just as the revolution in genetic engineering was getting under way. A quarter of a century later, it may well be possible to

Test flight of a remote-controlled 'drone'. Originally designed for reconnaissance, such aircraft are hard to detect, and could be rapidly adapted to carry a compact but devastating biological payload.

re-arrange the DNA of the bubonic plague bacillus, or of its flea vector, so that the spread of the disease can be precisely controlled. For instance (and this is pure speculation), it may be possible to create a flea/bacillus combination that can infect no more than a few people – a kind of 'three strikes and you're out' effect. This could be done by creating a mule flea – one incapable of reproducing – with a very short life-span, carrying a microbe of awesome virulence and total immunity to antibiotics. The plague might then reach the guaranteed-lethal pneumonic stage in every infection, but not be amplified by an expanding and migrating vector. Follow-up troops would need only an effective vaccine (which could be devised in tandem

with the flea/bacillus combination), and the patience to wait for the disease to burn itself out in the target population, before initiating an occupation. With expertise and equipment to modify microbes so readily available, biological weapons become increasingly attractive to states that lack either the means or the money to join the nuclear club.

The biological armory

Even a deterrent that one hopes one never has to use still has to have some credibility. You cannot rattle a saber if your scabbard is empty. Designer bugs, created with special vulnerabilities to bespoke (and above-top-secret) vaccines, were little more than fantasies in the early 1970s. Nevertheless, the mic-

The Pentagon in Washington, DC, hub of the US armed forces. Experiments have shown that the entire US government machine is extremely vulnerable to attack by airborne biological weapons.

robes that appealed to the military a quarter of a century ago are the ones whose military usefulness has been most researched. And because there was a body of knowledge on which to build, they have remained favorites with those countries that have continued to develop bioactive weapons.

Weapons designers have considered a range of biological agents for their military potential. The notion of using disease as a weapon is scarcely new: since at least Roman times soldiers have poisoned wells and springs with corpses of humans and animals to aggravate their enemies, and according to legend the first biological ballistic missiles were deployed in 1346, when the Tartars marked the end of their siege of Kaffa by catapulting plague-ridden corpses into the city. Specially designed chemical weapons appeared in World War I; of the 280,000 dough-boys who died in France, a quarter were killed by chlorine or mustard gas. The first people to use the discoveries of medical science to slaughter their fellow humans were the Japanese.

In 1932 Japan set up a puppet state in Manchuria, China. In 1935, the secret research Unit 731, under the command of General Shirô Ishii, opened at Harbin, in the remote north of the region. Three of Unit 731's eight divisions were separately concerned with bacteriological research, warfare research and field experiments, and the mass-production and storage of bacteria. They investigated the effects of bubonic plague, anthrax, botulins, brucellosis (undulant fever), cholera, dysentery, smallpox and typhus and their vectors (especially insects), along with potential antidotes and the effects of other drugs, chemical toxins, frost-bite, and plant and animal diseases. The remote location was chosen so that the Japanese scientists would disturb no one by conducting their experiments on living human beings. Some 3000 Chinese prisoners, whom the Japanese called *marutas* ('logs'), were killed by the Harbin researchers, who did not balk at vivisection in order to inspect the internal organs of those dying from their infections.

Conventional metal bombs with explosives tended to kill the microbes, so for frontline work Unit 731 devel-oped the *Ha*, a steel bomb containing 1500 cylindrical pellets immersed in anthrax or tetanus emulsion. For use against civilians anthrax-infected chocolates were made, as was the *Uji*, a 25kg (55lb) porcelain bomb that could contain up to 30,000 plague-infected fleas, or a large number of tetanus, dysentery or typhoid bacteria or anthrax bacilli. A small charge ex-ploded it in the air above the target.

During the 1942 Chekiang cam-paign against Chinese forces the Japanese had the chance to try their new-fangled weapons. Huge quantities of microbes were poured into wells, reservoirs and rivers by retreating troops, and *Uji* bombs were dropped from the air. Some 10,000 Japanese soldiers died as a result of inadvertently moving into a contaminated area, but Chinese losses were said to be 'incalcu-lable'. The Americans became aware of this interest in biological warfare in 1939, when the Japanese attempted to acquire some yellow fever virus in the USA. By the close of 1943, the USA itself had produced 225kg (500lb) bombs for anthrax and botulin mic-robes; and, at the end of World War II, the USA gave Japanese scientists from Unit 731 immunity from prosecution for war crimes in return for their exper-tise (and silence).

Secret wars

The UK too had begun research into bacteriological weapons, initially in 1934, with the aim of stockpiling vaccines against a possible large-scale airborne biological assault on the British Isles. In 1942 it was decided to respond to such an assault by spreading anthrax among the German livestock herds, and 5000 anthrax-filled cattle cakes were produced for the purpose.

Anthrax bombs of different sizes were also built and tested, most notoriously on the Scottish isle of Gruinard. The exercises revealed how easily biological warfare could backfire on the aggressor, for the island's soil became saturated with anthrax spores, and was not con-sidered entirely safe until 1987.

After World War II the UK maintained that its interest in biologi-cal warfare was purely defensive, although papers released in early 1997 show this to be untrue. Alerted to the post-war Soviet decision to develop offensive biological weapons, the British chiefs of staff decided to do the same, despite what they called 'the problem of international commit-ments'. They saw biological weapons as a useful follow-up to a nuclear attack, when their effect 'on a highly disorga-nized population, of greatly lowered morale and diminished physical resis-tance could be devastating'. While Britain's Porton Down defensive research facility became well known, much more secretive and elaborately guarded establishments in the far west of the country were never mentioned in public and were rumored to be the center for offensive operations and weapons storage.

The former Soviet Union, stretched to the limit during World War II, began to develop biological weapons in the late 1940s. What the Russians called 'scientific-experimental bases' were founded in Sverdlovsk (now Ekaterinburg), Kirov and Zagorsk to investigate anthrax, tularemia, brucel-losis, plague, typhus, and other pathogens. Production lines for agents and munitions were set up at Sverd-lovsk and Zagorsk, while agents and delivery systems were tested on Vozrozhdenie Island in the Aral Sea.

None of these experimental activities was barred under international law, as defined by the Geneva Protocol of 1925; only Japan actually acted illegally. The use of chlorine and mustard gas in World War I had led to the Protocol. Although mainly concerned with chemical weapons, it also renounced the use of bacteriological weapons in war. It did not, however, prohibit their development or manufacture, and it made no mention of weapons based on viruses, toxins or parasites. And, of course, it bound only those who signed it.

Word of honor

This last problem has bedeviled the Protocol's successor, the Biological Weapons Convention (BWC) of 1972, signed by 118 nations including the Soviet Union. This outlaws the development, production and stockpiling of biological and toxin weapons as well as their use, and provides for the destruction of existing stocks. Unfortunately, the BWC provides no means of verifying that signatories actually abide by it. Under the codename *Biopreparat*, the Soviet bloc continued its biological warfare research and expanded its capability until the Communist regime collapsed in 1991. Some 30,000 scientists, engineers and technicians were employed by the project.

There were a number of clues even in the public domain that this was happening. In 1977, five years after the BWC was signed, virus hunter Joe McCormick of the US Centers for Disease Control met four Soviet 'scientists' at the USSR's embassy in Monrovia, Liberia, who were ostensibly there to investigate Lassa fever.

McCormick was certain of the credentials of one of the quartet; but at least one of the others knew no basic biology at all. Once away from the embassy they explained that they wanted Lassa antibodies, reagents and virus samples. McCormick suggested they apply, in writing, to the CDC in Atlanta. He was to be pestered by Soviet researchers for over a year for samples of the Lassa virus and, after each meeting, by the CIA. McCormick was convinced both were afraid the other was interested in adding Lassa to its biological armory. Given that there was some evidence that, in certain circumstances, the virus could be transmitted simply by inhalation, the interest was understandable. Besides, Lassa had no cure apart from the serum of survivors, was lethal to nine out of 10 non-immune victims, and needed only a tiny 'dose' to create an infection.

Poisons have been in the inventory of the spy and the assassin from time immemorial. The BWC does not address 'non-military' applications, although Soviet/Russian research has long been developing 'products' intended for covert use against troublesome diplomats, politicians, business executives and even dissenters. In 1978 in the UK, Georgi Markov, a Bulgarian exile, was walking to a radio studio in London from which he regularly broadcast to his homeland on the BBC World Service. He suddenly felt a sharp pain in his leg. Turning

Gruinard Island, off the west coast of Scotland. Used as a proving ground for anthrax weapons during World War II, the island remained poisoned and uninhabitable for more than 40 years after the war's end.

around, he confronted a man picking up an umbrella. The man apologized and went on his way. Markov became ill that night and died several days later. The autopsy found, in his leg, a small metal pellet coated with ricin, a toxic biological substance derived from the castor-oil plant.

Another incident occurred early in April 1979 with hair-raising implications for public safety. According to a Russian emigrant newspaper, there was an explosion in a research compound in Sverdlovsk in Russia. The complex had already been photographed by spy satellite, and curiously for a Soviet military site had animal pens and an air-conditioning system. In the days following the explosion, reports of an outbreak of anthrax surfaced. Victims suffered temperatures as high as 42°C (108°F), and were dead within hours of reaching hospital. Up to 1000 people were said to have died.

The USA suggested that the outbreak was caused by an accident in a biological warfare production plant at the Sverdlovsk site. The USSR vehemently denied this had happened, pointing out that anthrax was endemic in the region and claiming that the outbreak was caused by tainted meat bought on the black market, and poor hygiene among the population. Many Western journalists and scientists argued that the known facts supported the Soviet claims.

However, in 1992 Russian President Boris Yeltsin admitted that the incident had indeed been the result of an accident involving anthrax developed for biological warfare. Yeltsin then signed a decree that recommitted Russia to the BCW. Then, in 1994, three defectors revealed that a biological warfare program is still under way

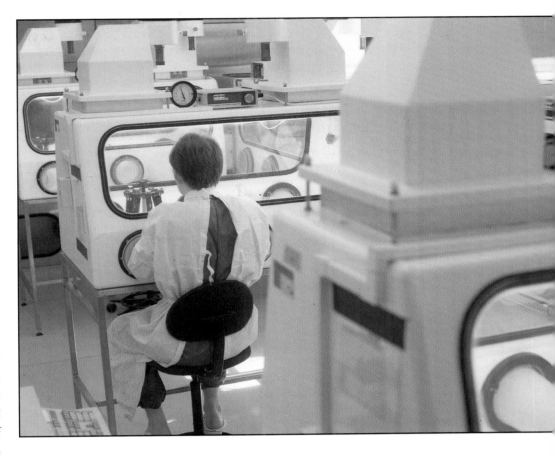

Inside the high-security virus laboratory at Porton Down in the UK. Lethal microbes are in the sealed units. These allow scientists to perform experiments without the need for full-body suits.

in Russia. It allegedly concentrates on a 'super-plague', which according to US intelligence sources is based on a strain of anthrax for which the West has no antidote. Yeltsin responded that he knew nothing of any biological warfare research. The defectors agreed, implying that the Russian military is running the program without Yeltsin's knowledge or consent.

In all these programs, the names of a handful of pathogens crop up time and again. In the 1960s those standardized and stockpiled by the USA were representative of the biological agents that had emerged as favorites with weapons designers everywhere, and that remain the subject of research today. Their general characteristics are given in the table overleaf.

These seven agents were selected from a huge range of appropriate diseases, and it is possible that other

countries have developed other agents for military use. As we noted earlier, it was suspected that the Soviet Union had been conducting considerable research into hemorrhagic fever viruses such as Lassa and Ebola; how far this was taken to create standard agents for use in weapons is not known. These viruses would very likely have been investigated by US military scientists too, had they not been constrained by the 1972 BWC, which came into force before most of the hemorrhagic fevers emerged from the wild.

In addition to disease agents, weapons designers have paid a good

US BIOLOGICAL WEAPONS FULLY DEVELOPED BY 1969

DISEASE (Agent)	INCUBATION PERIOD	EFFECTS	PERIOD SURVIVORS INCAPACITATED	MILITARY CONSIDERATIONS
Anthrax (*Bacillus anthracis*)	2–3 days	Lethal – 95–100% mortality	4–5 weeks	May contaminate ground; rapid decay rate in air
Bubonic/pneumonic plague (*Yersinia pestis*)	2–6 days	Lethal – 95–100% mortality in pneumonic form	1–5 weeks	Potentially uncontrollable
Yellow fever (arbovirus; mosquito vector)	3–6 days	Lethal – 40–100% mortality	1–2 weeks	Potentially uncontrollable if virus enters new animal reservoir; devastating to virgin (non-immune or unvaccinated) populations
Tularemia (rabbit fever) (*Francisella tularensis*)	2–10 days	Lethal – 30–40% mortality	8–13 weeks	Illness lasts approximately a month; drug-resistant forms exist; hardy bacteria can survive in soil for long periods
Brucellosis (undulant fever) (*Brucella suis*)	7–60 days	Incapacitating; 1–2% mortality	8–12 weeks	Recurrent fever over about a month; may last 12 months, and relapses may occur for years. Usual transmission through contaminated meat or milk; no vaccine available
Q-fever (*Coxiella burnetti*)	15–18 days	Incapacitating; 0–1% mortality	1–2 weeks	Highly infectious; easily grown in high concentrations; could be deployed in combination with other agents
Venezuelan equine encephalitis (arbovirus; tick vector)	3–6 days	Incapacitating; 0–2% mortality	1–2 weeks	Flu-like symptoms with nausea; highly infectious

deal of attention to botulinum toxins from bacteria and saxitoxin, a poison found in shellfish. Both are extremely lethal even in very small doses and have been considered for 'poison-tipping' small-arms ammunition. While strictly regarded as chemical weapons, both are, of course, derived from living creatures.

To blight an enemy's agriculture, the USA developed standardized agents and, presumably, delivery systems for rice blast (*Pyricularia oryzae* fungus), and black stem rust (*Puccinia graminis tritici* fungus) to attack cereals. Other crops targeted by biological weapons designers include tobacco (presumably for covert economic warfare rather than for use in a shooting conflict), sugar beet, corn and potatoes. The USA produced no agents or delivery systems to attack livestock, although rinderpest (cattle plague) and Newcastle disease, which attacks poultry, were intensively studied during World War II. Other potentially useful diseases included foot-and-mouth for use against cattle and pigs, heartwater against cattle, water buffalo, sheep and goats, and aspergillosis (lung disease) against poultry. Altogether some 60 biological agents have been assessed as suitable for 'weaponization'.

On the battlefield

Unlike chemical weapons and nerve gases, biological weapons have been used for certain only once in anger against combat troops and civilians, by Japan in 1942. In May 1951, during the Korean war, the North Korean Government accused the USA of dispensing large quantities of insects, spiders and caterpillars behind the lines in North Korea to spread plague, cholera, typhus and other diseases among Communist troops and civilians; confessions from US prisoners of war were cited to back the claim. The Soviet Union, China and the Koreans refused to allow field inspection teams from the Red Cross or WHO or from a panel of neutral and non-aligned countries to verify the accusations, although they continued to be made until at least December 1952. No one has since seriously believed that the charges had any substance. Spiders and caterpillars do not figure largely in the literature on biological weaponry. But the threat of biological attack seemed very real to the United Nations coalition forces preparing to liberate Kuwait from Iraqi occupation in Operation Desert Storm in 1991.

By then it was widely believed in intelligence circles that Iraq had a biological warfare program, one that had concentrated on weaponizing botulinum toxin and anthrax. By 2 August 1990, when the Iraqi army invaded Kuwait, the Iraqis had spent close to one hundred million dollars on their offensive biological warfare program and had a significant stockpile of biological warfare agents. This information came from several intelligence sources, the most telling of which was a defecting Iraqi microbiologist. He told a British newspaper reporter that as early as 1983 Iraqi scientists had begun developing and testing biological warfare agents, including botulinum, salmonella, and anthrax. 'Friends told me they had found a way to make anthrax even more toxic,' he said. 'I know they experimented on sheep with *Clostridium botulinum* type C (the source of botulinum toxin).' The defector said he himself had solved technical problems in 'weaponization and deployment' of biological warfare agents – a claim that was confirmed after the war by the Iraqi Government.

The Iraqi dictator, Saddam Hussein, repeatedly told the world that any battle launched by UN forces would be the 'mother of all wars', and the coalition military commanders took this to mean that no holds would be barred. The possibility that biological and chemical weapons would be used was deemed very real. UN coalition troops were given a mixture of inoculations, but the reality of the threat became obvious to the outside world when television pictures showed Israeli citizens wearing gas masks in preparation for missile attacks.

After the war, it emerged that an Iraqi Scud missile with a warhead filled with nerve gas had exploded inside Israel on 18 January 1991, although only three people died as a result. The fact had been kept secret lest outrage in the Israeli media were to provoke an uncontrollable escalation in the war and cause political chaos among the coalition nations, which included several of Israel's traditional enemies.

A major challenge to the military commanders was how to destroy Iraqi stockpiles of biological munitions and agents before they could be deployed. Dropping a precision-guided bomb on suspected storage bunkers would have been easy enough to do. The real problem was how to destroy the weapons without releasing the lethal agents themselves and killing either Iraqi civilians or coalition troops ('collateral damage'). The solution came from computer modeling, which showed that the right bombing approach would cause the storage bunkers to collapse in such a way that the infectious agents would not escape. All the suspected bunkers were attacked, and there were no confirmed reports of 'collateral damage' from biological agents. There was one unconfirmed news report of illness and death among Iraqi guards after a biological warfare facility in Baghdad was bombed.

Of rather less comfort to UN coalition troops on the ground was their lack of ability to locate biological weapons on the battlefield, before they were used. As Lt Col Robert P. Kadlec, MD, USAF, has noted:

When US troops deployed to Saudi Arabia during Operation Desert Shield, they did not have an operational capability to detect any biological agents.

During Desert Storm, the United States fielded only a rudimentary developmental detector system. This system could detect only two of several possible Iraqi BW threats. In addition to the limited scope of this detector, it took between 13 and 24 hours after the attack to determine the presence and identify the BW agent. There was no capability to provide any

real-time or advanced warning of a biological attack. During the Gulf War, the first likely indication of an attack was ill and dying soldiers. The most advanced detection equipment was fielded by the British Army, but that too was taken straight from a development project.

Questions from the Gulf

At the time of writing it remained an open question whether Saddam Hussein did or did not unleash his biological weapons. He was warned on 23 December 1990 by US Secretary of Defense Dick Cheney: 'Were Saddam Hussein foolish enough to use weapons of mass destruction, the US response would be absolutely overwhelming and it would be devastating.' Nonetheless testimony before various US Senate inquiries into 'Gulf War Syndrome' (GWS) indicates that such weapons may have used by the Iraqis.

Most countries that sent troops to fight in Operation Desert Storm now have veterans suffering from undiagnosable, debilitating illnesses. Of the 690,000 US troops who went to the Gulf, more than 6500 had died by the end of 1996, and more than 80,000 were suffering from GWS. Their symptoms included respiratory and stomach illnesses, nerve damage, rashes, joint pain, short-term memory loss and stress. What is especially disturbing about GWS is that in some cases it appears to be contagious, with members of veterans' families reporting the onset of similar symptoms, and newborn children being affected too. One of the most daunting difficulties in pinpointing the nature of GWS lies in diagnosing which effects are caused by substances released in combat, and which may be the outcome of the elaborate cocktails of unproven vaccines and protective drugs given to troops during the campaign.

After the ceasefire, Iraqi representatives admitted to UN inspectors that they had indeed had a sizable store of anthrax and botulism agents, but they claimed to have destroyed it lest microbes were spread over Iraq by coalition bombing. Iraq's deception over its nuclear research program would suggest that the country still has a large amount of biological warfare agents at its disposal. The problem is to prove it. The equipment and techniques used in developing biological weapons can be just as easily used for legitimate peaceful purposes. During the war, Iraq made much propaganda out of the bombing of a 'baby milk factory'. CNN reporter Peter Arnett's visit to the devastated site raised public doubts about whether this was a legitimate target. In fact the Abu Gharyb infant formula plant was a dual-use operation, fully capable of producing biological weapons. As this case showed, biological warfare programs can easily be hidden within legitimate facilities. Even with on-site inspections the chances of discovery are small unless the visitors know precisely where to go – and are permitted entry in the first place.

In due course, it became apparent that Iraq had indeed been economical with the truth. After the defection in 1995 of Saddam Hussein's son-in-law, Hussein Kamal al-Majid, the leader of Iraq's programs for weapons of mass destruction, it was learned that besides anthrax and botulinum, Iraq possessed a carcinogen called aflatoxin; ricin, which leads to liver and kidney failure as well as genetic problems, and enteroviruses, which can cause blind-

ness. Before Operation Desert Storm, Iraq had armed 191 missiles, shells and bombs with biological agents to use against coalition forces. Iraq was also developing new ways to disperse biological agents by aircraft and aerosol spraying, as well as a new type of shrapnel that would release germs into open wounds.

This arsenal was enough to kill all of the world's population several times over. It included 720 liters (158gal) of anthrax bacteria in concentrated form, 24,000 liters (5300gal) of botulinum – enough, in theory, to kill as many as 15 billion people – and 17 tonnes of media (used to grow germs) that Iraq bought in 1990. Lethal microbes grown from this quantity of media could kill up to 60 million people. Iraq, it transpired after the war, had not only had more biological agents than the Desert Storm coalition's intelligence had believed, but more storage and production sites as well.

Still more disconcerting was the UN inspectors' discovery that Iraq's biological weapons program was able to flourish through the help of a huge web of global suppliers, which may still be operating despite years of sanctions and embargoes. For example, Iraq may have also acquired any one of a number of the Soviet 'Novichok' series of ultra-lethal toxins that, even in minute doses, can be debilitating. In addition to inducing eye malfunctions, vomiting, memory loss, involuntary movements, and internal organ dysfunction, these toxins can have mutagenic effects, and they have no known antidotes. It is to culprits like this that sufferers from Gulf War Syndrome look when considering the disturbingly high proportion of abnormal children borne to them since the

conflict. There is also some evidence that Iraq was working on genetically altered microbes – novel agents, created by altering DNA, plasmids and vectors, and specifically intended to avoid detection. Several shipments of biological materials that may have been used to carry out such a program were licensed for export from the USA to the Iraq Atomic Energy Commission. In such a program, common intestinal bacteria such as *Escherichia coli* could be altered to produce viral, bacterial, or other toxins, and would be difficult to treat. If Iraq was successful in developing such agents, diagnosis will continue to elude physicians who, in investigating GWS, test for traditional illnesses.

The terrorist threat

The ease with which biological weapons research and production can be concealed is a major attraction for terrorists. Nothing demonstrated this with greater clarity than the events of 20 March 1995 in Tokyo, Japan.

In a co-ordinated operation, a number of people stepped off five crowded subway trains during the morning rush-hour, leaving behind carefully punctured plastic bags containing diluted sarin, a lethal nerve agent. The gas killed 12 people and injured over 5000. Nearly a month later, on 19 April, more than 400 subway riders in Yokohama were sent to local hospitals suffering from eye irritation, respiration problems, and dizziness. In July, police found two gas emission devices in Tokyo subway stations. One contained a timer and bags of sodium cyanide and sulfuric acid. When mixed together, these form deadly cyanide gas.

Members of a bizarre quasi-Buddhist

cult called Aum Shinri Kyo ('Supreme Truth') were charged with the 20 March and 19 April attacks. Searches of property owned by Aum revealed that the cult had, quite legally, stockpiled tonnes of chemicals used to make sarin. Aum Shinri Kyo had hidden its gas manufacturing plant in a shrine to a sect goddess. Investigators also found a biological weapons research lab containing an incubator, an electron microscope, media for fermenting or growing cultures, and cultures of the deadly botulinum toxin. Aum had been apparently planning a still more devastating offensive.

Shoko Asahara, who founded Aum Shinri Kyo in 1987 and is a professed admirer of Hitler, prophesied that a series of tragic events would occur, including floods, food shortages, economic failures, and the spread of strange diseases, culminating in a nuclear war in 1997. The earthquake near Kobe in January 1995 was, he maintained, one of these portentous events. Asahara's prophesies follow a well trodden path through the confused and malignant undergrowth of far-right conspiracy theory: influential Jewish financiers are out to create Armageddon by using secret societies such as the Freemasons to set the highly profitable 'war industry' in motion; and in the last great battle Eastern Buddhist civilization will be defeated by Western Christendom. Asahara – like many a milleniarist prophet before him – tells his followers in Aum that in the face of this annihilation, they alone will be 'saved'.

Aum's terrorist acts appear to have been an attempt to increase the group's power by fulfilling their own prophecies of doom, and to stir up social unrest. The agent the cult used was from the chemical warfare armory but, according to Jonathan Vankin and John Whalen, who monitor trends in conspiracy beliefs:

Asahara prophesied that Aum would run Japan by the turn of the century, and it's now disturbingly clear that they were not skimping on preparations for the *coup d'etat*. Inside buildings designated as

Troops of the United Nations coalition force are vaccinated against chemical and biological agents prior to Operation Desert Storm in 1991. Veterans believe the drugs did them more harm than good.

religious facilities were full-scale chemical and biological warfare laboratories. [Furthermore] a TV report said that an Aum group had also visited Zaire last December [1994], and that Aum publications showed a keen interest in the Ebola virus.

Two thoughts flashed like a nuclear pulse across the collective mind of the world's military and security communities on 20 March 1995: the attack could have occurred in London, Paris, New York, Tel Aviv, Rio, Moscow... and here was living proof that a renegade civilian group could acquire the means to wage biological warfare. In fact, this was not the first time that terrorists had acquired biological weapons. In a paper titled 'The Biological Weapon: A Poor Nation's Weapon of Mass Destruction', Lt Col Terry N. Mayer USAF reports:

In 1984, the French authorities made a startling discovery that demonstrates how vulnerable the world is to biological terrorism. The Paris Police raided a residence suspected of being a safe house for the German Red Army Faction. As they conducted their search, they found documents that revealed a strong working knowledge of lethal biological agents. As the police continued the search to the bathroom, they came across a bathtub containing many flasks filled with what turned out to be *Clostridium botulinum*, the microorganism that produces botulism, one of the most lethal biological substances known to man.

Indeed, the US and British authorities had for decades been well aware of how vulnerable their cities are to biological attack.

During the 1950s and 1960s various simulated biological agents were released in or over US cities including Minneapolis, St Louis, and Washington, DC, partly to discover how their presence could be detected, and partly to learn how effective 'live' agents might be. In one of the biggest experiments, on 26 and 27 September 1950, the US Army sprayed *Serratia marcescens* bacteria from a boat off the coast of San Francisco. The organism produces a red/pink pigment when grown on certain media, which makes identification (and a measurement of its dispersal) a simple matter, and the Army insisted that the bacteria were harmless. At one point, 5000 particles per minute were released from the sea toward the shore.

On 29 September, patients began appearing at Stanford University Hospital in San Francisco with *Serratia marcescens* infections. One man, Edward J. Nevin, died. The cause was kept secret, being simply described as 'a mystery to doctors'. Of greater import to the military was that the experiment showed that nearly everyone within the target area was 'infected' with the test organism. Today, *Serratia marcescens* is associated with gastrointestinal disorders, septic arthritis, and bacterial endocarditis (inflammation of the heart valves and cavity), and is no longer used by the military as a simulant.

In Minneapolis, residents apparently accepted the US Army's amazingly implausible cover story for the tests – they were told a harmless smoke was being tested to find out if cities could be hidden from radar-guided missiles. In 1966 *Bacillus subtilis*, a substitute for anthrax-producing *Bacillus anthracis*, was released into the subway system of

New York City, to determine how vulnerable it was to attack. Results showed that the entire underground system could be infected even if the agent were released in only one station: the trains acted like a piston as they traveled the tunnels, pushing a column of infected air in front of them from one stop to another. In an earlier series of experiments in 1955, the CIA had released *Bordetella pertussis* bacteria, which cause whooping cough, along the Gulf Coast region of Florida. The number of cases of whooping cough tripled that year. Infections rose from 339 to 1080, but deaths from the disease leaped from one in 1954 to 12 in 1955.

The British carried out similar secret experiments from the 1940s until at least the early 1960s. In 22 tests near the coast of Antigua in 1948, animals were towed in a boat behind a Royal Navy ship and subjected to clouds of bacteria and viruses. At least one person on shore was infected as a result. In 1952, Porton Down scientists released smoke over the city of Salisbury, Wiltshire, to gauge the 'travel' of toxic clouds in built-up areas; the study concluded that 'the dosage received inside buildings is roughly similar to that outside, and...little protection is afforded by houses.' Some commentators have questioned whether the substance was indeed smoke, for in other experiments a harmless form of *Escherichia coli* bacteria, *Bacillus globigii* (which lives on hay), and *Serratia marcescens* – the same microbe sprayed at San Francisco – were released in public places. In one trial they were let loose over the River Thames in central London, and in another were sprayed over Lyme Bay, Dorset. In 1963, foreshadowing the CIA's research in

Victims of the Aum Shinri Kyo cult's attack with sarin nerve gas in the Tokyo subway, 20 March 1995. The Aum sect was also allegedly researching ways of creating Ebola virus and botulinum toxin weapons.

the New York subway, 'harmless' bacteria were tested in London's tube.

Disaster nearly struck during 'Operation Cauldron' in 1952, when bubonic plague and brucellosis agents were tested at sea 'about half a mile [0.8km]' off the coast of western Scotland. The plague bacillus had just been sprayed from one ship toward monkeys aboard another, when the 400-tonne trawler *Carella*, setting out for Icelandic waters, rounded a headland and steamed straight through the cloud of pathogens. A Royal Navy destroyer with vaccines and treatments aboard was sent racing from its base 650km (400 miles) away to shadow the *Carella* and eavesdrop on its radio transmissions for any hint of an emergency. Fortunately, the fishermen escaped infection.

Bringing it all back home

It is probably fair to say that until 1993, for most of the American public, terrorist attacks were something that happened elsewhere. On 26 February 1993, a car bomb exploded in the underground parking garage at the World Trade Center in New York City. Six people were killed, and 1000 injured. The perpetrators were members of a small Islamic extremist group and were soon apprehended. The psychological effect of that attack was negligible compared to the response triggered by the 2250kg (5000lb) bomb that ripped a huge hole in the Alfred Murrah federal office building in

Oklahoma City on the morning of 19 April 1995. The blast had been calculated to strike just as thousands of people were arriving for work. The outrage was especially horrifying, not least because Americans were soon arrested and indicted for the murder of the 169 people, including 15 children, who died in the attack.

Col Mayer considers what might have happened in New York and in Tokyo had those responsible been but a

fraction more sophisticated in their approach to biological weapons:

If the intent of the terrorists had been to demonstrate how vulnerable the population of the United States is, the addition of biological agents to the conventional attack would really have terrified leaders and other citizens in the United States.

Col Mayer drives the lesson home:

Desert Storm also highlighted the

153

name it. And then any crackpot with a few thousand dollars' worth of equipment and a college biology education under his belt could manufacture bugs that would make Ebola look like a walk round the park.'

Far-fetched, even outlandish claims have been made for the miracles that genetic engineering is supposedly able to accomplish. For example, an article in the *Wall Street Journal* in 1984 maintained that:

> Soviet scientists were attempting to recombine the venom-producing genes from cobra snakes with ordinary viruses [such as influenza] and bacteria: such an organism would infect the body and surreptitiously produce paralytic cobra neurotoxin.

This kind of claim smacks of disinformation and propaganda from the Soviets themselves; or perhaps it is an urban legend. The realistic way biologists will create more deadly and more frightening microbes for biological warfare is much further within the boundaries of the possible, and a good deal simpler. It is a practical matter of improving on what already exists – taking an already well researched agent and accelerating its incubation rate, increasing its virulence or toxicity (say by producing a guaranteed-lethal edition of the flu virus) or overcoming available vaccines.

The USA abandoned the development of offensive biological weapons in 1969, destroyed its stocks of agents,

shortfall in the ability to strike a biological warfare storage facility with confidence that massive numbers of innocent civilians would not be killed (collateral damage) as a result. The United States is impotent to prevent a biological warfare terrorist attack against the population unless there is specific intelligence to forewarn of the attack. Additionally, following a biological warfare attack, there are many agents that medicine can't treat today.

The worry that weapons of mass destruction were disturbingly simple to construct had been voiced to a reporter by the CDC's Dr Karl Johnson in 1988: 'It's only a matter of months – years, at most – before people nail down the genes for virulence and airborne transmission in influenza, Ebola, Lassa, you

and became a prime mover in organizing the Biological Weapons Convention of 1972. The reason offered in public was that biological weapons had little military effectiveness. The reality was that the Nixon administration feared that a second arms race was about to begin and run out of control (and over budget) as the emerging art of genetic engineering got into its stride. In the event, the Soviets persisted with their research regardless of the BWC but, as they admitted later, never caught up with Western achievements in genetic engineering. (They were similarly dogged in microelectronics, computer software design and aerospace metallurgy.) Even without the spur of an arms race, scientific curiosity and insight combined with commercial acumen and demand so that by 1992 five major new biological technologies had emerged:

- Gene and protein sequencing: discovering the order of constituent chemicals in genetic material.
- Genetic engineering: cutting and splicing DNA, transferring genes from one organism to another, and achieving the desired effect from these changes.
- Cell fusion: producing a new cell with new characteristics from two parent cells, for example to create new varieties of plant, or 'monoclonal' antibodies that attack only specific pathogens (especially useful to diagnose diseases).
- Protein engineering: altering the structure and therefore the properties of proteins (which include enzymes and hormones) by manipulating the DNA that controls their production.

- Fermentation and cell culture: techniques of growing large numbers of cells or viruses.

In a manner paralleled by the rise of the computer software industry, a host of small, specialist laboratories and consultancies now operates in this field. Among its achievements are bespoke vaccines, growth hormones to counter dwarfism in children, diagnostic kits for AIDS, crops resistant to herbicides, insects and viruses, screening systems for animal infections, and animal growth hormones.

Public enemies

It does not take much imagination to see how any of these techniques can be applied to develop biological weapons. The action of toxic enzymes can be intensified, and a monoclonal antibody made to counter it, for distribution to friendly troops only; fermentation and culturing systems can produce agents, vaccines and treatments in vast numbers; genes controlling all manner of useful attributes in bacteria, viruses or their vectors can be manipulated and their functions amplified. The equipment is pretty much the same, whatever the subject of study, so all that demands security, concealment or disguise are the ingredients – the anthrax spores, fever viruses or pathogenic parasites that one is developing. Even then, in just an hour a lab could be cleared of all suspicious material and look like any medical or pharmaceutical research lab. Mass-production

Demonstrators outside the UK's biological warfare research station at Porton Down in 1965. The work there was purely defensive, but the UK had a super-secret offensive program under way elsewhere.

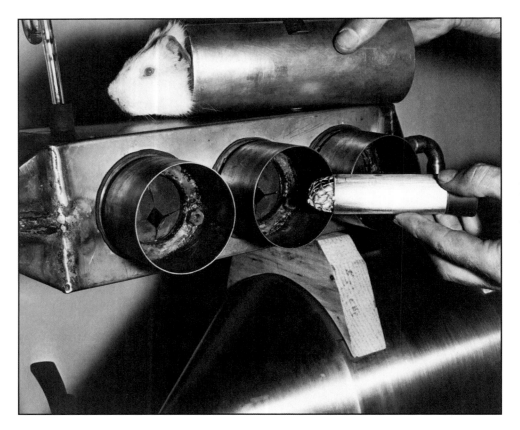

A rodent is exposed to disease agents at the US Navy's Medical Research Unit in 1946. US Army and CIA scientists released microbes into the human population in the USA, with sometimes disastrous effects.

of organisms can be done on a relatively small scale, and at surprising speed. A seed culture of anthrax bacteria could be grown to mass quantities in around 96 hours.

When governments are intent on this kind of research and development it is virtually impossible for inspectors to know whether lethal organisms are being studied in order to enhance and mass-produce them, or in order to take reasonable and prudent defensive measures against them. Even a research project that starts out with genuinely defensive intent can rapidly be inverted to employ its findings in offensive munitions. Observers have questioned the true intent of many research programs under way within the US military itself on precisely these grounds. What applies to the difficulties in detecting state-run biological warfare projects applies several times over to similar projects run by

clandestine groups determined to stay out of official reach.

If biotechnology labs and production lines are difficult to identify, for terrorist cadres the weapons themselves have a significant tactical advantage over explosives. Biological agents are not only the poor man's nukes; they are the poor man's stealth technology too. Until recently they were virtually undetectable while in transit. Anyone could, for example, carry a biological agent into the USA in a briefcase or checked luggage, since there is no mechanism currently used in standard customs, immigration, drug scan, or bomb search procedures that will detect it. The only way to find it would be a physical search by a well trained officer – and a very lucky one, for airlines and shipping companies are unlikely to subject the traveling public to routine examinations of this nature.

However, the technology now exists

to fill this gap in security. The Los Alamos National Laboratory and Bio-Rad Laboratories Inc announced in April 1996 that they were developing a 'flow cytometry unit' that could be operated by two people and would 'rapidly identify single bacterial cells, viruses and toxins'. The equipment for this task usually fills an entire lab, but the new 'robust, compact instrument' employs miniaturized electronics and improved optics to create 'a scaled-down unit with higher sensitivity and greater speed than previously possible', in the developers' words. Flow cytometry, which the Los Alamos laboratory pioneered, uses a laser to detect special biochemical tags that identify specific types of molecules, cells or other biological material.

The US Army has requested 150 of the new cytometric units, and began testing three prototypes in July 1996. If the detectors live up to the claims, it still remains to be seen whether commercial airlines and aviation authorities will regard the threat of biochemical terrorism as sufficiently potent to find funds to install such devices in airports.

Thieves and moles

The largest problem facing independent terrorists is acquiring the deadly microbes in the first place. For the dedicated, this is hardly insurmountable. Most exist in nature, and if field-work is beyond one's means then the next obvious routes are theft, or infiltrating a suitably qualified sympathizer into any one of the hundreds of independent companies working in biotechnology. The most efficient method is probably to acquire a patron state. If the IRA can negotiate the delivery of shiploads of conventional arms and ammunition from Libya, then another terrorist group can surely find an outlaw government willing to supply the basic ingredients for biological weapons.

Unsubstantiated rumor already says that Aum Shinri Kyo acquired some of their war materials from renegades within the Russian military establishment. The fate of Russian biotechnicians and scientists in the wake of the break-up of the Soviet empire, and the growing appeal of biological weapons to smaller nations, are other challenges yet to be met by both politicians and the intelligence community.

Apart from these risks, the proliferation of biological weaponry raises quite straightforward questions of public safety. We know that astonishingly irresponsible experiments by US agencies in the 1950s and 1960s killed innocent people. We know that an accident in the Soviet complex at Sverdlovsk in 1979 resulted in at least 1000 deaths. We also know that after Operation Desert Storm, UN inspectors charged with dismantling Iraq's capacity for mass destruction discovered that those working with some of the world's deadliest microbes and toxins were failing to take the most basic safety measures, even to protect themselves. No doubt similar lack of care is being exercised in other secret facilities elsewhere, and would likely be the norm in a makeshift terrorist lab. Even if none of these weapons is ever used, the risk of accident increases as long as they proliferate. It would take only one technician infected with an incurable disease to begin a pandemic. And that accident need not occur in a lab; it could happen on an aircraft, or in the street, if the weapons are held by amateurs.

The creators of biological weapons may have sown the wind; but it is we who will reap the whirlwind.

Microbes in storage at a center for tropical diseases on the outskirts of Paris, France. Such locations must now guard against intrusion and theft by terrorists, as well as against the inadvertent escape of diseases.

EPILOGUE

THE PESTILENCE WITHIN

We seem to face a future fraught with horrors – antibiotics that do us more harm than good, a global AIDS epidemic that indirectly threatens the economy of the West as well as millions of lives in Africa and Asia, the resurgence of long-forgotten diseases in the Americas and Europe, all occurring against a backcloth of increasing environmental and political breakdown. What can we do, individually and collectively, to protect ourselves against this spectrum of threats?

Faced with a catalogue of potential disasters as comprehensive as the one we have explored in this book, a person could be forgiven for an extreme reaction to extreme circumstances. Crawling into bed and refusing to come out, or spiriting oneself and one's loved ones away to an isolated island paradise are natural desires, but they evaporate as realistic options on a few seconds' mature consideration. We have to live in the real world, in the here and now. It is equally understandable that we should try to identify those responsible for this disquieting state of affairs. As we shall see, identifying the guilty may be emotionally

Drug capsules are checked on the assembly line prior to packaging. Drug companies are often accused of having an exclusive interest in profit, but actually fund a major part of pharmaceutical research.

gratifying, but rarely satisfies the criteria of natural justice – or even reason, on occasion. We need to assess the real causes of emergent and re-emergent diseases and, rather than look around for the nearest available scapegoat, ponder what we as individuals may be able to do to reduce the risks involved, both for ourselves and for the sake of future generations.

Pointing the finger

As we saw in Chapter One, when the people of 14th-century Europe found themselves reeling before the Black Death, their religion-drenched culture led them either to blame themselves and their sins for the catastrophe visited on them by an angry God, or to lash out at the Jews who, they thought, were estranged from God. From there it was not difficult to turn Jewish people into 'limbs of Satan' intent on destroying good Christians.

The classic case of passing the buck among diseases is surely syphilis. Known in England and Germany as the French pox, and among the French as Spanish pox, it was reckoned by the Dutch to be a product of German inns. The Japanese called it the Portuguese disease, the Persians said it was the Turkish pox, and the Poles named it after the Russians. As early as 1524, just three decades after the appearance of syphilis in Europe, one tract listed over 200 names for the disease, all of them identifying it with a specific place. This kind of blaming took place at the level of folklore. It can be understood as a reaction – a closing of ranks – against the incursions of strangers during the early years of the great Age of Exploration. At the same time it was believed that syphilis came from the New World. So perhaps the disease also represented the fear that went with the excitement of discover-

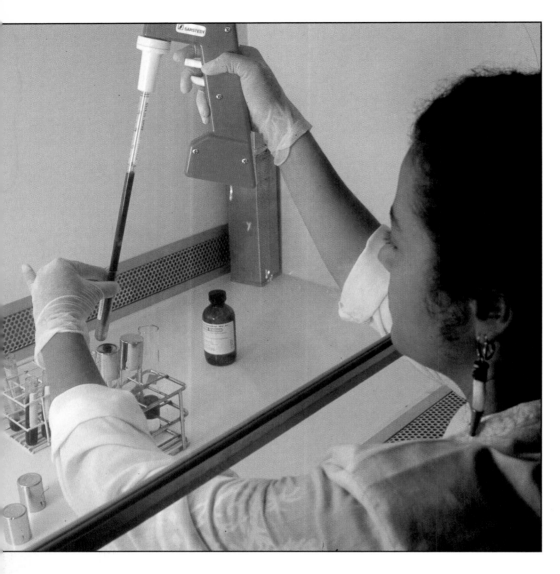

The medical profession became the focus of this discontent and fear. *Cordons sanitaires* and other measures designed to keep cholera out provoked riots in Russia and Hungary, where physicians, army officers, magistrates and nobles were killed. In Prussia, a rumor spread that physicians were being paid three silver thalers for every person under their care who died of cholera. Doctors were stoned in Paris, France. In India, cholera was said to be not a disease at all, but a campaign to poison rebellious subjects of British rule. In Britain itself it was believed doctors were using the disease as a cover to murder patients and sell their bodies for dissection in medical schools. As the epidemics retreated, so did the conspiracy theories, if not the state of mind that produced them.

In the USA and Europe in the 1980s and 1990s a similar reaction set in against AIDS.

AIDS and genocide

One of the first AIDS conspiracy theorists was British doctor John Seale, who published an article in the *Journal of the Royal Society of Medicine* in 1985 that claimed the US Army had concocted HIV out of genetic material from viruses causing bovine leukemia, visna in sheep, lentiviruses from horses and goats, and human T-cell leukemia/lymphoma virus. The recipe had been cooked up at Fort Detrick, Maryland, in 1977. Lying behind Seale's thesis were two articles that

ing the Americas, a sign of the break with the old order of the Middle Ages. Yet there was no suggestion that it was being introduced deliberately.

Nonetheless, conspiracy theories die hard. When cholera raged throughout Europe in the 19th century, it seemed to the rich and successful that it was a physical manifestation of some kind of moral pollution. The poor, overwhelmingly, were the ones whom cholera struck down. The districts in which they lived stank – not surprisingly, given the prevailing conditions. The rich did not, by and large, catch cholera, and that, to them, demonstrated their moral superiority over the poor. Such attitudes were easy to maintain, as the better-off had very little direct contact with those over whom they wielded power.

The wretches at the bottom of the heap inevitably suffered more from such crude defensive measures against the disease as quarantines and *cordons sanitaires* than did the wealthy. Resentment among the poor at rocketing food prices soon turned to a search for causes – for someone to blame for their woes. Rumors began to circulate that cholera was caused by a poison that had deliberately been spread by the rich to rid themselves of a troublesome underclass.

appeared in 1985 in *Literaturnaya Gazeta*, the journal of the Soviet Writers' Union, and told much the same story. According to Professor S. Drozdov of the Research Institute of Poliomyelitis and Encephalitis in Moscow, the CIA had let the virus loose by testing it on federal prisoners in the USA and in the field in Africa.

None of these claims bore much relation to scientific facts or history. The earliest identified AIDS cases date back to 1959, when the concept of genetic coding was unknown. Reverse transcriptase was discovered in 1970, and retroviruses were found in people in 1978. But it was not until 1983 that the technique of polymerase chain reaction was invented, revolutionizing research into, and manipulation of, DNA. Essentially the cloning technology that the 'invention' of HIV requires did not exist in 1977. In 1986, the Soviets admitted they had their own cases of AIDS, and after the fall of the Berlin Wall in 1989 the Soviet Academy of Sciences apologized for the episode, which it admitted had been inspired by the KGB. The US State Department had already concluded as much, and believed the accusations were designed to discredit the USA in developing countries.

But facts have never stood in the way of a good conspiracy theory. In 1996 Dr Leonard G. Horowitz, a dental health expert and former faculty member of Tufts and Harvard Universities, published (at his own expense) a 592-page 'exposé' of the links between AIDS, the National Institutes of Health, US biological warfare research, and an almost inevitable list of several favorite targets of conspiracy addicts, such as the Rockefeller family, the CIA, the Council on Foreign Relations, and the Nixon administrations of 1968–74. According to Dr Horowitz's book – titled *Emerging Viruses: AIDS & Ebola: Nature, Accident or Intentional?* – AIDS researcher Dr Robert Gallo did not discover HIV in 1984, but had already invented it by 1971. (One is amazed that Dr Gallo has refrained from legal action.) The virus was deployed in Africa as a means of population control, and the whole plot was originally put together by Dr Henry Kissinger as early as 1969. Dr Horowitz also claims that 'the world's most feared and deadly viruses' – Marburg and Ebola – were likewise man-made.

In a joint essay, Professors Dorothy Nelkin of New York University and Sander L. Gilman of Cornell University have pointed out that in this context 'blaming' is 'a means to make mysterious and devastating diseases comprehensible and therefore possibly controllable'. Even when plagues were believed to be the work of a wrathful God, the ultimate cause was deemed to be human wickedness, which did lie within human power to control. 'But diseases are never fully understood,' say Professors Nelkin and Gilman and, despite our medical science, 'we still make moral judgments for misfortune.... If responsibility can be fixed, perhaps something – discipline, prudence, isolation – can be done.' When confronted by intractable, invisible and potentially universal afflictions like AIDS,

These are situations where medical science has failed to serve as a source of definitive understanding and control, so people try to create their own order and to reduce their own sense of vulnerability. In

Panning for sapphires in the African jungle. Human invasions of the wild invite hidden diseases to emerge, and only massive investment by the West in vaccination and other public health programs will contain them.

effect, placing blame defines the normal, establishes the boundaries of healthy behavior and appropriate social relationships, and distinguishes the observer from the cause of fear.

However, this does not mean that the perceptions of what is 'normal', 'healthy' or 'appropriate' are necessarily humane or morally defensible. Blame is most often poured on those who are feared, powerful, or simply unconventional. Fear of intrusive and uncontrollable 'big government' and big business is clear enough in the outbursts of Dr Horowitz. In these conspiracy theories, 'disease' is partly, but not merely, a handy pretext for venting the underlying and pre-existing fear and rage. 'Disease' is also an irresistible metaphor for the moral and political corruption that is seen to foster all these alleged plots against 'the people'.

In the case of AIDS, the blaming ritual has amalgamated moral disgust and social and racial stereotyping. The Reagan administration's unwillingness to commit funds to HIV and AIDS research stemmed from a belief that AIDS would never affect heterosexuals, despite growing evidence to the contrary. Behind them stood a phalanx of bigots who proclaimed that gays had brought their plague upon themselves: television evangelist and Moral Majority leader Jerry Falwell declared: 'AIDS is God's punishment. The scripture is clear: We do reap it in our flesh when we violate the laws of God.' Alabama senator Jeremiah Denton reportedly said, 'Let the faggots die.'

By the late 1980s, the claim that AIDS was a product of biological warfare experiments in Africa had become established as folklore. On the political fringe, groups such as the United Front Against Racism and

Capitalist Oppression maintained that AIDS was 'bio-warfare directed mainly against gays' by the CIA. But by this time the threat to heterosexuals was widely recognized, and so among many African Americans the legend grew – along with the disproportionate spread of AIDS in the black community – that the biological 'war' was a genocidal attack on them. This belief was not limited to separatists or black nationalists, although it was endorsed by them. Stephen Thomas and Sandra Quinn, from the University of Maryland, polled black Americans in seven states between 1988 and 1990 on attitudes to the disease. Nearly 40 per cent of the black college students surveyed in Washington, DC, agreed with the statement: 'I believe there is some truth in reports that the AIDS virus was produced in a germ-warfare laboratory.' Still more disturbing was the finding that of 999 black churchgoers, one third agreed strongly with the statement: 'I believe AIDS is a form of genocide against the black race.'

Against this backcloth it becomes all the more urgent to promote some rational, fact-based approach to the causes of AIDS and emerging diseases, and the ways of combating them.

Scapegoats in industry

As we have seen, the factors that contribute to the appearance of any disease are highly complex – and not always obvious. Although, for example, it had long been recognized that plagues and epidemics could have dramatic historical consequences, it was not until the 1970s that the idea gained ground that disruptive human activities can release or promote disease. One instance of this is the pandemic of influenza of 1918–19: it began among French soldiers on the Western Front in World War I and would not have spanned the globe, killing more than 20 million people, but for the presence in northern France of US and African troops, who took the bug home with them.

In the history of medical disasters, no one is easier to accuse than the drug companies. Enormously wealthy, spanning continents, exerting tremendous if largely invisible political influence, they can readily be charged with putting profit before human welfare. The quinolone family of antibiotics is an example of drugs that have a useful purpose but carry a burden of unquantifiable risk.

Quinolones are synthetic, man-made drugs with no parallel in nature, and they are 'mutagenic' – they work by interfering with bacterial DNA. While no evidence has surfaced yet that quinolones can interrupt the functioning of human DNA, they are known to affect a wide range of bacteria. Dr Tore Midvedt of the Karolinska Institute in Stockholm, Sweden, wrote in *The Lancet* in 1989:

> More than ten million patients [have] received ciprofloxacin, just one quinolone. Some of these drugs are used in veterinary medicine and in fish farming.... It is astonishing that so little is known about their fate.... If not broken down, quinolones must end up somewhere, but I know of no studies of their ultimate fate. I am

surprised that drug registration authorities have allowed introduction of such potent drugs without asking this question. The potential hazardous biological effects of quinolones should not be underestimated.

Quinolones continued to concern Dr Midvedt, and he established that by 1992 in the fish farms of Norway alone somewhere between 10 and 20 tonnes of quinolones had been used to prevent and treat infections among the fish, which live crammed gill-to-gill in large underwater cages. Every investigation of the fate of the drugs showed that they stayed active in the water, 'just below the surface, for months and for years'. The effect on marine life is incalculable. We have no idea what we may have started breeding out there.

In 1990 the annual global production of antibiotics was 35,000 tonnes; it is projected to be 50,000 tonnes in the year 2000. In 1990 those drugs represented a turnover of eighteen billion dollars, and in 2000 they will be worth forty and a half billion dollars. Looking at these figures it is tempting to blame the greed of the drug companies for everything from superbugs to the potentially nightmarish contamination of the coastal waters of Norway, and anywhere else fish are farmed and kept nominally healthy with antibiotics. But it is also too easy to do that. We are the ones who want salmon – and every other kind of farmed animal flesh – on our plates, as cheaply as possible. The fish farms, and the intensively reared pigs and cattle that are fed growth-promoting antibiotics, are there because *we* create a market for them. We also create and sustain a market in medications that are slowly becoming self-defeating if not actually

dangerous, because we do not save antibiotics for serious illnesses and surgery. Instead, we want instant cures for minor infections that, left alone, are more likely than not to cure themselves. The answer is in our hands, in both cases.

If people want to change the direction that commercial enterprises take, they can buy shares in them, attend shareholders' meetings, write letters, organize boycotts, and make noise. There is nothing new, actionable or illegal about any of these activities, but they do take tremendous energy and commitment. And they should never be undertaken by anyone not absolutely familiar with the scientific arguments on both sides.

When considering the causes of, and the solutions to, the potential biological disasters that we face, we also have to remember that when both the antibiotic and the organochlorine revolutions took place, neither scientific knowledge nor popular sentiment had any grounds to suspect that disaster could ensue. The ironmasters, railroad builders and engineer-inventors of previous centuries likewise had no inkling that the grand achievements of the Industrial Revolution might begin to crumble under the combined weight of acid rain, global warming and ozone destruction. People – especially people long since gone to their graves – can hardly be put on trial for doing what they truly believed was best at the time. Especially as, by and large, we persist in taking advantage of the fruits of their enterprise and ingenuity. But we can all seek alternative sources of energy to coal or oil, and stop using chlorine bleach in our bathrooms, and plastics in our window frames, clothes, packaging or anywhere else we find organochlorines. We can also protest through all available channels when what seem to us to be unacceptable risks are taken in the name of progress. Knowing what we know now about the effects of DDT, antibiotics, or lead in gasoline, it really is up to scientists and doctors to prove that no harm will arise from their proposed innovations. And all of us should be demanding that they show us their proof.

New plagues: the real risks

While everyone can make a small contribution to reducing the multitude of threats to the environment, we still face the prospect that diseases long vanished from the world's most affluent nations will, for a myriad reasons, come creeping back. Have the previous chapters exaggerated the risks? And if they have not, what can be done to reduce them?

We might start by considering AIDS, which is unquestionably the nearest thing to a plague we are experiencing in the modern world. The disease appears to be out of control in Africa, is very likely so in parts of the former Soviet Union, and poses a real threat to the quality of life in South and Southeast Asia. In Europe, Australia, New Zealand and North America, education programs and public awareness have probably contained AIDS within high-risk groups. There is the hope that an effective treatment has been found, but it is likely to remain outside the economic reach of all but a minority in Third World countries. As we have noted, if a large part of the world's poorest countries succumbs to AIDS, the richest will not escape the pinch, because 'the West' depends so heavily

on the developing world for the raw materials and cheap labor that support its way of life.

From this perspective, we could anticipate several possibilities. It may be that a 'hollowing out' of Africa and parts of Asia will occur, in which the suffering and dying will receive little or no help, while the inevitable collapse of existing political orders will give way to a permanent state of conflict between rival warlords. In other words a situation like that prevailing in Somalia in Africa, or Cambodia in Asia, will spread across large areas of the respective continents.

If that happens, the West will have to make some hard choices. It might accept a fall or change in its own standards of living and security as supplies of raw materials dry up, and accept that large areas of the world will become inaccessible, beyond the reach of diplomatic, economic, and humanitarian assistance. To put it bluntly, these areas would be written off. Alternatively, economic imperatives would prevail. The supply of raw materials could be secured by reverting to ancient colonial practices – establishing heavily defended enclaves within which copper, chromium, cobalt, gold and other strategic metals and minerals could be extracted, perhaps by expatriate labor, in relative safety. Life in the new colonial powers would be noticeably more expensive, but it would continue much as before. The liberal conscience of the West may not be able to tolerate this option, however, but a third possibility at least remains open. That is to reconstruct the ruined and increasingly anarchic Soviet empire, which is rich in minerals – not as a political unit, but as an economic resource, for the benefit of

its people and the West alike. This would involve a scheme at least as ambitious as the Marshall Plan that helped to rebuild Europe after World War II.

More humanitarian alternatives in the countries most afflicted by AIDS are entirely dependent on political will. Both the determination and the funds will have to be found to tackle diseases of all kinds, not only AIDS, at source – at length, and in ways that do not invite them to return with still greater virulence. To achieve such a huge ambition, money, imagination and human resources would be required on a massive scale, and (perhaps most critically) not just in the West. Deeply rooted and jealously guarded habits of corruption would have to be broken: the West would no longer be able to turn a blind eye to the venality of a Milton Obote or a Mobutu Sese Seko in Africa and their equivalents in Asia, who have become billionaires by pocketing foreign aid funds while their subjects have suffered, starved and died. The chances of achieving that depth of reform are minute, but without it the possibility of breaking the grip of disease in the Third World is equally slim.

Such prospects are bleak. But no one knows how realistic these speculations and projections are. It is certainly possible that the projections of the future extent of HIV infections in the Third World will turn out to be extremely pessimistic. Comparing the chilling predictions made in the mid-1980s with the reality that came to pass in the Europe and the USA is quite instructive.

In 1986, Drs Anne Johnson and Michael Adler of London's Middlesex Hospital had produced figures suggest-

ing that by 1992 there would be 30,000 HIV infections in the UK and an accumulated death toll of 9000 AIDS sufferers. In fact, the total of new HIV infections reported between 1986 and 1992 amounted to 14,119, and even by the end of 1995 there had been 'only' 7346 deaths from AIDS in the UK since the disease emerged.

In the USA in June 1986, health officials were predicting that the number of annual deaths from AIDS would increase by 10 times within five years. In that year, just over 12,000 people died from the disease; in 1991, five years later, 36,242 people died.

The calculations had been wildly wrong – partly, perhaps, because in 1986 AIDS deaths in the USA were nearly double those of 1985, while cases of full-blown AIDS had been doubling every year from 1982 to 1985, and leapt from 11,843 in 1985 to 19,149 in 1986. The outlook was indeed grim, but the predictions did not take into account the effects of public education, the self-limiting nature of the disease within high-risk groups, or the sometimes heroic efforts of members of the gay community to persuade their fellows of the virtues of caution. Educational endeavors had

Greenpeace demonstrators act out the effect of nuclear pollution. Environmentalists have led the way in showing how direct, peaceful action can bring about changes in government and corporate policy.

been so successful that in a survey of American adults for *Time* magazine in December 1996, 90 per cent of the respondents agreed that 'Getting AIDS is something everyone needs to worry about'. Between 1992 and 1996, the growth rate of HIV and AIDS cases in North America and in Australia and New Zealand dropped by 13 and 14 per cent respectively, while in western Europe the rate had grown by only 2 per cent. In the USA, new HIV infections during 1996 still came overwhelmingly (83 per cent) from homosexuals and those who took drugs intravenously.

Globally, however, 75 per cent of new HIV cases in 1996 were acquired by heterosexual transmission. While the developed world largely had AIDS under control, the rest did not. The predictions of WHO have constantly been revised upward over the years in the light of unexpectedly high, and fast, rates of infection. In June 1990, for example, WHO estimated that by the end of the century there would be 15–20 million HIV infections world-

wide and 5–6 million cases of AIDS. By the end of 1996, WHO was suggesting that there could be 30–40 million HIV infections worldwide in the year 2000. Others were still more discouraged. Indian researchers believed that HIV cases might reach 15 million, and perhaps 50 million, on the subcontinent alone. One can see why both WHO and the Indian doctors are pessimistic: between 1992 and 1996, HIV infections rose by 261 per cent to 5.2 million in South and Southeast Asia, for example; over 30 per cent occurred among women; and 143,000 people in the region died of AIDS in 1996. Even so, no one can yet say whether these gloomy prognostications will turn out to be accurate, or if the

rate of infection will flatten out in due course, as it has elsewhere.

Rude good health

One of the most difficult aspects of predicting the spread of diseases is knowing whom they will kill and whom they will not – and why. AIDS may have run like wildfire through the gay community in the early 1980s because a significant proportion of those people's immune systems had

The Rev. Billy Graham, one of many homophobic Christians who believed AIDS was an inevitable punishment for sexual deviance. 'AIDS is a judgment of God,' thundered the renowned evangelist.

already been battered by a succession of sexually transmitted diseases – and further taxed by their treatments with antibiotics. AIDS may be rampaging through central Africa and southern Asia today for a similar reason: these are regions where people are constantly assaulted by hostile bacteria, viruses and parasites, where subsistence diets are the norm, where clean water is rare or non-existent – where the average human body is already living at the very margins of tolerance.

Individuals are extremely variable in their tolerance of diseases. An astounding instance occurred in London during a 19th-century cholera epidemic and was recorded by Dr John Snow. The nurse of a cholera patient became exhausted, and in seeking some refreshment she inadvertently drank some of the 'rice-water' that had been evacuated from the bowels of her patient. Apart from possibly fainting away at the thought of what she had just done, the nurse was unaffected.

No one would willingly take such risks. But it is also true that the vaunted superbugs that infest many hospitals – and whose existence no one doubts – do tend to remain there. Doctors, nurses and their families are not constantly being incapacitated by these particularly hostile bacteria, and nor are the friends and relations of patients. But these are healthy people living mainly in a bug-free environment – unlike the patients, whose immune systems are at their lowest ebb through sickness or the major physical and mental trauma of surgery.

Keeping oneself healthy, not surprisingly, would therefore appear to make up a crucial part of the battle against the microbes. Most of us can take some comfort from our own fitness. In

reviewing the prospects for survival should dengue, yellow fever, malaria, cholera and other diseases return to temperate climates, we can also take some refuge in statistics. Not everyone in an affected community actually catches these diseases. And apart from very rare infections like anthrax or pneumonic plague – the favorite tools of the weapons designers – their mortality rate is usually well below 100 per cent. Even yellow fever offers a six in 10 chance of survival, while thanks to effective treatment the 1991 cholera epidemic in Peru killed only one in 100 patients. Outbreaks of lethal, virulent diseases are nothing to rejoice over, but they certainly do not spell inescapable doom.

Outflanking the microbes

There are also grounds for hope that the battle against other diseases is not altogether lost.

Although more and more disease-causing microbes are becoming 'super-bugs', scientists haven't given up on the dream of discovering or even creating new antibiotics that will sidestep the bugs' resistance to drugs. For instance, in November 1996, researchers at Merck Research Labs and Duke University Medical Center in North Carolina reported in *Science* magazine on a new class of experimental antibiotics that they are developing. Scientists have discovered that the drug-resistant cells secrete a lipid (a liquid containing oils and fats) that forms a protective coating on the bacteria's outer membrane.

Dr Christian Raetz, chairman of biochemistry at Duke Medical School said: 'The coating is necessary for the bacteria, and without it they start dying.' In preliminary tests, two of the

antibiotic compounds being studied – labeled L-573,655 and L-161,240 – penetrated this oily coating and blocked an enzyme, deacetylase, that is crucial for maintaining the structure of the outer membrane of resistant bacteria such as *Escherichia coli*. Both compounds were successfully used to cure mice infected with normally lethal doses of the same microbe. Many more test-tube and animal experiments will have to be completed before clinical trials can begin, to establish whether the compounds are safe and effective in humans, but at least some progress has been made.

New lines of research in vaccines are also beginning to show promising results. Conjugate or DNA vaccines give special cause for hope. In an article published in summer 1996 in *Emerging Infectious Diseases*, Dr Robert G. Whalen, director of research at the French National Center for Scientific Research in Paris, explained how the new vaccines are produced: 'These methods involve the deliberate introduction of a DNA plasmid carrying a protein coding gene.' The plasmid inserts itself into healthy cells in the body and makes them generate antigens in sufficient quantity to create an effective immune response. 'This procedure,' says Dr Whalen, 'known as a DNA vaccine, is perhaps better described as DNA-mediated or DNA-based immunization.'

Microbiologist Matthew Waldor of the New England Medical Center and his colleague, John Mekalanos, believe that cholera 01 bacteria became lethal when a virus invaded its genes and turned the *Vibrio* into a poison factory. Their work was instrumental in the development of a cholera vaccine with a 'partially deleted toxin gene'. Strains of cholera were specially created by deleting the gene carrying the cholera toxin and other possible toxins from the bacterial chromosome. The resulting mutant strain was much weaker than the original, but still able to make the body produce antibodies that were effective against cholera 01 bacteria. The vaccine, tested in 6500 people, appears to be both safe and highly protective, and trials are continuing.

Even more encouraging is a two-year trial of a vaccine against the particularly virulent cholera 0139, begun by Waldor and Mekalanos in 1996. They have already published research results showing how they inserted a transposon into 0139 bacteria to create the basis of the vaccine. Derivatives of the modified *Vibrio* strain are 'predicted to be safe, antibiotic-sensitive, vaccines' for cholera 0139. It is reported that 100 US Army volunteers had tried the vaccine 'with no resulting illness'.

'DNA vaccines have distinct advantages,' says Dr Whalen. They can be manufactured far more easily than vaccines consisting of inert viruses or bacteria, cell fragments, or genetically engineered, mass-produced proteins. 'Since almost all plasmids can be manufactured in essentially the same way, substantial economies of scale can be achieved.'

Dr Whalen says that if DNA methods were used for human vaccination, 'the cost of production and delivery of vaccines would be reduced, thus allowing vaccines to reach areas of the world somewhat deprived of preventive public health measures.... Today's research method can be tomorrow's vaccine. DNA vaccines will be within the means of many more populations and countries.' In other words, there really is hope that the price of these

new vaccines can be held down. Furthermore, Dr Whalen pointed that only two years passed between the first published description of a DNA vaccine and the beginning of the first clinical trial. 'This short time span bodes well for the ability of public health agencies all over the world to bring scientific research to bear on diseases relevant to their own situation and to disease prevention.'

Other examples of new DNA vaccines being developed include two therapeutic ones for treating chronic hepatitis B, which have been shown to be safe for use in people. A 1996 study by SmithKline Beecham Biologicals of Risensart, Belgium, showed both vaccines caused only 'mild local adverse effects' in most patients. One month after vaccination, all subjects in the study had developed antibodies to hepatitis B. The vaccines were entering a second phase of trials in 1997.

At the time of writing, researchers were also plowing ahead in developing new vaccines against drug-resistant *Pneumococcus* and strep B bacteria. The US National Institute of Allergy and Infectious Diseases (NIAID) reported in November 1996 that its scientists had made a 'major step toward developing a vaccine to prevent infections with Group B *streptococci* bacteria, an important cause of infant disease and death.... An experimental vaccine against one type of Group B strep stimulated strong immune responses in human volunteers.' In later laboratory experiments, antibodies from the volunteers neutralized the same type of Group B strep bacteria and prevented infection in newborn mice that were exposed to it. 'This work provides the most promising evidence to date that we're getting

closer to finding an effective vaccine,' reported Dr Pamela McInnes of NIAID.

In the first report of its kind, *State of the World's Vaccines*, WHO said in 1996: 'Over the next 15 years, revolutionary new vaccines generated by scientific advances could save the lives of some 8 million children who now die each year from infectious diseases.'

The WHO report says four ingredients are needed to make global immunization against diseases a success: more government and private donor funding, donations targeted to the neediest countries, drug makers holding drug prices down, according to a country's ability to pay; and increased education around the world on the value of vaccination. WHO says the results of failure may be devastating, but Dr Hiroshi Nakajima, WHO's director-general, prefers to be mildly optimistic. 'If our organizations and our partners can give the world a better understanding of the value of vaccines...the success of the past 20 years in saving millions of children's lives will be dwarfed by the successes of the next two decades.'

Slamming the door

None of the foregoing is any cause for complacency. Keeping microbes out of a country in the first place is one of the cheapest and simplest forms of protection. No such system can be foolproof, but it need not be onerous or unduly bureaucratic. If we can set up reasonably trouble-free ways to guard airliners against bombs we can surely do something similar with diseases. It used to be the case that no one could enter the USA legally without a certificate of smallpox vaccination. How expensive or inconvenient would it be to insist that travelers from certain parts of the world be certified as free from a list of especially dangerous diseases? But then which parts of the world would we be talking about? And which diseases? Would they include HIV infections, or re-emergent diseases like yellow fever and malaria, or only new 'nightmare' risks such as Ebola fever?

One of the more troubling opportunities for unknown and perhaps uncontrollable infections lies in a moral and legislative limbo between the duties of government and the responsibility of individual citizens.

That is the activity of medical and scientific élites who will tend to do whatever is not specifically prohibited by law in the interests of what they perceive as progress. Their motives are not questionable, but the way they discharge their responsibilities can leave much to be desired, and merely invite legislation and its attendant, often uninformed and self-serving, controversy.

For example, since the 1960s there have been attempts to transplant primate organs into ailing human beings. As person-to-person trans-

plants became routinely successful, demand for human organs exceeded supply, and there was increasing pressure to find a reliable source of animal organs. In the early 1990s, surgeons at the University of Pittsburgh performed experimental transplants on two men, replacing

Security staff check luggage by hand at Japan's Kansai International airport. The technology now exists to make a laser-operated search for biological and chemical weapons a swift, simple part of airport routine.

New technology combines a drug with an aerosol propellant. Dispensing drugs by aerosol in poor countries could drastically reduce the risks of epidemics breaking out through the use of dirty hypodermics.

pathogens that are infectious to humans. You assume it's something that can kill you. But then in the next breath we turn around and ship a baboon up to Pittsburgh, they open it up, probably every human in the operating room is exposed to whatever is in there, and they stick its liver into a human. Does that seem rational?'

The answer must be no, given that transplants are carried out with the patient doused in drugs that suppress the immune system, to reduce the odds of the recipient rejecting the new organ. There is also the risk that monkey viruses could pick up genetic material from those in humans to create all sorts of unforeseen superbugs.

The ultimate lesson to be learned from the prospect of new and revived plagues stalking the world is that we have to take responsibility for our relationship with nature, and for our own lives. On the one hand that means doing all we can to halt activities such as the destruction of the world's rain forests or the whittling away of the ozone layer. On the other hand it may mean that New Yorkers must learn to live without air conditioning and to sleep under mosquito nets, and that air travel reverts to being a privilege of a global élite. Many may suffer, but humanity will very likely survive. Meanwhile, we should be aware, and wary. There is nothing to be gained, and almost everything to be lost, if human life is reduced to nothing more than survival.

their livers – which had collapsed from hepatitis B – with ones from baboons. Doctors considered the operations a breakthrough for, although the patients died, they did not do so as a result of problems associated with the transplants. However, officials at the Southwest Foundation, which supplied the baboons, were considerably less than impressed. They knew that one of

the animals used was infected with a number of viruses closely related to those that cause disease in humans: these included the baboon form of herpes B, the simian AIDS virus, and simian cytomegalovirus.

Journalist Laurie Garrett quotes the reaction of one Southwest Foundation scientist, Jon Allan: 'We assume as a given that these primates carry

GLOSSARY

Words in **bold** refer to another entry in the Glossary

abscess – collection of pus anywhere in the body, isolated by damaged and inflamed tissue, and usually caused by **bacteria**

AIDS – Acquired Immune Deficiency **Syndrome**; caused by **HIV**, which destroys **cells** vital to the **immune system** and allows normally harmless **infections** to reach lethal proportions

algae – primitive, mainly aquatic plants that range in size from single **cells** to huge seaweeds; microscopic algae may give off **toxins**

amino acid – constituent of **proteins** in living things; some can be made by the body, but others can be obtained only from proteins in the diet

amyl nitrites – muscle relaxants, taken by inhaling; also known as 'poppers' and 'snappers'. Widely used by gays to facilitate anal intercourse

anemia – disorder caused by reduced amount of oxygen-bearing pigment in the blood

anesthetic – agent that reduces sensation in whole or part of the body

anthrax – **infectious disease** of animals that can be transmitted to humans, where it attacks the lungs, bringing on pneumonia, or the skin, where it causes severe ulceration

antibiotic – drug that destroys or fatally disables **bacteria**

antibody – special blood **protein** produced in response to the presence of a specific foreign body (such as a **virus**), and which destroys the invader

antigen – a substance or foreign body (usually a **protein**) treated as a threat by the **immune system**, which produces an **antibody** to destroy it

antiseptic – chemical that kills harmful **microbes** but does not damage skin or body tissue

antiserum – **serum** that contains **antibodies** against a specific **microbe**

arbovirus – short for *arthropod-borne* **virus**, i.e. a virus carried by an insect, such as those causing **yellow fever** or encephalitis

arthritis – inflammation of the joints; may be caused by over 200 **diseases**

autopsy – examination of a body to determine the cause of death

bacillus – member of a family of **spore**-bearing, rod-shaped **bacteria**

bacteria – micro-organisms whose **cell nucleus** is not self-contained; most are harmless, but some produce **toxins** that cause **disease**

barefoot doctor – worker with limited training in health care, giving basic treatment and **diagnosis** for referral to qualified physicians

bartonellosis – infectious **disease** transmitted by sandflies; in one form causes **fever**, **anemia**, enlargement of the liver, spleen, and **lymph** nodes, and can be fatal

biopsy – removal of small sample of living tissue for analysis

biotechnology – production of living things using biological processes, e.g. producing **antibiotics** from fungi, or **cloning** hormones

botulism – potentially fatal poisoning, caused by the **toxin** from *Clostridium botulinum* **bacteria**, which affects parts of the central nervous system

bubo – swollen, inflamed **lymph** node in the groin or armpit; one of the **symptoms** of bubonic **plague**

cancer – malignant, uncontrolled growth of **cells** that invade and destroy surrounding tissues; the focus of the growth is called a tumor

capillary vein – very narrow blood vessel with a wall only one **cell** thick, to allow exchange of oxygen, salts, etc., between body tissues and the bloodstream

carcinogen – substance that causes **cancer** when tissues are exposed to it

catheter – tube used to drain fluid from, or inject it into, the body, or to sample blood from the heart and take blood pressure within the heart's chambers

CD4 – the **protein** molecule on a **T-helper cell** that detects **antigens** in the body, and onto which **HIV** binds before invading the cell

CDC – Centers for Disease Control, the US national preventative health agency in Atlanta, Georgia

cell – the basic unit of living things. It contains jelly-like **cytoplasm**, in which is suspended the **nucleus**; a membrane holds the cell together

CFC – chlorofluorocarbons, a group of **organochlorine** substances; implicated in the destruction of the **ozone** layer in the upper atmosphere

chromosome – a threadlike structure, composed of **proteins** and **DNA**, with **genes** arranged along its length, found in the **nucleus** of a **cell**; when the cell divides, each chromosome reproduces itself exactly

cirrhosis – formation of fibrous tissue in the liver in response to the death of some of its **cells**; condition impairs liver function and is incurable

cloning – reproduction of a **cell** or other biochemical unit (such as an enzyme) that is identical to the original. *See also* monoclonal antibody

colitis – inflammation of the colon (large intestine)

commensal organism – one living closely with another without benefit or harm to either, e.g. **bacteria** in the gut

congenital – any condition present from birth; may be inherited, or may be the result of environmental factors

contagious disease – **disease** transmitted by touching an infected person

cordon sanitaire – guarded, physical isolation of infected persons from the uninfected

cryptosporidiosis – diarrheal **infection** caused by **protozoa**

cyst – sac or enclosed cavity

cystitis – inflammation of the bladder, most often caused by *Escherichia coli* **bacteria**

cytomegalovirus – (abbreviation CMV) a **herpesvirus**, usually creating mild cold-like **symptoms** and more severe ones in **HIV-positive** patients; can produce **congenital** defects in children born to women infected during pregnancy

cytoplasm – jelly-like substance contained within a **cell** and surrounding the **nucleus**

DDT – dichlorodiphenyltrichloroethane, an **organochlorine** used as a pesticide

DHF/DSS – dengue hemorrhagic fever/dengue shock **syndrome**; severe forms of dengue fever caused by a **virus** carried by *Aëdes aegypti*, *Aëdes albopictus*, and *Aëdes polynesiensis* mosquitoes

diagnosis – determination of the nature of a disorder through analysis of **symptoms**, medical history, laboratory tests, X-rays, etc.

diphtheria – severe, highly **contagious** disease caused by **bacteria**, which release a **toxin** into the bloodstream and cause a membrane to form across the throat. Death from heart failure may occur within four days of first **symptoms**

disease – disorder (other than one caused by injury) with a specific cause and recognizable **symptoms**; the objective fact of having an **illness**

DNA – deoxyribonucleic acid, which forms **chromosomes**; consisting of two intertwined strands of chemicals, called nucleotides, DNA contains the chemical information necessary for living things to reproduce

dysentery – diarrheal **disease** of the intestines; may be caused by an amoeba (**protozoon**) – *see Entamoeba histolytica* – or by **bacteria**

electrolytic salts – salts containing sodium, potassium, etc. that make up the chemical composition of the body. When lost through severe vomiting or diarrhea, electrolytic salts may fall to dangerously low levels, but can rapidly be replaced if taken dissolved with glucose in water

electron micrograph – image produced on a photographic plate by an **electron microscope**

electron microscope – device that uses a beam of electrons rather than light to create an image of a specimen, which is magnified many thousands of times, held in a vacuum

emetic – agent that causes vomiting

endemic disease – persistent disorder occurring among people in a particular area

Entamoeba histolytica – single-celled animal (amoeba) that invades the intestinal wall and causes amoebic **dysentery**

enterovirus – **virus** that enters the stomach and intestines and invades the central nervous system

enzyme – essential **protein** that speeds up a biological reaction without itself being altered, usually by binding on to a substance and converting it into another

enzyme-linked immuno-sorbent assay (ELISA) – technique for diagnosing **disease**. Blood **plasma** from the patient is added to a specific **antigen**; if the **antibodies** are in the plasma (indicating the presence of the **infection**) they will bind to the antigen. **Enzymes** are then added that will in turn bind to the resulting complex. The presence of the enzymes, and therefore the disease, will show up when they are washed with a dye

epidemic – unexpected or unusual outbreak of a **disease**, usually on a large scale, in a particular time and place

epidemiologist – doctor who studies **epidemics** to establish origins, causes, and modes of transmission, in order to find ways of prevention and control

Epstein-Barr virus – **herpesvirus** that causes glandular **fever**, and may be responsible for some forms of **hepatitis** and **cancer**

Factor VIII – substance normally present in blood but absent in hemophiliacs; contributes to coagulation of the blood

fever – rise in body temperature above normal (37°C/98.6°F in humans)

fluke – parasitic flatworm of the Trematoda group; flukes may migrate to the liver, gut, and lungs, and can cause a variety of **diseases**

fulminant – describes a condition or **symptom** that arises suddenly, is very severe, and persists for only a short time

fumigation – using gas or vapor to kill animals or **microbes** infesting clothes or a building

gastric – relating to or affecting the stomach

gastro-intestinal infection – **infection** of the stomach and intestines, e.g. gastro-enteritis; inflammation of those organs

gene – segment of **DNA**, carried on a **chromosome**, that performs or manages a specific function within the body, e.g. regulator genes control **protein** production

genetic code – information carried by **DNA** and **RNA** to dictate the sequence of **amino acids** in **proteins**. A fault or change in the sequence creates a **mutation**

genetic engineering – insertion of **genes** from one organism into the **DNA** of another in order to transfer specific characteristics

genome – whole of an organism's genetic material, consisting of its **genes**

germ – micro-organism, especially one that causes **diseases**

giardia lamblia – parasitic **protozoon** that infests the small intestine; causes diarrhea, nausea, and related **symptoms**

GRID – Gay-Related Immunodeficiency Disease; early name for **AIDS**, abandoned when it became clear that AIDS was not exclusive to gays

hemorrhage – bleeding; commonly used as shorthand term to describe internal bleeding

hepatitis – inflammation of the liver; may be caused by **bacteria, viruses,** or failures of the **immune system**; chronic hepatitis can lead to **cirrhosis**

herpesvirus – group of **viruses** that cause herpes and chickenpox; includes **cytomegalovirus** and **Epstein-Barr virus**

HIV – Human Immunodeficiency Virus; **retrovirus** responsible for **AIDS**

HIV-positive – having **HIV** in the body, as evidenced by tests for the presence of HIV **antibodies** showing a 'positive' result

hormone – substance produced by endocrine glands and carried by the blood to various parts of the body to regulate or modify their structure or function

illness – **disease**; and, as defined by medical anthropologists, the subjective experience of suffering from a disease

immune system – complex system of **cells** produced by the **thymus**, bone marrow, **lymph nodes**, spleen, tonsils, and other organs to detect **antigens** when they enter the body, alert and organize **antibodies**, and destroy the invaders

immunity – the ability of the body to resist **infection** and **disease**; depends on effective functioning of white blood cells and **antibodies**

immunofluorescence – technique to detect **antibodies** or **antigens** in body tissue; antibodies are 'labeled' with a fluorescent dye so that, when they bind to the antigen, they are visible through an ultraviolet microscope

immunosuppression – reduction of the body's capacity to resist **infection**

impetigo – highly **contagious bacterial infection** of the skin; **symptoms** may be a light brown crust, or blisters

infection – presence in the body of potentially harmful **microbes**; infection does not always lead to **disease**

infectious disease – a **disease** that can be transmitted from one person to another by any available route – touch, breathing, insects, exchange of body fluids, etc.

inflammation – physical reaction to injury or **infection**; pain, heat, redness, and swelling occur as blood vessels dilate to facilitate the arrival and operation of white blood **cells** and other agents of the **immune** system

injectionist – quack doctor selling treatments given by hypodermic needle with minimal **diagnosis** and often using inappropriate drugs

inoculation – deliberate **infection** with a small amount of **antigen**, to create a mild disorder and stimulate the production of enough **antibodies** to protect against further infection

intensive-care unit – hospital unit with specialist staff and equipment to provide constant monitoring of and immediate response to severely ill or injured patients

Kaposi's sarcoma – malignant tumor in blood vessels in the skin, common in **AIDS** patients

kidney dialysis – mechanical system for filtering waste products and poisons normally removed from the bloodstream by the kidneys

lesion – area of tissue damaged by **disease** or wounding

lymph nodes – series of filters in the body that remove foreign particles from lymph, which bathes the body tissues, and is derived from blood; also produce lymphocytes (white blood cells), which are part of the **immune system**

macrophage – large scavenger cells, crucial to the **immune system**; some remain in fixed positions, others roam through the body to gather when needed at infected sites, to consume **bacteria** and other foreign bodies in the blood or tissues

mastoid – thin protruding bone or 'process', full of air spaces, connected to the middle ear, from which **bacteria** may travel to cause **infection**

meningitis – inflammation of the meninges, the three layers of membrane that enclose the skull and spinal cord; may be caused by **bacteria** or **viruses**, and can be fatal

miasma – noxious emanation, once believed to rise from the soil and cause **disease**

microbe – micro-organism; a living thing too small to be seen with the naked eye

microbiologist – one who studies the science of **microbes** or micro-organisms

monoclonal antibody – **antibody** produced by **cloning** from lymphocytes (white blood cells) and consisting of a single type of **protein**

mucous membrane – moist membrane that lines tubes and cavities in the body, such as the mouth, stomach, intestines, or sinuses

mutation – change in form or behavior of an organism that is caused by a difference between its **DNA** and that of the previous generation

non-specific urethritis – inflammation of the urethra (the tract taking urine from the bladder) through unspecified, sexually transmitted bacterial infections

nucleus – part of a **cell** that contains **DNA** and **RNA**, separated from the **cytoplasm** by a double membrane

oedema – excessive accumulation of fluid in body tissues; also known as dropsy

organochlorine – chemical compound of chlorine and carbon that reacts with few other chemicals but accumulates in fatty tissues of animals and causes genetic defects

ozone – poisonous gas; each molecule is composed of three atoms of oxygen; the ozone layer in the upper atmosphere filters out ultraviolet light

pandemic – **epidemic** that spreads across a region or continent or the world

parasite – organism that feeds on or shelters in another and damages its host's tissues or functions

pathogen – parasitic **microbe** that causes **disease**

pathology – study of **diseases** and their processes

PCBs – polychlorinated biphenyls, a group of **organochlorine** substances

petri dish – flat, shallow, circular lidded dish of glass or plastic used in the laboratory to hold a medium on which **bacteria** can be grown

plague – outbreak of **disease** so devastating that it causes social disruption; the term is also commonly used as an abbreviation for bubonic plague

plankton – tiny plants and animals living near the surface of fresh and salt water

plasma – pale yellow fluid in which blood cells are suspended, consisting of a solution of salts, **proteins** and trace substances

plasmid – free particle of genetic material that can incorporate itself into the **DNA** in a **cell nucleus** and alter the cell's properties or behavior

polymerase chain reaction – technique of treating the **DNA** of a single cell with an **enzyme** that causes the DNA to replicate many times over. The **genes** of the amplified DNA can then be identified and analyzed with relative ease

prophylactic – preventative treatment, measure or implement

protease – **enzyme** that breaks down **protein**

protein – biochemical compound of hydrogen, carbon, oxygen, and nitrogen, and sometimes sulfur and phosphorus; protein molecules consist of **amino acids**. Proteins form the basic material of all body tissues, and in the form of **enzymes** and **hormones** act as managers of body functions

protozoon – (plural protozoa) microscopic single-celled animal

PVC – polyvinyl chloride, an **organochlorine** substance, implicated as a disrupter of **hormone** functions

quarantine – period during which people or animals are kept in isolation, to give time for **symptoms** of a **disease** to appear, or to ensure they are clear of **infection**

retrovirus – **virus** that contains **RNA** and uses a special 'reverse transcriptase' **enzyme** to convert the **RNA** to **DNA**, which then attaches itself to the DNA of its host **cell** and triggers replication of the virus

rickettsia – spherical or rod-shaped **parasite** that resembles **bacteria** but (like a **virus**) cannot reproduce outside its host; infected ticks and lice transmit them to people; they cause **diseases** such as Q fever and **typhus**

RNA – ribonucleic acid; found in the **cytoplasm** and **nucleus** of **cells**, and manages the production of **proteins**; also the genetic material of some **viruses**

scarlet fever – highly contagious **disease** caused by *Streptococcus* **bacteria**; **symptoms** include scarlet rash, **fever**, nausea, and sore throat; can lead to ear and kidney **infections**, and may be fatal

seropositivity – condition in which positive signs of the presence of **disease** have been detected by tests on blood **serum**

serum – fluid that separates from clotted blood, or from blood **plasma** that is left to stand; similar to plasma, but lacks coagulants

Shigella flexneri – **bacteria** that cause shigellosis, a form of **dysentery**

SIDA – French acronym for **AIDS**

simian virus – **virus** affecting monkeys and other primates

smallpox – potentially fatal viral **disease**; **symptoms** are high **fever** and spots that become pustules and burst, leaving scars

spirochete – spiral-shaped bacterium

spore – reproductive agent of some plants and **microbes**

STD – sexually transmitted **disease**(s), e.g. syphilis, gonorrhea, **AIDS**

steroid drugs – drugs with **protein**-building effects similar to male **hormones**

sulfa drugs – family of drugs used to combat **bacterial infections**

superbugs – **bacteria** that have undergone **mutations** and other changes that give them extremely high resistance to drugs intended to destroy them

superinfection – **infection** occurring during treatment for another infection; may occur when normally harmless **microbes** become **pathogenic** as drugs remove other microbes that control them, or when drug-resistant microbes intensify the original infection

symptom – indication of a **disease** noticed by the patient (indications observed by the physician alone are called 'signs')

syndrome – literally 'running together'; a particular combination of **symptoms** and signs that, occurring together, indicate a specific **disease**

T-helper cell – **immune-system cell**, produced by the **thymus**, that alerts and directs **antibodies** when an **antigen** is detected; the cell invaded by **HIV**

thymus – organ at the root of the neck that produces white blood cells; part of the body's **immune system**

toxic – poisonous or potentially lethal

toxin – poison produced by a living organism

typhoid fever – **infection** of the digestive system caused by *Salmonella typhi* **bacteria**; can cause erosion of intestinal walls, leading to **hemorrhage** and death

typhus – group of potentially fatal **infections** caused by **rickettsiae** that are transmitted through lice, fleas, ticks, and mites; **symptoms** include a rash, **fever**, and delirium

ulcer – break in skin or **mucous membrane** that does not heal

vaccine – specially prepared, weakened (and usually dead) forms of **bacteria** or **viruses**, or of **toxins**, that produce few or no **symptoms** but stimulate the production of **antibodies**, so creating an **immunity** to **diseases**

VD – venereal **disease**; *see* STD

vector – animal (often an insect) that transmits **microbes** to people or other animals, e.g. the mosquitoes that, when they feed on blood, inject **parasites** causing malaria

virulence – informal measure of the severity of **symptoms** of **infection** produced by a **microbe**

virus – minute particle consisting of a core of genetic material enclosed in a shell of **proteins**; can replicate only within a living **cell**; many are harmless, some cause only mild **infections**, while others cause extremely virulent, often fatal **diseases** in plants, animals, and people

WHO – World Health Organization, based in Geneva, Switzerland; monitors **disease** outbreaks internationally and co-ordinates efforts at prevention and treatment

FURTHER READING

Berridge, Virginia: *AIDS in the UK*, Oxford University Press, 1996

Cannon, Geoffrey: *Superbug*, Virgin, 1995

Colborn, T., Dumanoski, D, & Myers, J.P.: *Our Stolen Future*, Little, Brown, 1996

Conner, S. & Kingman, S: *The Search for the Virus*, Penguin, 1988

Dando, Malcolm: *Biological Warfare in the 21st Century*, Brassey's, 1994

Epstein, Steven: *Impure Science*, University of California Press, 1996

Fisher-Hoch, S. & McCormick, J.B: *The Virus Hunters*, Bloomsbury, 1996

Ford, P. & Howell, M.: *Medical Mysteries*, Viking, 1985

Garrett, Laurie: *The Coming Plague*, Penguin, 1995

Goldsmith, E. & Hildyard, N.: *The Earth Report 2*, Mitchell Beazley, 1990

Gould, Peter: *The Slow Plague*, Blackwell, 1993

Karlen, Arno: *Plague's Progress*, Victor Gollancz, 1995

MacGarvin, Malcom: *The North Sea*, Collins & Brown, 1991

Mack, Arien (ed): *In Time of Plague*, New York University Press, 1991

McKeown, Thomas: *The Origins of Human Disease*, Basil Blackwell, 1988

McNeill, William H.: *Plagues and Peoples*, Basil Blackwell, 1977

Mandell, G.A., Douglas, R., & Bennett, J.E. (eds) *Principles and Practices of Infectious Diseases*, 4th Edition, Churchill Livingston, 1995

Martin, Elizabeth A. (ed): *Concise Oxford Medical Dictionary*, Oxford University Press, 1996

Porter, Roy: *Disease, Medicine and Society in England, 1550-1860*, Cambridge University Press, 1995

Preston, Richard: *The Hot Zone*, Random House, 1994

Rosenberg, Charles: *Explaining Epidemics*, Cambridge University Press, 1992

Smith, Dr Tony (ed.): *British Medical Association Complete Family Health Encyclopedia*, Dorling Kindersley, 1995

ter Haar, Barend: *The Future of Biological Weapons*, Praeger, 1991

Wills, Christopher: *Plagues*, HarperCollins, 1996

Some particularly useful sites on the World Wide Web were:

Outbreak (http://www.outbreak.org) for details of current epidemics of new and resurgent disease

Fifty Greatest Conspiracies of All Time (http://www.conspire.com) for information on Aum Shinri Kyo

Centers for Disease Control (http://www.cdc.gov) for health statistics of all kinds

Time Magazine's archive on CompuServe (GO TIME)

Greenpeace Climate Crisis home page (http://www.greenpeace.org/ ~climate) for information on global warming

The National AIDS Manual (http://www.nam.org.uk) for details of the latest AIDS drug trials and treatments and how they work

Gulf War Veterans' Association (http://www.gulfwar.org) for details of Gulf War Syndrome

US Air Force (http://cdsar.af.mil/battle) for texts on biological warfare by Lt Col Terry N. Mayer, USAF and Lt Col Robert P. Kadlec, MD, USAF from *Battlefield of the Future*

ACKNOWLEDGEMENTS

Special thanks, first, to my consultants, Professor Roy Porter of the Wellcome Institute for the History of Medicine, London, and Dr Fiona Payne of St Thomas's Hospital, London, for gently correcting my errors and omissions, and to Professor Porter in particular for introducing me to books and angles on history of which I would otherwise have been unaware. Thanks too for incidental (but sometimes crucial!) information, advice, support and useful pointers to Dr Richard Cummings, Colonel Peter Darman, Dr Peter Gould, Sally Harper, Dr Malcolm MacGarvin, Shelagh Meyer, Bob Rickard, Dr Barbara Skew, Henry Graham Smith of the National AIDS Manual, Dr Christine Stevenson, and the staff of the Terrence Higgins Trust and Glaxo Wellcome. Any errors or omissions that remain are my very own.

To Vicky Hanson at Brown Packaging Books and to my editor, Lesley Riley, who had to deal not only my writing but with but me as well – extra special thanks for everything (although an award for heroism might be more appropriate).

INDEX